SPECIFYING INTERIORS

SPECIFYING INTERIORS

A Guide to Construction
and FF&E for Commercial
Interiors Projects

Maryrose McGowan

Drawings by Kelsey Kruse

JOHN WILEY & SONS, INC.
New York • Chichester • Brisbane • Toronto • Singapore

The *Architectural Woodwork Quality Standards,* published by the
Architectural Woodwork Institute (AWI), is frequently updated.
Readers should contact AWI at 1952 Isaac Newton Square, Reston,
Virginia 22090, to determine if the Standards have been updated
since the 6th Edition, Version 1.1. The following figures can be
found on the pages indicated in the *Architectural Woodwork Quality
Standards:*

> *Figure 3.2: Section 100, pg. 37; Table 3.10: Section 100, pg. 36;
> Figures 3.15&3.16: Section 200, pg. 60; Figure 3.17: Section 200, pg. 61;
> Figure 5.1: Section 400, pg. 93.*

This text is printed on acid-free paper.

This publication is designed to provide accurate and
authoritative information in regard to the subject
matter covered. It is sold with the understanding that
the publisher is not engaged in rendering legal, accounting,
or other professional services. If legal advice or other
expert assistance is required, the services of a competent
professional person should be sought.

Library of Congress Cataloging-in-Publication Data:
McGowan, Maryrose.
   Specifying interiors: a guide to construction and FF&E for
commercial interiors projects / Maryrose McGowan.
      p.   cm.
   Includes bibliographical references and index.
   ISBN 0-471-10619-4
   1. Commercial buildings—Specifications.   I. Title.
TH4311.M34   1996
725′.2—dc20   96-24631

Printed in the United States of America

10 9 8 7 6 5 4 3 2 1

To John
and to my parents,
Mary and Jack McGowan,
and
Nora and John McGing

Contents

Preface

When the focus of my career shifted to commercial interiors, it was immediately clear that, being trained as an architect, I was inadequately prepared for my new pursuit. In fact, my background was limiting me. Like many others, I attempted to understand contract interiors in the context of (or, to be more direct, as a stepchild of) new building construction. Consequently, the complexities of this comparatively new profession were trivialized. Then the search for a deeper understanding of the contemporary practice of commercial interior design began — from its origins to its manifestation through the selection and specification of finishes and furniture. That exploration resulted in a deep appreciation for the commercial interior design profession, and in the book before you.

Commercial interiors practice is a sophisticated and efficient contract delivery approach. It requires the intricate coordination of construction and FF&E contracts, which are often developed simultaneously. By its nature, this practice can respond almost immediately to market demands. As a means of serving the client, it is an inherently more flexible system than new building construction.

This book is an introduction to the contemporary commercial interiors project. It is intended for all students of commercial interiors, those in formal architecture and interior design training programs, as well as those who continue their study through practice.

Acknowledgments

I am deeply grateful to the late Dr. Albert Bush-Brown, who opened the door that was to become this book. The following people have generously shared their talents and my enthusiasm for this project:

My editor, Amanda Miller, and associate managing editor, Donna Conte; Sarah Bader, architect; Dr. F. H. Kruse, chemist; Constantine Seremetis, cartographer; William Mulherin of Benjamin Moore & Co., Inc.; Herb Stoudt of Tarkett; Kay Villa of the American Textile Manufacturers Institute; Tom McGing, for his tireless and unrecognized contributions to the commercial interiors industry; Dennis Bradway of Mannington; Patricia Neumann and Gladys Finley of Southwest Research Institute, for their substantial contributions to the "Flammability Standards" section; Don Weber of Stretchwall; Hank Hildebrandt, Coordinator of the Interior Design Program, University of Cincinnati; Matthew Schottelkotte, AIA of GBBN, Cincinnati, Ohio; Charles Kimball, Graham Scott, and Cliff Simonton of Interface Flooring Systems, Inc.; Bob Dempsey of the Congoleum Corporation; Woody Vaughn; Mary Klinoff, whose strong hands pushed and prodded me towards the completion of this project; and most especially, to Christopher G. Smith, AIA, and the Masterspec Interiors Review Committee, whose dedication to the advancement of specifications for commercial interiors practice is my constant inspiration.

Maryrose McGowan

Cambridge, Massachusetts
June 1995

CHAPTER 1

Commercial Interiors Projects

In response to market demands, commercial interiors practice has developed creative solutions for increased flexibility. To support the turnover in tenant space, the building shell (exterior) and core (shared service space) have evolved as separate from the office floors they support. This separation of base building from leased space continues to meet today's requirements.

Up until the 1950s, adapting office space to suit a tenant's needs involved little more than putting a fresh coat of paint on the walls of existing offices. Today, speculative office building interiors are designed with maximum flexibility, anticipating the wide range of tenants that will inhabit them. Each space is then adapted, or built-out, to suit its tenant.

Contemporary base buildings incorporate sophisticated floor duct systems for routing utility wires to freestanding workstations; floor-to-ceiling partitions are no longer required to act as chases for electrical wire or data cable. Movable and demountable partition systems are available as replacements for constructed gypsum board walls. Moreover, the use of systems furniture offers an even easier solution to the problem of relocating walls without downtime or the creation of construction debris.

The separation of base building and infill can be traced through a series of technologic and economic events. As the economy developed, technology and the interior design profession responded with solutions.

The industrial revolution indirectly prompted the emergence of the service industry. By the late 1840s, less than a quarter of the world's population was dependent on agriculture as a means to make a living. The service sector—law, accounting, banking and the like—grew in proportion to burgeoning businesses.

After first invading the home—office on the lower level, residence above—small businesses moved to commercial office space, which still imitated the domestic layout. But by 1860, the Sun Fire Insurance Company had opened an office in London that had been designed specifically to support the work of its 80-person staff. However, it was the advent of the steel-frame office building 25 years later that launched the first great step in the development of commercial interiors.

Heralding the future of the skyscraper, the Home Insurance Building was built around a light-weight steel frame. Designed by William LeBaron Jenney, this 10-story building was constructed in Chicago between 1883 and 1885. The new skeletal framing system offered several advantages. Masonry curtain wall exteriors and fire-resistant steel structural members responded to increasing national concern for the prevention of fire in dense urban areas—the great Chicago fire had decimated the city in October 1871 (Figure 1.1). Steel structural systems also offered unprecedented flexibility in interior space. For the first time, interior partitions were easily moved, because the interior walls did not have to be bearing walls. Tenant spaces could be adapted to the individual needs of their inhabitants.

By the end of the nineteenth century, electric elevators were familiar amenities in many office buildings. Commercial rental rates no longer decreased with each additional flight of stairs to be climbed. During the

Figure 1.1 The American Type Founders offices in New York City, 1902. At the turn of the century, concern grew about the incidence of fires in office buildings. This typical commercial interior includes wood furniture and flooring. Gaslights and smoking materials were common ignition sources. Steelcase.

Figure 1.2 Secretarial desk set designed by Frank Lloyd Wright for the Johnson Wax headquarters building, a forerunner of systems furniture. The three-legged chair design was controversial at the time. Steelcase.

Figure 1.3 The "Great Workroom" of the Johnson Wax headquarters building, Racine, Wisconsin. Steelcase.

economic prosperity of the 1920s, speculative office buildings became a popular form of investment.

Most of the skyscrapers of the 1930s and 1940s incorporated flexible partitioning requirements. For example, the Philadelphia Savings Fund Society Building, designed by William Lescaze and George Howe and built in the early 1930s, incorporated movable partitions designed specifically for the project. Varying tenants' needs were anticipated by the base building designer and the interior designer.

In the mid-1930s, the Johnson Wax headquarters building, designed by Frank Lloyd Wright, included specially made furniture (Figures 1.2 and 1.3). The desk and chair set, manufactured by Steelcase, was an integral part of the interior design and supported the worker's tasks. Other furniture man-

Figure 1.4 Multiple 15 desk and C-line chairs, mid–1940s. The first modular office furniture (based on multiples of 15 inches) built by Steelcase. Steelcase.

Figure 1.5 The Merchandise Mart, Chicago, Illinois. Courtesy of the Merchandise Mart.

ufacturers worked with architects to respond to the furnishing needs of the modern, flexible office. Thonet worked with Le Corbusier and Otto Wagner to improve the office environment, and in the United States, Raymond Loewy teamed up with the Gestetner Furniture Company.

Furniture manufacturers were producing sophisticated products that targeted the increasingly complex needs of commercial interiors (Figure 1.4). In 1942, Herman Miller introduced its first furniture product for the modern office, a component system called the Executive Office Group, designed by Gilbert Rohde. Standard distribution channels were not equipped to sell these complex office furnishings. Many of these early furniture systems had important features that were not apparent to the casual observer. Few understood the product, and so for the first time, fur-

Figure 1.6 Action Office, introduced in 1964. Designed by Robert Probst, it was a radically different office furniture design, defining work areas with modular panels. Courtesy of Herman Miller, Inc.

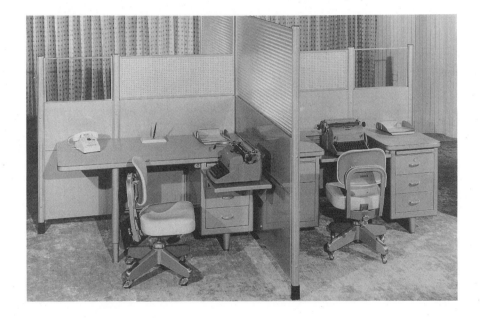

Figure 1.7 Convertiwalls desk system, early 1960s. Steel or glass panels are connected by slotted posts that are wired to accommodate telephones and business machines. Attachments such as shelves and chalkboards are added without using tools. Steelcase.

niture manufacturers were marketing furniture directly to architects and interior designers through showrooms and trade shows.

Designer showrooms as we know them today (open only to architects and interior designers, or "to the trade"), were well established by the 1940s. The Merchandise Mart, completed in 1931, catered exclusively to the wholesale trade (Figure 1.5). The largest building in the world at the time of its completion, the Mart continues to host the NEOCON trade show annually.

The Executive Office Group component furniture system responded to a changing lifestyle requiring more mobility and less space. Twenty-five years after its introduction, the radically different Action Office furniture line was marketed (Figures 1.6 and 1.7). Still in production today, Action

Office enables a quick and efficient response to change by the reconfiguration of modular panels. "Open plan" office furniture, or systems furniture as it is called today, defines and separates work spaces without the use of constructed partitions. Today, it is estimated that more than 30% of U.S. businesses use systems furniture.

The practice of commercial interior design today is a specialty. It reflects the increasingly complex synthesis of construction and furnishings, of base building and tenant space. With the decline in new construction starts and the dwindling availability of prime urban real estate, tenant work will continue to be a primary focus for many design practices.

BASE BUILDING AND TENANT IMPROVEMENTS

The commercial office building shell and core, which include essential services, such as the heating, ventilating, and air conditioning (HVAC) system, elevators, and toilet rooms, is commonly referred to as the **base building**. **Tenant improvements** are those materials and constructions that form the infill responding to the tenant's needs which are not part of the base building.

The **base building standard**, or building standard, is a package of typical tenant improvements provided by, and sometimes required by, the landlord. By standardizing such building components as suite entry doors, suite signage, lighting fixtures, and window treatments, the landlord can maintain coherence in design and consistency in maintenance routines throughout the building. The designation **above base building standard** refers to items that are not included in the base building standard. These usually exceed the base building standard in quality or quantity.

A significant point of negotiation between a leasing agent (or property manager) and a prospective tenant is determining who will pay for construction costs for building out the tenant's space. Usually, there is a **tenant improvement allowance** to cover standard items that will be installed at no cost to the tenant. The quantity of tenant improvements is usually described per square foot of rentable space; for instance, 1 telephone jack for every 10 sq m (125 sq ft) leased, 1 door every 30 sq m (300 sq ft), and so on. If such a quantitative approach is not used, the allowance may be stated as a certain amount of money to be provided by the owner per square foot of leased space.

The Lease and the Work Letter

A **lease** is an agreement between the property owner and the tenant. It gives the tenant the right to the exclusive use and occupancy of a specified space for a stated period of time in return for a stipulated rent. Virtually every lease provision is subject to negotiation.

There are standard improvements that landlords provide to tenants as part of the rental rate. The document that describes these improvements to the rented space is the **work letter**, which is attached to and becomes part of the lease. The quantity and quality of the materials or construction are described in the work letter (Figure 1.8). The lease and attached work letter are frequently the subject of intense negotiation.

Building Standard Work Letter for Garden Court Towers

The following tenant work shall be provided by and at the expense of the landlord and included in the stated base rent:

1)Standard interior partitions—One lineal foot consisting of steel studs, ½" gypsum wallboard on each side to ceiling height, taped and spackled for every 10 square feet leased.

2) Standard demising partitions—One lineal foot for every 60 square feet leased.

3) Standard interior doors with frame and hardware—One for every 400 square feet leased.

4) Standard corridor doors with frame and hardware—One for every 1,200 square feet.

5) Standard acoustical ceiling—Exposed grid suspended system with 2' by 2' acoustical lay-in tegular tiles throughout the demised premises.

6) Standard recessed lighting fixtures—One for every 80 square feet leased.

7) Duplex electrical outlets—One for every 120 square feet leased.

8) Light switches—One for every 200 square feet leased.

9) Telephone outlets—One for every 200 square feet leased.

10 Wall finishes—One prime coat and 2 coats building standard latex paint. Colors shall be selected by the Tenant from building standard selections allowing one color per room and up to three colors per suite.

11) Venetian blinds—One standard 1-inch slat, furnished and installed at all windows.

12) Flooring—Building standard carpet or vinyl throughout. Color shall be selected by Tenant from building standard samples.

13) Suite entry identification—Plaque for each Tenant indicating suite number and firm name. Standard lettering and design shall be used throughout the building.

Figure 1.8 Sample work letter.

Measuring Commercial Office Space

There are about a dozen different methods of measuring commercial office space in current use. All methods make similar distinctions between gross area, usable area, and rentable area, but they differ in how these areas are calculated. Generally, the gross area is the floor area construction, the rentable area is the revenue-producing floor area, and usable areas are those that are occupiable.

The **building gross area**, defined as the "construction area" by the Building Owners and Managers Association (BOMA), is the floor area within the exterior face of the building including the thickness of the exterior wall. It is the total constructed space. This measurement is used in evaluating building efficiency and comparing construction costs among various projects. The floor area that the tenant pays rent on is the **rentable area**, usually defined as the interior floor area excluding vertical penetrations through the floor (e.g., air shafts, elevators, and stairways). This measurement is used to determine the income-producing capability of a building. The **usable area** is the floor area that is inhabitable by the tenant. This measurement is used in planning and designing the space.

It is critical to understand which method is used for a particular project. The method of measurement determines the rental rate agreed to in the lease and often affects the provisions of the work letter. Square footage calculations frequently form the basis of the designer's fee. ANSI Z65.1 *Standard Method for Measuring Floor Areas in Office Buildings*, commonly known as the BOMA method, is widely accepted in commercial real estate. The International Facility Management Association (IFMA) measurements and classifications are consistent with the BOMA method but describe some tenant-oriented measurements in greater detail. A summary of five of the most common measurement methods is illustrated in Figure 1.9.

Figure 1.9 Various methods of floor area measurements. The main features of the measurement systems of the following organizations are diagrammed: Real Estate Board of New York (REBNY), the Building Owners and Managers Association (BOMA), the Washington, D.C., Area Realtors (WDCAR), the General Services Administration (GSA), and the International Facility Management Association (IFMA). Solid-line boxes designate the terms defined in a standard. Dotted-line boxes surround terms that are not mentioned but are included by implication. Boxes that straddle two shaded areas represent those terms that a standard splits between the two categories. Terms in boxes outside the shaded areas are not recognized by a standard. Copyright © 1993 Lawrence W. Vanderburgh, Facility Transitions, 5453 Hildebrand Court, Columbia, MD 21044. Phone (410) 730-7965.

Space Measurement Systems Compared

© Facility Transitions, Columbia, Maryland 1993

rented by measurement (BASE RENT / SPACE ALLOCATED)

BOMA

exterior wall	
interior columns & bldg projns	
convec-tors	
TENANT SPACE	
demising walls	
stores	to bldg line

space on ext. wall >5'-0" ht.
exterior wall
interior columns & projns
convec-tors
TENANT SPACE
demising walls

WDCAR

exterior wall
interior columns & projns
convec-tors
TENANT SPACE
demising walls
bsmts
stores

to bldg line

REBNY

convec-tors <50% wall length
interior columns & projns
demising walls
storage type
special type
office type

circulation

| stores |

GSA

exterior wall
interior columns projns & convctrs
net assignbl
second'y circl'n
demising walls
stores

IFMA

---

allocated pro rata (ADDED TO BASE RENT)

corridor walls	
public corridors	
walls enclosg floor service	
floor service areas	
bldg lobbies & atriums	

corridor walls
public corridors
walls enclosg floor service
floor service areas
bldg lobbies & atriums

corridor walls
public corridors
walls enclosg floor service
floor service areas
bldg lobbies & atriums

joint use
corridor walls
public corridors

corridor walls
primary circl'n (public corridors)
walls enclosg floor service
floor service areas
bldg lobbies & atriums

---

amortized base bldg cost OVERHEAD (BUILT INTO BASE RENT)

BOMA

bsmts & stor.
amenity spaces
walls enclos'g vertical penetr'ns
major vertical penetr'ns
bldg service areas
mech pent-house
ext. wall
exterior balc's & skywalks

WDCAR

bsmts
amenity spaces
walls enclos'g vertical penetr'ns
retail & direct to ext.
major vertical penetr'ns
bldg service areas
mech pent-house
ext. wall

REBNY

extra if room ht. >1.25 x avg. clg. ht.

other

other HVAC space, incl shafts
mech pent-house
walls between rentbl & non-rent
arcades & plazas
amenity spaces
some vertical penetr'ns
bldg service areas
ext. wall

GSA

convec-tors >50% wall length
walls enclosg floor service
floor service areas
bldg lobbies & atriums
walls enclos'g vertical penetr'ns
major vertical penetr'ns
bldg service areas
mech pent-house
ext. wall (entire)
open porches & docks
enclosed walks, mezz & parking decks

IFMA

bldg service areas
walls enclos'g vertical penetr'ns
major vertical penetr'ns
loading docks
mech pent-house
non-dominant ext. wall
inter-stitial space

9

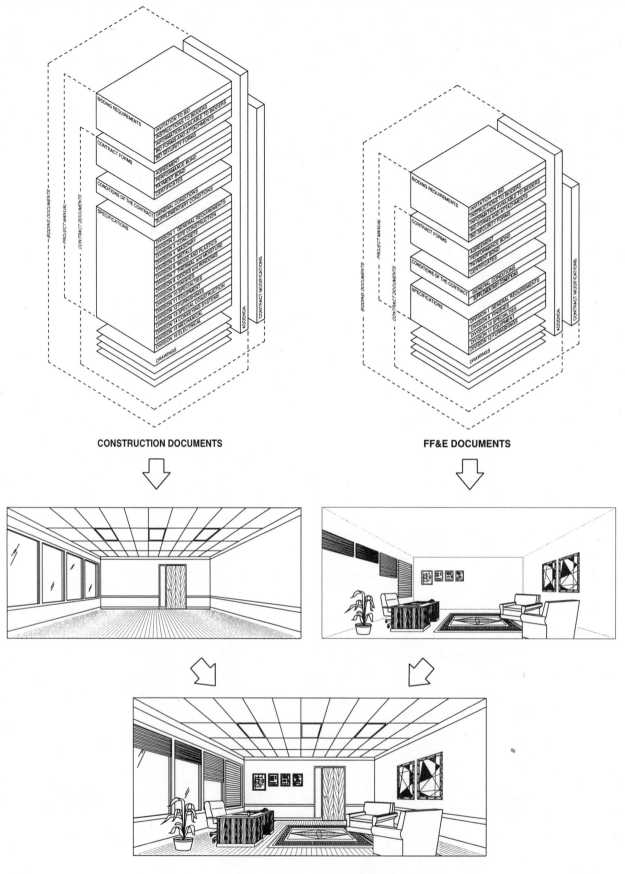

Figure 1.10 Complete commercial interiors project with both sets of contract documents. Construction documents diagram reprinted from the Construction Specifications Institute (CSI) *Manual of Practice*, with permission from CSI, 1955.

10

The contract documents describe the proposed construction or furniture, furnishings, and equipment installation. They include the written (specifications) and the graphic (drawings) documentation that communicate the design of the project. There are two sets of contract documents that a designer must prepare for a complete commercial interiors project (Figure 1.10):

- The construction contract documents
- The furniture, furnishings, and equipment (FF&E) contract documents

Table 1.1 is a comparison of the phases of a construction contract and FF&E contract, from predesign through contract administration.

The agreement between the owner and the construction contractor is the contract for construction (Figure 1.11). The construction contractor's responsibilities are described in AIA A201 *The General Conditions of the Contract for Construction* (see Appendix B). The construction contractor is responsible for supervising and directing the construction of the project. This includes providing labor, materials, equipment, tools, water, heat, utilities, and other facilities and safety features. The construction contractor employs the various trades required to accomplish the work of the contract or makes agreements with subcontractors. The work of these specialty contractors, such as electricians, plumbers, painters, carpenters, and carpet installers, is coordinated by the general contractor.

The Contract for Construction

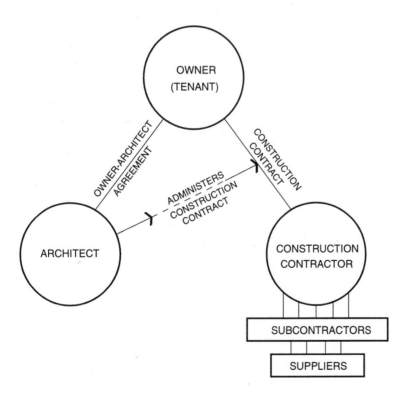

Figure 1.11 Construction contract.

TABLE 1.1   COMPARISON OF CONSTRUCTION CONTRACT AND FF&E CONTRACT BY PROJECT PHASE

Construction Contract for Interiors	FF&E Contract	Architect	Tenant	FF&E or Construction Contractor
PREDESIGN				
PROGRAMMING		P	A	
Select Building	*Not Applicable*	R	P	
Work Letter/Lease Negotiation	Space Planning or Test Layouts	P	R, A	
Site Survey	FF&E Inventory	P		
Building Standards	Work Station Standards		R	
SCHEMATIC DESIGN				
Conceptual Design		P	A	
Initial Plans		P	A	
Conceptual Elevations		P	A	
Outline Specifications		P	A	
Consultant Coordination Acoustical Electrical Mechanical Structural	Consultant Coordination Planting (interior landscaping) Signage Furniture Project Manager	P		
Preliminary Pricing		P	R, A	
Meetings/Presentation		P	R, A	
DESIGN DEVELOPMENT				
Not Applicable	Research FF&E	P	R, A	
Construct Mockups	Install Mockups/Manufacturer Presentation	R, A	A	P
Definitive Construction Documents	Definitive FF&E Documents	P	R, A	
Definitive Construction Specifications	Definitive FF&E Specifications	P	R, A	
Develop Budget for Construction	Develop Budget for FF&E	R	P	
CONTRACT DOCUMENTS				
Final Construction Drawings	Final FF&E Drawings	P	R, A	
Final Construction Specifications	Final FF&E Specifications	P	R, A	
Prepare Bid Documents **Unit Prices** (adjustment to contract made by change order during contract administration) —These prices are determined by bidder. **Alternates** (options that are priced separately) —Alternates are accepted by tenant. **Allowances** (monies reserved in contract) —Tenant allows for work not determined at time of bid.	Prepare Bid Documents **Unit Prices**—Bids are itemized as unit prices. Cost per item is determined by contractor's discounted price. **Alternates**—Less commonly used. Costs are known during design phase and are factor in item selection. **Allowances**—Less commonly used. Tenant can use allowances for budgeting purposes.	P	R, A	R

Construction Contract for Interiors	FF&E Contract	Architect	Tenant	FF&E or Construction Contractor
BIDDING OR NEGOTIATION				
Prequalification of Bidders		A		
Issue Addenda		P	A	R
Receive Bids		R	P, A	
Bid Review/Analysis		P	R	
Confirm Performance Bond			P	
Confirm Insurance			P	
Award Contracts		R	P	
Submit Construction Schedule	Submit P.O. Tracking Report	R		P
CONTRACT ADMINISTRATION				
CONSTRUCTION	INSTALLATION			
Determine Deposits/Orders for Long Lead Items	Determine Deposits for FF&E Orders	R	P	
Set Up Temporary Facilities	Determine Staging Area		A	P
Project Coordination Contractor responsible for sub-contractors.	Project Coordination (Tenant coordinates FF&E contractors and their work with construction contractor.)	R		P
Construction Meetings	Job Progress Meetings	R, A	A	P
Submittal Review		R, A		P
Review Project Progress		P	A	
Product Substitutions Proposed by contractor.	(Typically not permitted. Contractor points out reason why substitution must be made. Architect proposes substitute to tenant.)	R, A	A	P
Authorize Payments	P.O.'s may not be submitted to architect for approval	R, A		P
Issue Certificates of Payments	Tenant pays P.O. invoice	R, A		P
Contract Document Revision		P	A	
Issue Change Orders	Issue, revise, or cancel P.O.'s	R, A	A	P
Determine Substantial Completion	Tenant pays P.O. invoice	A		P
Not Applicable	P.O. Coordination	R, A		P
Prepare Punchlist		P	A	R
Not Applicable	Move Coordination	P	A	
Determine Final Completion	Tenant pays final P.O. invoice	A		P

P=Performs task; R=Reviews; A=Approves.

Source: Reproduced with permission of the American Institute of Architects, 1735 New York Avenue, N.W., Washington, D.C. 20006 under license number 95050. This license expires June 30, 1996.

In addition to orchestrating various construction activities, construction contractors perform a variety of administrative tasks. The general contractor is usually responsible for securing and paying for the building permit and other permits required for completion of the project. He or she is usually responsible for the preparation of a construction schedule and must prepare and submit shop drawings and samples for the architect's approval. **Shop drawings** illustrate specific situations or details of a project. They are prepared by the construction contractor, one of the subcontractors, or the product manufacturer or supplier, and submitted to the designer. **Samples** are examples of the materials or workmanship; these are used to verify selections and to establish standards by which the completed work will be judged. Shop drawings and samples are not contract documents. They are submitted to demonstrate the way in which the construction contractor intends to accomplish the design expressed by the contract documents.

The traditional approach to a construction project is the **design-award-build** sequence of events. The designer fully documents the project in the contract documents, which include the construction drawings and specifications. Proposals to build the project are requested from construction contractors. These bids are evaluated, a contractor is selected, and a construction contract between the successful bidder and the owner is signed. The "owner" (the term used on the agreement forms) in most cases is the tenant, but, depending on the terms of the lease and work letter, can be the landlord. The architect is usually retained to administer the contract for construction between the owner and the construction contractor.

New methods of contracting for construction projects are continually being developed in response to tighter construction budgets and schedules. Two of the more recent and creative approaches are the fast-track and design/build methods.

It is often necessary to begin construction as soon as possible because of accelerated occupancy schedules or the high cost of financing a project. In the **fast-track** approach to construction, building begins before the project design is complete. Separate construction contracts are defined, and contract documents are prepared for each phase. Items that will be the last to be installed or constructed—for example, custom casework—will be the last to be fully designed and bid. The design schedule extends into the construction schedule, reducing the duration of the project. Fast tracking often increases construction costs due to decreased labor efficiency.

In **design/build** projects, one party is responsible for both the design and the construction of the interior (Figure 1.12). The design/build firm may be a construction company with in-house designers or one that has hired a design firm consultant. The advantage of this method of construction contracting is that the contractor is involved with the project from the initial stages. Costs, material availability, and scheduling can be estimated much more accurately.

Construction for commercial interiors on leased properties is referred to by various names, including tenant build-out work, tenant fit-up, or ten-

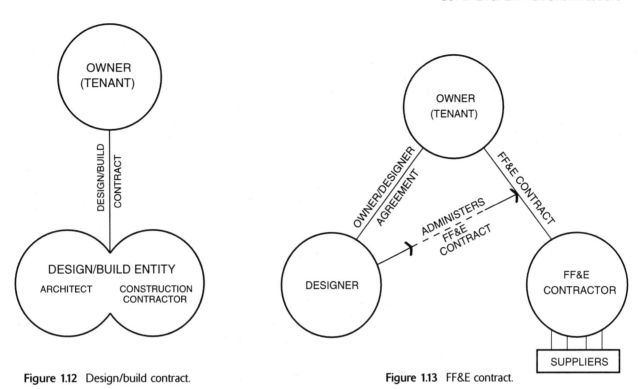

Figure 1.12 Design/build contract.

Figure 1.13 FF&E contract.

ant improvements. Lease provisions often require that the prime, or general, contractor and the subcontractors be approved by the landlord. In some cases, landlords retain contractors to build all tenant spaces in their buildings.

PROCUREMENT OF FF&E

The FF&E contractor is responsible for procuring, delivering, and installing the goods described in the FF&E contract. These responsibilities are detailed in documents AIA A271 and ASID ID320, titled the same, *The General Conditions of the Contract for Furniture, Furnishings and Equipment* (see Appendix C). The agreement between the owner and the FF&E contractor is typically administered by the designer (Figure 1.13). The FF&E contractor is often a furniture dealer but can also be a furniture manufacturer or a design professional (Figure 1.14).

The **furniture dealer** is the local or regional presence of the manufacturer. The dealer processes the sale and provides various support and follow-up services to the owner. In this way, the manufacturer concentrates on product development and production and the dealer focuses on sales and service. One of the services a dealer typically offers is warehousing the goods between the time manufacturing has been completed and the point at which the project site is ready to receive them for installation.

The Contract for Furniture, Furnishings, and Equipment (FF&E)

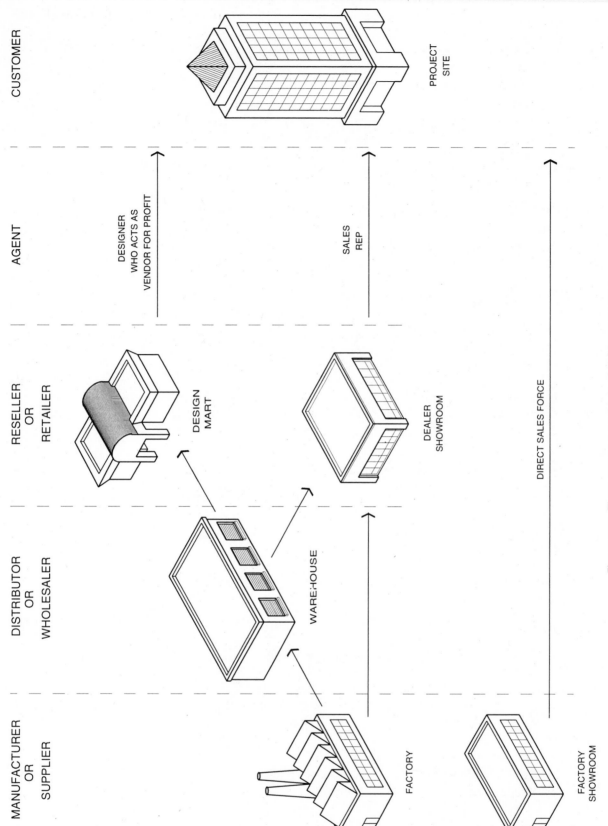

Figure 1.14 Three common methods of FF&E distribution.

CUSTOMER

PROJECT SITE

AGENT

DESIGNER WHO ACTS AS VENDOR FOR PROFIT

SALES REP

RESELLER OR RETAILER

DESIGN MART

DEALER SHOWROOM

DISTRIBUTOR OR WHOLESALER

WAREHOUSE

DIRECT SALES FORCE

MANUFACTURER OR SUPPLIER

FACTORY

FACTORY SHOWROOM

A **direct sales force** represents the manufacturer, not the manufacturer's dealer. Equipment is commonly procured directly from the manufacturer through a direct sales force. For example, a hospital bed manufacturer may not require a showroom to market a relatively expensive product with a limited user base. The sale may be effectively accomplished by having a sample bed sent to the hospital on a trial basis or by arranging a tour of the factory showroom.

The FF&E contractor prepares purchase orders based on the FF&E contract. A **purchase order** is the form used to obtain the required goods for the project (Figure 1.15). It contains a description of the goods, the supplier's catalog number, the number of items required, and the price. Separate purchase orders are prepared for each supplier involved in the project.

An **acknowledgment**, also referred to as a purchase order acknowledgment, is prepared by the supplier as confirmation of the purchase order (Figure 1.16). The acknowledgment must be verified by the FF&E contractor to make sure it is an accurate interpretation of the purchase order. If the purchase order acknowledgment is correct, the order is placed and the manufacturing process begins.

The FF&E contractor coordinates the requirements for C.O.M. (customer's own material). **C.O.M.** is material that is not supplied by the product manufacturer. It is purchased separately from the product and supplied to the product manufacturer for application. "Customer" in this case does not refer to the designer's customer, the owner, but refers to the manufacturer's customer, the party placing the order, which is the FF&E contractor. It is the FF&E contractor who is responsible for the acquisition and coordination of C.O.M.

The owner can also procure the required goods through their in-house purchasing departments. Large corporations can purchase products, for example, carpet, furniture, fabric, and light fixtures, and supply them to the contractor for installation. This allows a business to establish national accounts with vendors and reduce costs by buying in volume.

After the goods have been manufactured, they are packaged for delivery. An **invoice**, a bill requesting payment for the goods, is prepared by the manufacturer and sent to the FF&E contractor, typically at the same time the goods are shipped (Figure 1.17).

DELIVERY AND INSTALLATION OF FF&E

The Uniform Commercial Code (UCC) (see "Contract Law and Commercial Law," page 27) defines many of the terms and sets forth the procedures used in the delivery of goods. **Delivery** is defined by the UCC as *voluntary transfer of possession* (UCC 1-201). Delivery does not necessarily indicate ownership. **Title** means *ownership*. If you have title to goods, you own them. For example, a manufacturer delivers furniture to a carrier for transportation to its destination. The manufacturer is not transferring title to the goods; therefore the carrier does not own the furniture. **Receipt** is defined as *taking physical possession of goods* (UCC 2-103).

⋃ herman miller   **purchase order**

Herman Miller Inc.   Zeeland, Michigan 49464
Systems for Office, Health Care, Laboratory and Industrial Environments
616 772 3300

both purchase order number and
part number must appear on all
boxes, packages, shipping documents,
invoices and correspondence

to   AMERICAN FURNITURE DEALER
239 HURON AVENUE
SPRINGFIELD, MA 10172

vendor number 4437

If unable to meet the "ship to arrive" date, please notify the undersigned purchasing agent/buyer as soon as possible.

confirming	account number		ship to arrive	via	f.o.b.		date of order
	398576		12/18/95	AIR FREIGHT	DESTINATION		10/17/95

quantity	our number	vendor number	description	u/m	unit price	total price
1	EE122PK.N4		Ergon III work chair with knee tilt Size: Mid Back Arms: FIxed Finish: Dark Tone Fabric: 4437 Burgundy		**$XXX.XX**	**$XXX.XX**

ship to   U.S. CORPORATION
601 MADISON AVENUE
SPRINGFIELD, MA 10173

Herman Miller Inc.

TOTAL   **$XXX.XX**

requestor   purchasing agent / buyer

acknowledge immediately   this order subject to provisions listed on reverse side

ZP01 R 5/83

Figure 1.15a Purchase order. Courtesy of Herman Miller, Inc.

R 2/93

1. **Application of Standard Terms.** Sales of the Company's products are made only on the Company's standard terms and conditions of sale which are contained in this document and in the Company's price book. Purchaser acknowledges receipt of the terms and conditions of the Herman Miller Promise® and understands that this order is covered by those terms and conditions. The standard terms and conditions may be modified or supplemented only by a written document separately signed by the Company's authorized personnel at its divisional headquarters. Any term or other condition contained in any purchase order or other form used by purchaser to order goods (including standard printed language) which is different from, in addition to, or in any way inconsistent with the Company's standard terms and conditions, shall be of no force or effect whatsoever.

2. **Prices and Payment.** Unless otherwise shown on the face hereof, prices stated in this document include domestic packing and freight, but exclude special or export packing, duties, taxes, redelivery or accessorial freight charges, unpacking and installation charges. Orders are invoiced at the time of shipment or at the time of first shipment in the case of multiple shipments and payment is due upon receipt of the Company's invoice. The Company will permit a discount only as indicated on the face of this document. Any balance remaining unpaid thirty (30) days after the invoice date will be considered in default.

3. **Taxes.** All sales, use, excise, and other applicable taxes (excluding only taxes on the net income of the Company) are the purchaser's responsibility and will be invoiced to the purchaser. If purchaser claims an exemption from such taxes, it shall be the purchaser's responsibility to furnish an appropriate exemption certificate to the Company.

4. **Changes and Cancellations.** After the date hereof, purchaser may not change or cancel the order for the goods shown on the face hereof without the written consent of the Company. Approved cancellations for products will be subject to the following cancellation charges:

20% standard items five (5) weeks or less before ship date

50% non-standard items from one week after acknowledgment up to five weeks before ship date; no cancellations or changes accepted on Rapid Response or Priority 10

Cancellation charges will be calculated based on the net acknowledgment value of the cancelled items. There are no cancellations or changes accepted on Rapid Response or Priority 10 orders.

5. **Shipment and Delivery.** All domestic shipments will be FOB factory. All shipments outside of the 48 contiguous states will be shipped FOB factory, surface freight included to the point of embarkation. The Company will select the method of domestic shipment, unless otherwise specified by purchaser. If added cost is incurred by reason of the Company's complying with a special shipment request by purchaser, such added cost will be invoiced to purchaser. Risk of loss shall pass to purchaser at the time the Company places the goods in the possession of a common carrier or at the time of tender of delivery to the purchaser in the case of delivery by the Company's vehicles.

6. **Storage.** In the event purchaser requests postponement of delivery of more than one (1) week beyond the scheduled shipping date after the goods have become work in process or at a time when the Company is then about to make shipment, the Company may transfer the goods to storage for the purchaser's account and at purchaser's risk and expense. Purchaser may elect to contract storage for up to 30 days after ship date at a charge of 3 percent of net invoice. Each additional month of storage will be available at a 1 1/2 percent per month charge. Orders which are postponed more than six months from the original scheduled ship date will be priced, invoiced, and paid for at the prices in effect on the date of shipment.

7. **Delays.** The shipping date specified on the face hereof represents the Company's best estimate of an approximate shipping date at the time of this acknowledgment. However, the Company shall not incur any obligation or liability to purchaser for failure to ship by any particular date unless such date has been formally established as a "Guaranteed Move-in" date as detailed in The Herman Miller Promise®. Said Guaranteed Move-In document must be signed by authorized company personnel. In addition, in no event, however, shall the Company be liable for any loss or damage resulting from any delay or failure in shipment or other failure to perform all or any part of the agreement between the parties with respect to the goods shown on the face of the order acknowledgment where such delay, failure, loss, or damage is the proximate result of any act of any governmental authority or political subdivison thereof, revolution, riot, civil disorder or disturbance, act of enemies, delay or default in transportation, strike, disputes among or between labor unions, or other labor disputes, delay or inability in obtaining materials and facilities, fire, flood, act of God, or any cause not within the reasonable control of the Company, whether of the class of causes enumerated or otherwise. Without limiting the generality of the foregoing, the Company may, without causing any breach or incurring liability,

allocate goods which are in short supply, irrespective of the reasons therefore, among purchasers in any manner which the Company in its sole discretion deems advisable.

8. **Suspension.** In the event purchaser defaults in the payment of any sum due the Company, or in the event purchaser's financial condition becomes unsatisfactory to the Company, the Company shall have the right at its option, upon notice to the purchaser, to defer or discontinue shipment of any goods until such time as the default is cured or the purchaser provides assurances of payment to the Company in such form, content and/or amounts as the Company, in its sole discretion, deems adequate.

9. **Claims.** The Company is not responsible for damage to goods which occurs in transit or in storage. It is the purchaser's responsibility to examine goods upon receipt and to file any claims with the carrier. Any claims against the Company for apparent defects, errors, or shortages must be made by the purchaser in writing within five (5) working days after any delivery. Failure by the purchaser to make any claim against the Company within five (5) days shall constitute acceptance of the goods and a waiver of any apparent defects, errors, or shortages.

10. **Returns.** Returns will not be allowed on product after 90 days following the invoice date. No return of goods will be accepted without written consent and shipping instructions from the Company. When return goods authorization is given, the product is to be shipped prepaid at the returnee's expense. Only unused product, in its original shipping container, will be accepted. A restocking charge of 25 percent of the net invoice price will be assessed on all authorized returns. The only "used" products accepted for return are those specified under the "Trade-in" provisions of The Herman Miller Promise®. An additional charge for restoring such goods will be made or no credit will be given if goods cannot be reused. Restocking charges will be calculated based on the net invoice value of the returned items.

11. **Warranty Matters.** The Company warrants its products to be free from defects in material and workmanship (including installation where performed by the Company's employees) for a period of one (1) year from the date of initial delivery. The following extended warranty periods apply to products manufactured and sold in the United States after April 29, 1991:

10 years Systems (excluding electrical components), storage, and furniture

5 years Seating, electrical components, height adjustment mechanisms, and lighting

3 years Veneer, vinyl, leather, and other covering materials for workmanship only

Natural variations occuring in wood, marble, and leather shall not be considered defects; the Company does not warrant the colorfastness or matching of the colors, grades, or textures of such materials. No warranties are made with respect to nonstandard material selected by and used at the request of purchaser.

The Company's obligation and the purchaser's remedy pursuant to this warranty are limited to repair or replacement at the Company's option, FOB the Company's plant, for products which, when used normally and pursuant to the Company's published instructions, prove to be defective within the first year of the warranty period and to furnish necessary repair parts for products which prove to be defective within the remainder of the extended warranty period. Purchasers may be required to establish that a claim is within the warranty period by producing the invoice for the product or such other evidence as may be reasonably satisfactory to the Company.

The Company makes no warranties to purchasers who acquire products for personal, family, or household purposes. THERE ARE NO OTHER WARRANTIES EXCEPT AS EXPRESSLY SET FORTH ABOVE, EITHER EXPRESS OR IMPLIED, INCLUDING ANY WARRANTY OF MERCHANTABILITY OR FITNESS FOR ANY PARTICULAR PURPOSE. The remedies stated herein are expressly agreed to be exclusive as a condition of sale and the Company's liability with respect to its products or installation services might not exceed that expressly set forth above irrespective of the theory upon which any claim might be based, including breach of contract, warranty, negligence or strict liability in tort. Under no circumstances shall the Company be liable for any incidental or consequential damages.

12. **Miscellaneous.** It is the purchaser's responsibility to check this document for accuracy, correct fabric and finish selections, etc. The order acknowledgment shows approximate shipping date of items ordered. Shipping dates are assigned to orders based on the item having the longest manufacturing lead time. Orders with customer's own material (COM), missing or incorrect information (finish selections, fabric selections, etc.) will be scheduled for manufacturing upon receipt of COM or correct and complete information. Purchaser must indicate if multiple shipping schedules are required.

This document is intended as a complete, exclusive and final statement of the terms and conditions of Agreement between the Company and purchaser with respect to the purchase and sale of the goods shown on the face hereof. The transaction between the parties described herein shall be governed by and interpreted and construed in accordance with the laws of the State of Michigan.

Figure 1.15b The terms and conditions of the sale are usually printed on the back of the purchase order, the acknowledgment, and the invoice. Shipment and delivery conditions are defined. Courtesy of Herman Miller, Inc.

⊔ herman miller　　　acknowledgment

HERMAN MILLER INC
855 EAST MAIN AVENUE
ZEELAND　　　　　　MI 49464

customer	date	order number
I-021081	08-31-95	646740
	PAGE	1 OF　1

sold to

AMERICAN FURNITURE DEALER
239 HURON AVENUE
SPRINGFIELD, MA 10172

ship to

U.S. CORPORATION
601 MADISON AVENUE
SPRINGFIELD, MA 10173

AIR ASAP

FOB PLANT/PREPAID

It is the orderer's responsibility to check this document for accuracy, correct fabric selections, etc. Report claims immediately. This order is subject to the terms and conditions on the face and reverse side.

order date	your purchase order number	terms	deposit	type	we will ship week of or earlier
08-31-95	04-254-066-117-00000	NET 120 DAYS		FO	09-09-95

contract	ship to purchase order number	ship from	salesperson	territory	ship via
A10891	04-254-066-117-0000	ZEELAND, MI		9900	AIRFREIGHT

p/c	item number	quantity ordered	product number	product description	ship week	unit price	extended price
			NOTE: ORIG FO:638196/ENTRD BY:BC7144				
			CALL NBR:194510/RGR:N				
			AIR ASAP				
X	0001	2	E1250.38S	FINISHED END	09-09	$XX XX	$XX XX
			BU-SURFACE	FINI-BLACK UMBER			
X	0002	1	E1311.D	RECEPTACLE-8 WIRE,	09-09	$XX XX	$XX XX
			BU-SURFACE	FINI-BLACK UMBER			

X　T	08/01/95	ORDER VALUE IN USD	$XX XX
14			

Herman Miller Inc.　Zeeland, Michigan 49464　Systems and Furniture for Office and Health Care Environments　　　　　　dealer　　A0340A R 2/94
Telephone: 616 654 3300
Telex: 297706 HMIZ UR

Figure 1.16 Purchase order acknowledgment. Courtesy of Herman Miller, Inc.

⌐ herman miller invoice

HERMAN MILLER INC
855 EAST MAIN AVENUE   MI 49464
ZEELAND

customer	date	invoice number
D-025103	09-04-94	212017

PAGE 1 OF 1

sold to
AMERICAN FURNITURE DEALER
239 HURON AVENUE
SPRINGFIELD, MA 10172

ship to
U.S. CORPORATION
601 MADISON AVENUE
SPRINGFIELD, MA 10173

DELIVER BY 9/9/94

FOB PLANT/PREPAID

It is the orderer's responsibility to check this document for accuracy, correct fabric selections,etc. Report claims immediately. This order is subject to the terms and conditions on the face and reverse side. Federal employer I.D. 38-0837640.

order date	your purchase order number					terms	deposit	salesperson	territory	type	order number	ship date
08-23-94	01056941A					NET 120 DAYS			520F	FO	449750	09-02-94

contract number
A21086

ship to purchase order number

ship from
ZEELAND, MI

ship via
SHIPPER SUPREME

bill of lading number
00328664

item number	quantity this invoice	quantity remaining	quantity ordered	quantity previously invoiced	product number	product description	unit price	extended price
						*** FINAL SHIPMENT FOR FO **		
						NOTE: REF F.O. 449635		
						DELIVER BY 9/9/94		
0001	2	2	2		EQ405S	CHAIR-LO SPLIT UPH S	39 XX	$XX XX
						MT-BASE FINISH-MEDIUM TONE		
						MT-SHELL FINISH-MEDIUM TONE		
						T2-PACKAGING -MULTIPLE PACK OF TWO		
						M803-FABRIC -		
0002	1	1	1		EQ405S	CHAIR-LO SPLIT UPH S	$XX XX	$XX XX
						MT-BASE FINISH-MEDIUM TONE		
						MT-SHELL FINISH-MEDIUM TONE		
						T1-PACKAGING -PACKAGE OF ONE		
						M803-FABRIC -		

NET DUE ON 01-02-95

X T 14   12/01/93 FED-EMP-ID=38-0837640 C   TOTAL AMOUNT DUE USD $XXX XX
                        S=00000

HERMAN MILLER INC.
Remit to 855 E. MAIN STREET
ZEELAND, MI 49464

A0170A R 5/94

customer original

Herman Miller Inc.   Zeeland, Michigan 49464   Systems and Furniture for Office and Health Care Environments
Telephone: 616 654 3300
Telex: 297706 HMIZ UR

Figure 1.17 Invoice. Courtesy of Herman Miller, Inc.

21

A **carrier** is a transportation company. Carriers that operate in interstate commerce are regulated by the Interstate Commerce Commission (ICC). **Common carriers** offer transportation services to the general public. They are usually responsible for the goods they are shipping, whether or not they have been negligent. **Contract carriers** provide transportation only to those with whom they choose to do business. They do not insure the goods they transport unless they are contracted to do so. **Private carriers** are not in the transportation business. They own and operate trucks to transport their own goods. The ICC does not regulate private carriers.

With few exceptions, such as when goods are picked up by the buyer (see UCC 2-509 Appendix F), whoever has title to the goods bears the risk of their being lost, stolen, damaged, or destroyed. The risk of loss is commonly indicated by the abbreviation "F.O.B." The UCC defines F.O.B. as "free on board" (UCC 2-319). **F.O.B.** at a named place, indicates where title to the goods and risk loss or damage pass from the seller to the buyer, which is typically the FF&E contractor. The buyer pays the transportation costs from the point named in the F.O.B. "place" (Table 1.2).

When goods are sent **F.O.B. place of shipment**, the buyer owns the goods at the place of shipment (typically, the manufacturer's factory loading dock). The goods are given to the carrier (typically, a truck), and the seller is no longer responsible for the delivery of the goods or their condition upon arrival. The buyer pays for shipping. If the goods are stolen, damaged, or destroyed in transit, it is the buyer's responsibility to recover damages from the carrier. When the terms of shipment do not specify shipping point or destination, it is assumed to be F.O.B. *place of shipment.*

F.O.B. place of destination means the seller is responsible for delivering the goods. The cost of the goods includes shipping charges. If the goods are stolen, damaged, or destroyed in transit, it is the seller's responsibility to recover damages from the carrier (UCC 2-319) (Figure 1.18).

F.O.B. factory—freight prepaid means that the buyer has title to the goods during transit but that the supplier pays the transportation charges to the destination. In this way, the buyer has the convenience of not having to arrange for transportation and the supplier reduces its liability.

A **drop shipment** means the goods will be shipped to a destination different from that of the party who ordered and paid for them.

A **bill of lading** (Figure 1.19) is defined by the UCC as a document confirming the receipt of goods for shipment issued by a person engaged in the business of transporting (UCC 1-201). The supplier prepares the bill

TABLE 1.2   PASSAGE OF TITLE

	Seller Assumes Expense and Risk of . . .	Passage of Title Occurs at . . .	Price of Goods . . .
F.O.B. "the place of shipment"	Putting goods into the possession of the carrier at place of shipment	Place of shipment (typically manufacturer's factory loading dock)	Does not include shipping charges
F.O.B. "the place of destination"	Transporting the goods to the destination	Destination (typically the project site's loading dock)	Includes shipping charges

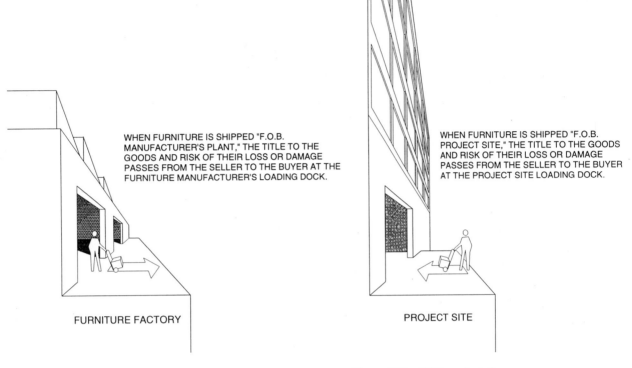

Figure 1.18a F.O.B. manufacturer's plant.

Figure 1.18b F.O.B. project site.

of lading. The carrier verifies that the goods loaded on its vehicle match those listed on the bill of lading. The bill of lading lists the number of boxes, crates, or packages. It is not meant to be used to verify that the goods being transported are the goods that were ordered. A **packing list** (Figure 1.20) is a detailed list of quantities and descriptions of the goods being delivered. It is used to check the items and it cross-references the bill of lading. The packing list is typically attached to the outside of the shipping package in a clear plastic envelope.

A **contract** is an agreement between two or more parties that is based on mutual promises to do (or refrain from doing) something that is neither illegal nor impossible. A contract is basically a promise that the law will enforce.

U.S. laws must conform to the U.S. Constitution and can originate from any of the three branches of government: executive, legislative, or judicial.

LAWS THAT AFFECT THE CONTRACTS FOR INTERIORS PROJECTS

CONSTITUTIONAL LAW

Sources of U.S. Law

A constitution is the basic law of a nation or state. **Constitutional law** is the supreme law of a nation. All forms of law must conform to the constitution. The U.S. Constitution establishes the organization of the federal government (Figure 1.21).

STRAIGHT BILL OF LADING—SHORT FORM—ORIGINAL—Not Negotiable
RECEIVED, subject to the classifications and lawfully filed tariffs in effect on the date of the issue of this Bill of Lading.

Bill of Lading number

00081673

from **herman miller** ZEELAND, MI 49464

date 09/05/95
PAGE 1

ship to   AMERICAN FURNITURE DEALER
239 HURON AVENUE
SPRINGFIELD, MA 10172

special delivery instructions	attention	Subject to Section 7 of Conditions of Applicable Bill of Lading, if this shipment is to be delivered to the consignee without recourse on the consignor, the consignor shall sign the following statement. The carrier shall not make delivery of this shipment without payment of freight and all other lawful charges.
AIR 05SEP95	tag	
☒ carton load ☐ bar load ☐ blanket wrap	URGENT	signature of consignor Herman Miller, Inc.

For payment of prepaid invoices, attach copy of Bill of Lading to freight bill and mail to:	freight charges All accessorial charges are collect unless requested in writing herein. Prepaid unless box is checked.
Herman Miller, Inc. 0850001 c/o CTI Logistics, Inc. PO Box 782, Aurora, IL 60507 telephone number (708) 851 3015 Freight bills without Bill of Lading copy will be returned.	☐

carrier name	vehicle number	account number(s)
SHIPPER SUPREME		

number of packages	kind of package, description of articles, special marks, and exceptions	item number	sub no	class	weight (subject to corrections)
NONE 1	Hazardous Material F FURN PART;NOI,OTHER THAN FOAM RUBBER OR PLA F.O./P.O. NUMBERS: 647187/10016709, COMMENTS:	83270		100	16.20

1

Herman Miller, Inc. shippers	total number of packages	total weight	total cube	carrier name _____
signature	1	16.20	1	signature/date

RECEIVED, subject to the classifications and lawfully filed tariffs in effect on the date of the issue of this Bill of Lading, the goods or the containers, vans, trailers, pallet units, or other packages said to contain goods herein, mentioned, in apparent good order and condition, except as otherwise indicated, to be transported, delivered or transhipped as provided herein. All of the provisions written, printed or stamped on either side hereof are part of this bill of lading contract.

apply pre-pro label here

BOL 00081673

permanent post office address of shipper 855 East Main Avenue, PO Box 302, Zeeland, MI 49464-0302

ZT09 R 12/92

Figure 1.19 Bill of lading. Courtesy of Herman Miller, Inc.

herman miller packing list

bill of lading	date	order number	page
00081673	09/05/95	647187	1

ship to

U.S. CORPORATION
601 MADISON AVENUE
SPRINGFIELD, MA 10173

sold to

AMERICAN FURNITURE DEALER
239 HURON AVENUE
SPRINGFIELD, MA 10172

ship to purchase order	carrier	trailer number	shipping identification
10016709	SHIPPER SUPREME		9524813328

shipping tag	shipped from	freight terms
URGENT	ZEELAND, MI	FOB PLANT/PREPAID

item number	product and description	quantity this shipment	carton count	tally
	NOTE: ORIG PO:625650/ENTRD BY:BB3052 CALL NBR:194583/RGR:N			
0001	234189 LOCKSET SERVICE	10	1	
	TOTAL WEIGHT THIS ORDER THIS SHIPMENT		16.20	
	TOTAL CARTONS THIS ORDER THIS SHIPMENT		1	

pulled by ______________________________

ZT30 R 12/92

Herman Miller Inc **Systems and Furniture for Office and Health Care Environments**
855 East Main Avenue PO Box 302 Zeeland MI 49464-0302
Telephone 616 654 3000

Figure 1.20 Packing list. Courtesy of Herman Miller, Inc.

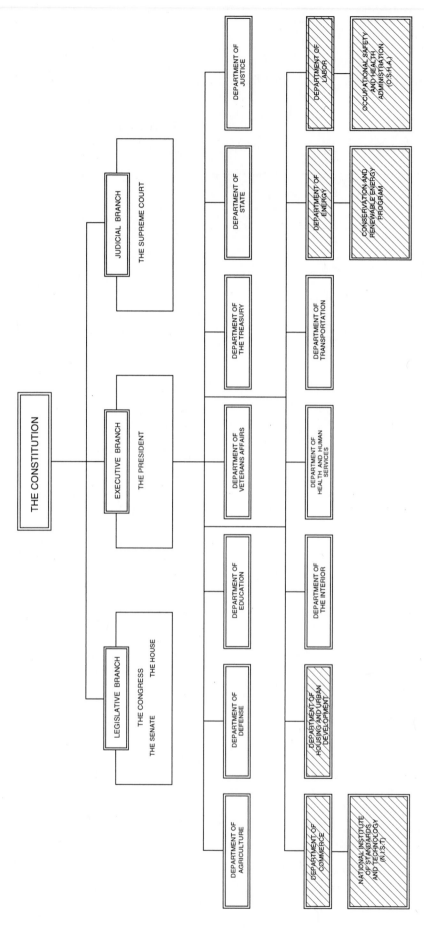

Figure 1.21 The U.S. Government. Shaded departments are involved in building regulations.

26

LEGISLATION: STATUTORY LAW

Laws passed by a legislature are known as **statutes**. At the federal level, these are the laws that are passed by Congress and signed by the president. At the state level, statutes are enacted by state legislative bodies. Statutory law also includes ordinances passed on the local level by cities and counties.

Because many different statutes are passed each year by each state's legislative body, there are significant differences in statutory law throughout the United States. This may present problems when parties from different states that are subject to different laws try to do business. The most important development in uniform legislation among the states has been the Uniform Commercial Code (UCC). The **Uniform Commercial Code** is the group of statutory laws governing sales transactions in the United States. **The UCC governs contracts for FF&E.**

COURT DECISIONS: COMMON LAW

Common law is based on the outcome of previous court cases under comparable circumstances. The tradition of common law dates back to the early English kings' attempts at establishing a fair system of rules that all courts in the kingdom could hold in common. Consistency was maintained by relying on previous legal decisions. These previous decisions, known as precedents, became model cases for the courts to follow when facing similar situations. **Common law, as modified by statute, governs contracts for construction.**

RULES OF AGENCIES, BOARDS, AND COMMISSIONS: ADMINISTRATIVE LAW

Contemporary society often presents problems so complex that neither legislators nor judges have the expertise to provide adequate counsel. To assist in this effort, legislators commonly delegate their power to others by creating administrative agencies, boards, and commissions. The rules made by administrative agencies comprise **administrative law** (See Table 2.1, page 42).

All contracts contain agreements, but not all agreements are contracts. An agreement may or may not be legally enforceable. To be enforceable, an agreement must conform to the law of contracts. Contract law is the framework for all commercial law. It serves as the basis for much of the law described in more specialized areas, such as the sale of goods.

If the subject of a contract is real estate or services, common law and certain statutory provisions govern. If the subject of a contract is goods, then the UCC applies. **Goods** are defined as all things (except money, stocks, and bonds) that are moveable. When a contract includes both goods and

CONTRACT LAW AND COMMERCIAL LAW

Sales Contracts and Services Contracts

services, the dominant element of the contract determines whether it is a sales contract or a services contract.

A **contract for construction**, which is between the owner and the construction contractor, is essentially an agreement to provide expertise and service and includes the purchase of construction materials. It is regulated by common law as modified by statute. A **contract for FF&E**, which is between the owner and the FF&E contractor, includes services such as warehousing, delivery, and installation, but it is primarily a sale-of-goods contract. A contract for FF&E is regulated by the UCC (Figure 1.22).

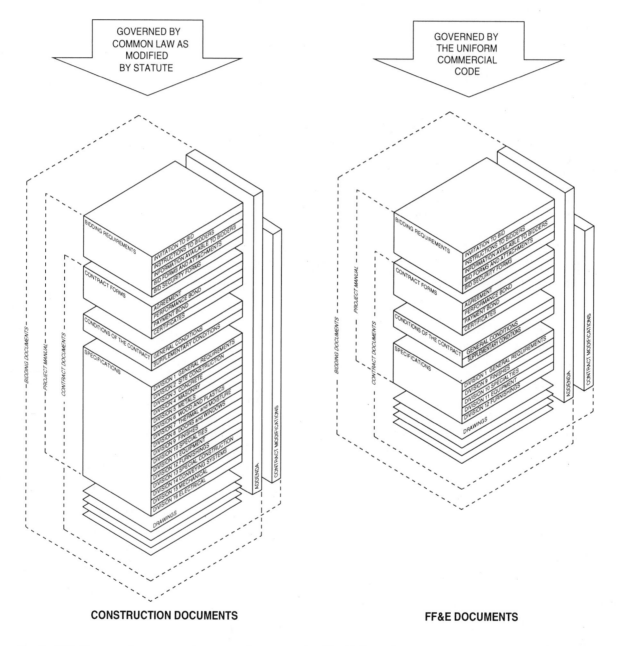

CONSTRUCTION DOCUMENTS   **FF&E DOCUMENTS**

Figure 1.22 Common law governs the contract for construction. The Uniform Commercial Code (UCC) governs the contract for FF&E. Construction documents diagram reprinted from the Construction Specifications Institute (CSI) *Manual of Practice*, with permission from CSI, 1995.

TABLE 1.3   THE UNIFORM COMMERCIAL CODE TABLE OF CONTENTS

Article Title	Content
Article 1: General Provisions	Purposes of the UCC
Article 2: Sales	Sale of goods
Article 2A: Leases	Leasing of goods
Article 3: Negotiable Instruments	Checks, cashier's checks, travelers checks, etc.
Article 4: Bank Deposits and Collections	Bank transactions
Article 4A: Funds Transfers	Payments through the banking system
Article 5: Letters of Credit	Credit issued by a bank or other entity
Article 6: Bulk Sales	Large inventory transfers
Article 7: Warehouse Receipts, Bills of Lading and Other Documents of Title	Title transfer
Article 8: Investment Securities	Stocks
Article 9: Secured Transactions; Sales of Accounts and Chattel Paper	Security interests in personal property
Article 10: Effective Date and Repealer	The conditions under which the UCC is in effect
Article 11: Effective Date and Transition Provisions	

The **Uniform Commercial Code (UCC)** is the set of statutes that governs the commercial transactions of all fifty states (except Louisiana, which has adopted only Articles 1, 3, 4, and 5, the District of Columbia, and the Virgin Islands). For practical purposes, the rules governing commercial transactions are consistent throughout the country because of the UCC. Table 1.3 lists the articles and contents of the UCC. Note that Article 2 of the UCC sets down the rules for buying and selling goods and is included in Appendix F.

In cases in which the UCC is silent, the common law of contracts and applicable state statutes govern. Common law rules and UCC provisions are quite often the same.

The UCC simplifies the law governing commercial transactions by making the fundamental rules of contract law less rigid. UCC provisions are more appropriate than common law for a variety of circumstances typical of sales transactions. Although many common law rules and UCC provisions are the same, there are some significant differences (Table 1.4).

Differences Between Contract Law and Commercial Law

Offer and Acceptance in Formation of Contract (UCC 2-206). Rules of commercial law regarding the way an offer is made and accepted are not as strict as those of contract law. In many cases, an enforceable sales contract can be made in any way—written, oral, or by conduct—that shows an agreement has been reached. Unless the original agreement is in writing with a stipulation that it may not be modified except by a signed contract, mutual promises are not required to modify a contract for the

TABLE 1.4   DIFFERENCES BETWEEN THE UCC AND CONTRACT LAW

UCC	Contract Law
Not all terms have to be included in the contract (UCC 2-204).	An offer must be definite enough for the parties (and the courts) to ascertain its essential terms when the contract is accepted.
Firm written offers by *merchants* for three months or less cannot be revoked (UCC 2-205).	An offer can be revoked any time before acceptance.
The price does not have to be included to have a contract (UCC 2-305).	Price must be included.
Variation in terms between the offer and the acceptance may not be a rejection (UCC 2-207).	Variation in terms between the offer and the acceptance act as a rejection of, and a counter offer to, the offer.
A modification for the sale-of-goods contract does not require mutual agreement (UCC 2-209).	Modification of common law contract requires mutual agreement.

sale of goods. In a sale-of-goods contract, the purchase price may be omitted and the amount of goods to be sold need not always be defined.

Additional Terms in Acceptance or Confirmation (UCC 2-207). Under the general rules of contract law, acceptance of an offer is an unconditional approval of all contract provisions. The UCC rules governing sale-of-goods contracts are more relaxed. In most sale-of-goods contracts, additional terms are treated as proposals for additions to the contract if none of the parties involved are merchants. If both parties are merchants, the additional terms become part of the contract unless there is an objection within a reasonable period of time.

In a few cases, the UCC applies differently to merchants than to consumers making purchases. A **merchant** is defined as a person who deals in a particular kind of goods or who claims to have knowledge or skills peculiar to those goods (UCC 2-104). A merchant is held to a higher standard of conduct than those who are not professional vendors. This is only one reason that the decision of a designer to act as a vendor for profit for furniture and furnishings deserves careful consideration.

For example suppose, a business's purchasing department places an order over the phone for some chairs. The dealer puts the verbal agreement in writing and sends it to the business for its signature. The purchasing department signs the contract and changes the delivery date. Because only one party in this contract is a merchant, the schedule modification is treated as a proposal. The contract is not modified until the furniture dealer agrees to the proposed delivery date. If, however, both parties are merchants—for example, if this scenario occurs between a furniture manufacturer and a furniture dealer—the changed delivery date becomes part of the contract unless an objection is raised within a reasonable period of time.

The UCC is the primary source for rules regarding warranties in commercial transactions. It defines two important types of warranties: express and implied.

Warranties

An **express warranty** is a representation about the quality of a product. There are three different ways to make an express warranty: by a statement of fact or promise, by a description of the goods, or by a sample or model (UCC 2-313).

An **implied warranty** is not offered by the seller; it is imposed by law. It is a warranty that is inferred from the nature of the transaction. Implied warranties are designed to promote fairness and honesty. There are two types of implied warranties: an implied warranty of merchantability and an implied warranty of fitness for a particular purpose.

An **implied warranty of merchantability** assures the buyer that the goods are fit for the ordinary purpose for which they are to be used. This warranty type applies only to sales made by merchants who deal in goods of the kind sold (UCC 2-314). For example, a furniture dealer makes an implied warranty of merchantability every time it sells a desk, but a neighbor selling the same desk at a yard sale does not. For a claim to be made for a breach of this type of warranty, a defect must exist at the time the goods are purchased.

When a buyer relies on a seller's judgment to select the goods, it is implied that the seller warrants that the goods will be fit for the purpose for which they are to be used. This creates the **implied warranty of fitness for a particular purpose**. This warranty type applies to both merchants and nonmerchants. If the seller knows how the buyer will use the goods and knows the buyer is relying on the seller's skill in selecting the goods, there is an implied warranty of fitness (UCC 2-315).

There are two sets of contract documents a designer must prepare for a complete commercial interiors project: the construction contract documents and the FF&E contract documents (see Figure 1.23). Although the laws governing these two contract types differ in significant ways, their organization is the same.

CONTRACT DOCUMENTS FOR COMMERCIAL INTERIORS PROJECTS

The bidding requirements instruct prospective bidders on the procedures that must be followed so that their bid will not be disqualified. The bidding requirements are not part of the contract. They are not enforceable during the administration of the contract. Bidding requirements typically include the following documents:

Invitation to Bid

Instruction to Bidders

Information Available to Bidders

Bid Forms and Attachments

Bid Security Forms

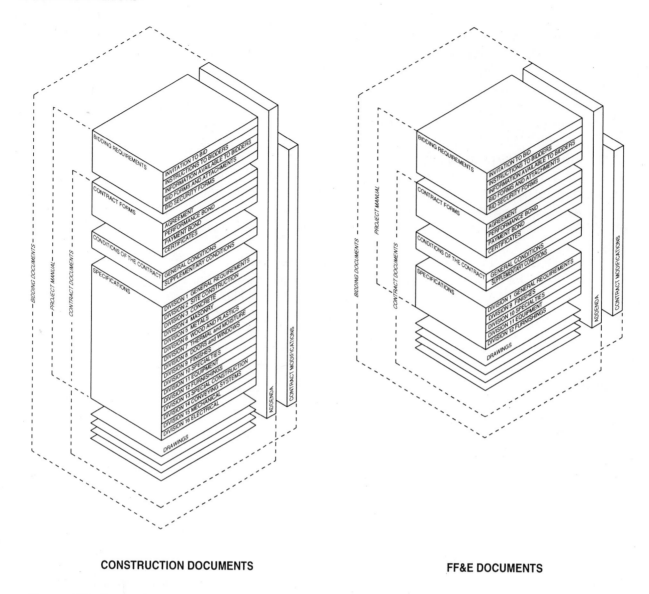

CONSTRUCTION DOCUMENTS   **FF&E DOCUMENTS**

Figure 1.23 Construction documents and FF&E documents. Construction documents diagram reprinted from the Construction Specifications Institute (CSI) *Manual of Practice*, with permission from CSI, 1995.

The **contract documents** describe the work included in the contract to the construction or FF&E contractor. They consist of the following:

- Contract Forms—the agreement, certificates of compliance with required regulations, and, more typically in construction contracts, performance bonds, and payment bonds
- Conditions of the Contract
- Specifications
- Drawings
- Contract Modifications

The **agreement** is between the owner and the contractor. It briefly describes the work of the contract and simply states the project schedule and the contract sum. The agreement includes the other contract documents (general conditions of the contract, specifications, drawings, and modifications) by reference. It is kept separate from the other contract documents because it contains information that the owner and the contractor may not want to be known by all the parties involved, specifically, the contract sum. Standard agreement and other contract forms are available, the most popular being those from the American Institute of Architects (AIA) (for construction and FF&E) and the American Society of Interior Designers (ASID) (for FF&E). These standard forms are designed to be compatible with standard forms of the general conditions (Table 1.5).

TABLE 1.5 STANDARD CONTRACT FORMS

Contract Type	General Conditions	Compatible Standard Forms
FF&E	ASID Document ID320, *General Conditions of the Contract for Furniture, Furnishings and Equipment*	ASID Document ID300, *Standard Form of Agreement Between Owner and Contractor for Furniture, Furnishings and Equipment*
		ASID Document ID310, *Abbreviated Owner-Contractor Agreement for Furniture, Furnishings and Equipment*
		ASID Document ID100, *Standard Form of Agreement for Interior Design Services*
		ASID Document ID330, *Instructions to Interiors Bidders*
		ASID Document ID325, *Guide for Interiors Supplementary Conditions*
	AIA Document A271, *General Conditions of the Contract for Furniture, Furnishings and Equipment*	AIA Document A171, *Owner-Contractor Agreement Form — Stipulated Sum — for Furniture, Furnishings, and Equipment*
		AIA Document A177, *Abbreviated Owner-Contractor Agreement Form — Stipulated Sum — for Furniture, Furnishings, and Equipment*
		AIA Document B171, *Standard Form of Agreement Between Owner and Architect for Interior Services*
		AIA Document B177, *Abbreviated Form of Agreement Between Owner and Architect for Interior Services*
		AIA Document A771, *Instructions to Interiors Bidders*
		AIA Document A571, *Guide for Interiors Supplementary Conditions*
Construction	AIA Document A201, *General Conditions for the Contract for Construction*	AIA Document A101, *Owner-Contractor Agreement Form — Stipulated Sum*
		AIA Document A107, *Abbreviated Owner-Contractor Agreement Form — Stipulated Sum — for Construction Projects of Limited Scope*
		AIA Document B141, *Standard Form of Agreement Between Owner and Architect*
		AIA Document B151, *Abbreviated Owner-Architect Agreement*
		AIA Document A701, *Instructions to Bidders*
		AIA Document A511, *Guide for Supplementary Conditions*

The **conditions of the contract** establish the duties and responsibilities of the construction or FF&E contractor, the owner, and the designer, even though the designer does not sign the owner-contractor agreement. The conditions of the contract include the general and supplementary conditions.

The **general conditions** are standardized documents. They contain those provisions that are common among contracts and are included without annotation. AIA A201 *General Conditions for the Contract for Construction* is widely used in the United States. AIA A271 and ASID ID320 *General Conditions of the Contract for Furniture, Furnishings and Equipment* provide a standard form for the FF&E contract. Although these two documents have the same title, they differ in subtle, but important, ways. The ASID version refers to the design professional as the "Designer" and makes no references to construction activity. The AIA version refers to the design professional as the "Architect," which is defined as the "entity lawfully practicing architecture" in AIA Document A201 (Article 4.1.1, 1987 edition).

The requirements for project administration are established in the general conditions. The responsibilities of the owner, contractor, and architect are described. The provisions these documents reflect contain common practice in the United States.

When the general conditions must be modified to address circumstances specific to a locality or project, **supplementary conditions** are included. They pertain to the unique nature of each project and may include such items as office procedures or progress payments. The supplementary conditions are not standard documents but are tailored to each project.

The design intent is conveyed in the specifications and drawings. These two parts of the contract documents are the focus of the designer's attention.

The **specifications** describe the quality of materials and their construction (for construction contracts) or installation (for FF&E contracts). They include information that cannot be communicated graphically in the drawings. Specifications are discussed in greater detail in the following section.

The **drawings** show the shape and form of the space, as well as the quantities, sizes, and locations of materials and products. Drawings for construction contracts include demolition plans, existing construction to be modified, new construction, elevations, sections, and details. Drawings for FF&E contracts include furniture and furnishing plans.

Contract modifications are changes to the construction or FF&E documents. Modifications made to the bidding documents are called **addenda**. Addenda are typically issued before the bids are open. There are three means of modifying a contract after it has been executed (signed):

Change order

Change directive

Supplemental instruction

A written modification altering the contract sum is called a **change order**. Only the owner can authorize a change order. When altering the contract sum or schedule is required but has not yet been agreed upon, the modification is called a **change directive**. Change orders often originate as change directives. When an interpretation or clarification is required of the designer and it does not involve altering the contract sum or schedule, it is called a **supplemental instruction**.

There are four basic types of specifications: proprietary, descriptive, performance, and reference standard. Most specifications incorporate features from more than one of the four types. For example, a proprietary specification for a particular fabric might also include reference standards for flammability and abrasion resistance.

Proprietary specifications require a specific product from a specific manufacturer indicated by a brand name or model number. The specifier has complete control over what will be incorporated in the project when a proprietary specification is used. FF&E specifications are commonly proprietary. For example, *Knoll Group, Studio Line, Barcelona Chair, with black leather upholstery* is a proprietary specification.

Descriptive specifications detail the requirements for material properties and workmanship. Manufacturers and products are not named. Descriptive specifications are the most difficult to write, because every aspect of the topic must be considered. For example, an acoustical ceiling tile would be specified by describing the tile material, pattern, finish, color, edge detail, thickness, and size.

Performance specifications describe the required results. They describe how a product or material is to perform, not necessarily what it is. The construction contractor or FF&E contractor has a choice of products, materials, and processes that will be used to achieve these results. Performance specifications typically make reference to industry standards. It is helpful to include standard test methods to ensure that performance requirements are met objectively. For example, an acoustical wall panel could be specified by describing its fire-test-performance characteristics, acoustical properties expressed by a noise reduction coefficient (NRC) value, and the abrasion resistance of its fabric covering. This specification type is relatively rare, because designers are most often concerned with a product's appearance as well as its performance.

Reference standard specifications are based on requirements set by an accepted authority. For example, by specifying compliance with ANSI A108 *Specifications for Installation of Ceramic Tile*, the requirements of the standard are included in the specification by reference. Reference standard specifications tend to be the briefest type of specifications. When referencing a standard, it is important that the specifier understand the standard and verify that all provisions of the standard apply to the project.

Specification writers often use master guide specifications such as Masterspec (a product of AIA Master Systems). Master guide specification systems help ensure the currency and accuracy of a specification and assist the specifier in formatting the document.

SPECIFICATIONS

Types of Specifications

Specification Formats

The Construction Specifications Institute (CSI) has established formats for specification information classifications (MasterFormat), sections (Section-Format), and pages (PageFormat). These three formats provide the basis for a complete, concise, and coordinated project manual in which information can be reliably and easily located.

SPECIFICATION INFORMATION CLASSIFICATION

In 1963, CSI introduced MasterFormat in an effort to standardize language, project manual organization, and data filing systems. **MasterFormat** is a list of numbers and titles that classify the materials and requirements of construction and FF&E projects. It is used to organize project specifications and file product information in the United States and Canada. MasterFormat is composed of 16 divisions, each identified by a five-digit numbering system. The first two digits indicate the division number; the last three denote the section location within the Division.

SPECIFICATION SECTION ORGANIZATION

SectionFormat organizes the information presented in each specification section into three parts: Part 1—General; Part 2—Products; and Part 3—Execution (Figure 1.24). Part 1—General describes the administrative and procedural requirements specific to the section. Part 2—Products contains the requirements for the appearance and performance attributes of the items included in the section. Part 3—Execution describes the preparation for and the construction or installation of items included in the section. Each part of the section is divided into articles. Article titles should be selected for inclusion based on their applicability.

SPECIFICATION PAGE ORGANIZATION

PageFormat organizes each page of the project manual. PageFormat includes recommendations for headers, footers, and part, article, and paragraph designations. Part and article titles are presented in capital letters. For ease in referencing information—for example, in correspondence or during contract administration—articles are numerically labeled with a designation consisting of the part number, a decimal point, and a two-digit number starting with 01 (Figure 1.25). Paragraphs are outlined using the traditional alphanumeric system (i.e., A.1.a.1).

PART 1 GENERAL

SUMMARY
 Section Includes
 Products Supplied But Not Installed
  Under This Section
 Products Installed But Not Supplied
  Under This Section
 Related Sections
 Allowances
 Unit Prices
 Measurement Procedures
 Payment Procedures
 Alternates/Alternatives*

REFERENCES

DEFINITIONS

SYSTEM DESCRIPTION
 Design Requirements
 Performance Requirements

SUBMITTALS
 Product Data
 Shop Drawings
 Samples
 Quality Assurance/Control Submittals
  Design Data, Test Reports,
  Certificates, Manufacturer's
  Instructions, Manufacturer's Field
  Reports
 Closeout Submittals

QUALITY ASSURANCE
 Qualifications
 Regulatory Requirements
 Certifications
 Field Samples
 Mock-ups
 Pre-Installation Meetings

**DELIVERY, STORAGE,
AND HANDLING**
 Packing, Shipping, Handling, and
  Unloading
 Acceptance at Site
 Storage and Protection

PROJECT/SITE* CONDITIONS
 Environmental Requirements
 Existing Conditions

SEQUENCING

SCHEDULING

WARRANTY
 Special Warranty

SYSTEM STARTUP

OWNER'S INSTRUCTIONS

COMMISSIONING

MAINTENANCE
 Extra Materials
 Maintenance Service

PART 2 PRODUCTS

MANUFACTURERS

EXISTING PRODUCTS

MATERIALS

MANUFACTURED UNITS

EQUIPMENT

COMPONENTS

ACCESSORIES

MIXES

FABRICATION
 Shop Assembly

FINISHES
 Shop Priming
 Shop Finishing

SOURCE QUALITY CONTROL
 Fabrication Tolerances
 Tests, Inspection
 Verification of Performance

PART 3 EXECUTION

ACCEPTABLE INSTALLERS

EXAMINATION
 Site Verification of Conditions

PREPARATION
 Protection
 Surface Preparation

ERECTION

INSTALLATION

APPLICATION

CONSTRUCTION
 Special Techniques
 Interface with Other Work
 Sequences of Operation
 Site Tolerances

REPAIR/RESTORATION

RE-INSTALLATION

FIELD QUALITY CONTROL
 Site Tests
 Inspection
 Manufacturer's Field Services

ADJUSTING

CLEANING

DEMONSTRATION

PROTECTION

SCHEDULES

Figure 1.24 SectionFormat Standard Article Titles. Reprinted from the Construction Specifications Institute (CSI) and Construction Specifications Canada (CSC), *SectionFormat* (1992 edition), with permission from CSI, 1995.

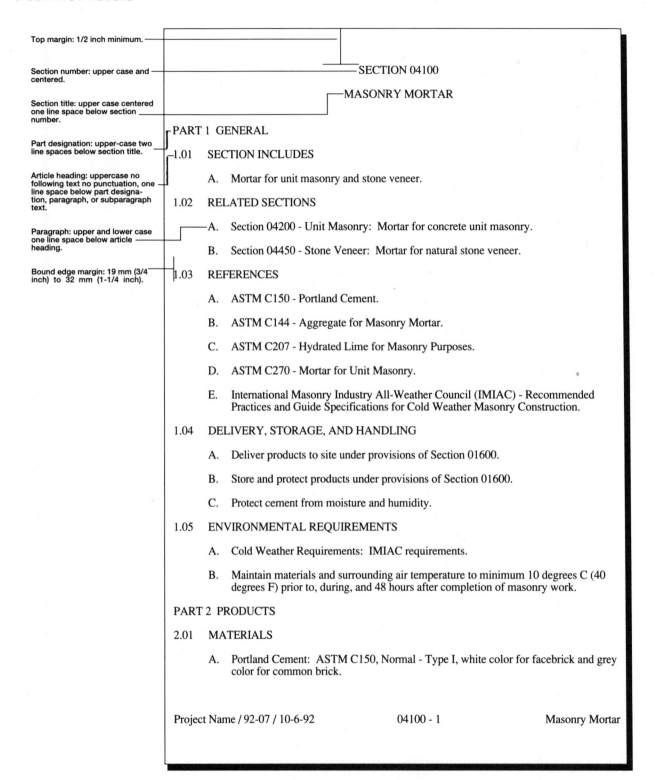

Top margin: 1/2 inch minimum.

Section number: upper case and centered.

Section title: upper case centered one line space below section number.

Part designation: upper-case two line spaces below section title.

Article heading: uppercase no following text no punctuation, one line space below part designation, paragraph, or subparagraph text.

Paragraph: upper and lower case one line space below article heading.

Bound edge margin: 19 mm (3/4 inch) to 32 mm (1-1/4 inch).

SECTION 04100

MASONRY MORTAR

PART 1 GENERAL

1.01   SECTION INCLUDES

    A.   Mortar for unit masonry and stone veneer.

1.02   RELATED SECTIONS

    A.   Section 04200 - Unit Masonry: Mortar for concrete unit masonry.

    B.   Section 04450 - Stone Veneer: Mortar for natural stone veneer.

1.03   REFERENCES

    A.   ASTM C150 - Portland Cement.

    B.   ASTM C144 - Aggregate for Masonry Mortar.

    C.   ASTM C207 - Hydrated Lime for Masonry Purposes.

    D.   ASTM C270 - Mortar for Unit Masonry.

    E.   International Masonry Industry All-Weather Council (IMIAC) - Recommended Practices and Guide Specifications for Cold Weather Masonry Construction.

1.04   DELIVERY, STORAGE, AND HANDLING

    A.   Deliver products to site under provisions of Section 01600.

    B.   Store and protect products under provisions of Section 01600.

    C.   Protect cement from moisture and humidity.

1.05   ENVIRONMENTAL REQUIREMENTS

    A.   Cold Weather Requirements: IMIAC requirements.

    B.   Maintain materials and surrounding air temperature to minimum 10 degrees C (40 degrees F) prior to, during, and 48 hours after completion of masonry work.

PART 2 PRODUCTS

2.01   MATERIALS

    A.   Portland Cement: ASTM C150, Normal - Type I, white color for facebrick and grey color for common brick.

Project Name / 92-07 / 10-6-92   04100 - 1   Masonry Mortar

Figure 1.25 Page Format. Sample text with explanatory notes. Reprinted from the Construction Specifications Institute (CSI) and Construction Specifications Canada (CSC), *PageFormat* (1992 edition), with permission from CSI, 1995.

B. Mortar aggregate: ASTM C144, standard masonry type; clean, dry; protected from dampness, freezing, or foreign matter.

C. Hydrated Lime: ASTM C207, Type S.

D. Water: Clean and potable.

E. Mortar Color: Mineral oxide pigment; chocolate brown color; "Great Stuff" manufactured by Acme Manufacturing Co. Ltd.

2.02 MIXES

A. Mortar for Load Bearing Walls and Partitions: ASTM C270, Type S, using proportion method.

B. Mortar for Non-load Bearing Walls and Partitions: ASTM C270, Type N, using proportion method.

2.03 MORTAR MIXING

A. Thoroughly mix mortar ingredients in quantities needed for immediate use in accordance with ASTM C270.

B. Add mortar color in accordance with manufacturer's instructions. Provide uniformity of mix and coloration.

C. Do not use anti-freeze compounds to lower the freezing point of mortar.

PART 3 EXECUTION

3.01 INSTALLATION

A. Install mortar in conjunction with Sections 04200 and 04450.

3.02 FIELD QUALITY CONTROL

A. Field testing will be performed under provisions of Section 01400.

End of section indication: upper case, centered two lines below the last line of section text.

END OF SECTION

Project name, number, and the date.

Project Name / 92-07 / 10-6-92   04100 - 2   Masonry Mortar

Page number: 5-digit section number with hyphen and sequential page number.

Section title on unbound margin.

Bottom margin: same as top margin.

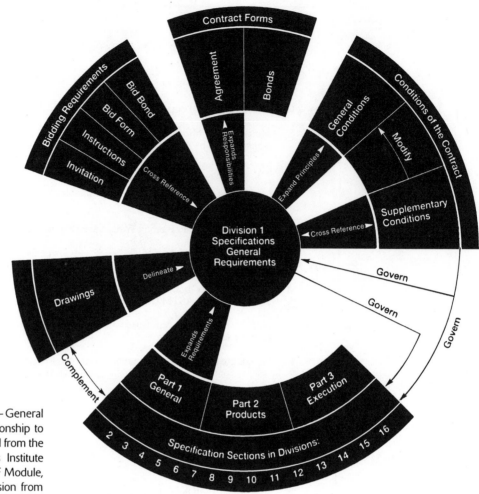

Figure 1.26 Division 1—General Requirements and its relationship to other documents. Reprinted from the Construction Specifications Institute (CSI) *Manual of Practice* (FF Module, 1992 edition), with permission from CSI, 1995.

Division 1 — General Requirements

The topics of Divisions 2 through 16 are included in a project specification only if they are relevant to the project. However, every project specification includes a Division 1—General Requirements. The specification sections of Division 1 govern the execution of sections in Divisions 2 through 16 (Figure 1.26). Division 1 contains the administrative and procedural requirements pertaining to all the specification sections and is the key to administering a construction or FF&E contract.

Notice that many Division 1 section titles are also article titles in Divisions 2 through 16. The Division 1 sections cover those aspects of the topic that apply to all specification sections in the project manual; the section articles cover those aspects that are peculiar to that section. For example, the Division 1 section "Submittals" describes information for use with all submittals: the transmittal form, how the submittals are to be numbered and identified, and the number of copies required. The section article "Submittals" describes which materials, finishes, or products discussed in that section should be submitted and what information the shop drawings or product data must contain.

CHAPTER 2

Regulations, Codes, and Standards

Contract documents must comply with a wide variety of regulations from all levels of government. It is the designer's responsibility to ensure that the design conforms to all applicable laws. These laws have been developed by government to help ensure the health, safety, and welfare of all citizens. Federal and state regulations, local zoning laws, building codes, and fire codes must be reviewed and applied to the specifics of each project.

Federal administrative bodies administer statutes enacted by Congress in specific areas. These agencies create rules, regulate and supervise, and render decisions that have the force of law (Table 2.1). The contract documents must conform to these regulations (Figure 2.1).

FEDERAL REGULATIONS

For example, to protect consumers from dangerous products, Congress passed the Consumer Product Safety Act in 1972. The act established the Consumer Product Safety Commission (CPSC), which has the authority to issue safety and performance standards that guard against injury from hazardous items. One such regulation under CPSC jurisdiction is that all carpet sold in the United States must pass the Methenamine Pill Test (see page 52). Passing this test helps to ensure that a carpet will not contribute substantially to the spread of a fire. Other agencies, boards, and commissions that address issues of concern to designers include the Environmental Protection Agency (EPA), in regard to issues of indoor air quality and toxic substances, and the Architectural and Transportation Barriers Compliance Board (ATBCB), in regard to accessibility standards.

TABLE 2.1   U.S. GOVERNMENT AGENCIES INVOLVED IN BUILDING REGULATIONS

Abbreviation	Title	Mission	Key Organization Departments
DOC	Department of Commerce	Encourages, serves, and promotes international trade, economic growth, and technologic development.	NIST (National Institute of Standards and Technology) assists industry in developing technology to improve product quality. NIST develops generic technology and measurement techniques and standards.
HUD	Department of Housing and Urban Development	Responsible for programs concerned with improvement and development of housing and communities.	
DOL	Department of Labor	Promotes and develops the welfare of wage earners to improve their working conditions and advance their opportunities for profitable employment.	OSHA (Occupational Safety and Health Administration) develops and issues regulations and conducts inspections to determine status of compliance with regulations.
DOE	Department of Energy	Provides the framework for a comprehensive national energy plan.	
Independent Establishments			
CPSC	Consumer Product Safety Commission	Protects the public against unreasonable risks of injury from consumer products.	
EPA	Environmental Protection Agency	Protects and enhances the environment; controls and abates pollution in air, water, and land caused by solid waste, pesticides, radiation, and toxic substances.	
FTC	Federal Trade Commission	Strives to maintain competitive enterprise by keeping competition free and fair.	
ICC	Interstate Commerce Commission	Regulates surface transportation, assuring shipping rates and services that are fair and reasonable.	
ATBCB	Architectural and Transportation Barriers Compliance Board	Develops accessibility standards.	

Building Codes

A **building code** sets forth minimum requirements for design and construction in order to protect public health and safety. Such codes describe requirements for fire protection, structural design, sanitary facilities, light, and ventilation. Building codes do not contain criteria to assure efficient, comfortable, or beautiful buildings.

Building codes have been in existence since the Babylonian king Hammurabi's ancient law of retaliation. The first recorded building codes,

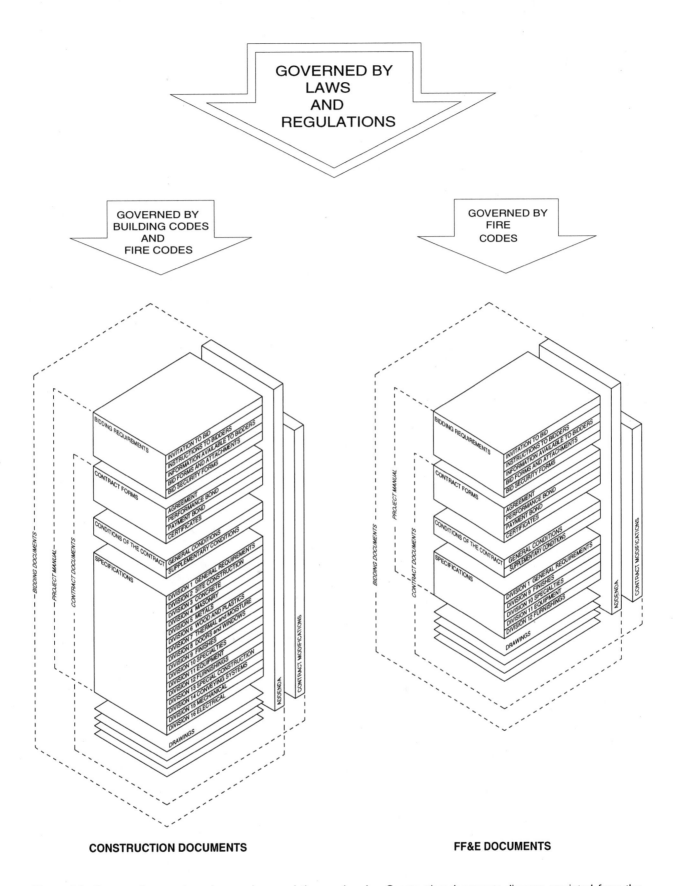

CONSTRUCTION DOCUMENTS

FF&E DOCUMENTS

Figure 2.1 Contract documents and governing regulations and codes. Construction documents diagram reprinted from the Construction Specifications Institute (CSI) *Manuel of Practice,* with permission from CSI, 1995.

dating from as early as 2000 B.C., concentrated on the prevention of building collapse. Modern building codes focus on protecting life and property from fire. They include provisions for exits for evacuation of occupants, the flame-spread requirements of interior finishes, and sprinkler systems. The first nationally recognized model building code written in the United States, entitled the National Building Code, was published in 1905 by the National Board of Fire Underwriters, a fire insurance industry concern.

Enforcing building codes and developing and revising them are two separate activities that are the responsibility of two separate entities. The administration and enforcement of building and other construction codes is typically performed by the local building department, including the chief building inspector and staff. This entity checks for code compliance, issues building permits, and inspects during and after completion of construction. Developing and updating code requirements is the responsibility of the model code organizations. There are three independent, nongovernmental organizations that maintain model building codes:

Building Officials and Code Administrators International (BOCA)
Southern Building Code Congress International (SBCCI)
International Conference of Building Officials (ICBO)

THE REVISION OF MODEL CODES

Generally, the three model codes are updated and published on a three-year cycle. Amendments are distributed in the two years between the issuing of the revised editions. Changing a model code is a consensus process. The model code organization appoints a committee, which listens to testimony and examines technical documentation regarding a proposed change. Anyone can submit a proposed change or testify at a model code hearing. The committee evaluates the information presented and makes its recommendations, which are then distributed to the members of the model code organization. Model code organization membership consists of building code enforcement officials, fire marshals and members of fire departments, trade associations, product and material manufacturers, architects, interior designers, builders, and any others who are concerned with the construction and furniture industries. Unchallenged recommendations are automatically approved; challenged recommendations are debated further.

Almost all building codes in the United States are adopted from one of the three model codes prepared by these organizations (Table 2.2). City, county, and state officials decide on which model code to adopt and, perhaps, amend. When a jurisdiction adopts a code, it becomes law (Figure 2.2).

The **BOCA National Building Code**, or the *Basic Building Code* as it is sometimes referred to, is published by Building Officials and Code Administrators International (BOCA). BOCA was organized in 1915 and is the oldest of the three code-sponsoring organizations. "National" in the

TABLE 2.2   MODEL CODE ORGANIZATIONS AND THEIR PUBLICATIONS

Sponsoring Organization	Model Building Code	Other Codes Offered by Sponsoring Organization
Building Officials and Code Administrators International (BOCA)	NBC—*National Building Code (or Basic Building Code)*	NFC—*National Fire Prevention Code (or Basic Fire Prevention Code)* NMC—*National Mechanical Code (or Basic Mechanical Code)* NPC—*National Plumbing Code (or Basic Plumbing Code)* NECC—*National Energy Conservation Code*
Southern Building Code Congress International (SBCCI)	SBC—*Standard Building Code*	SFC—*Standard Fire Prevention Code* SHC—*Standard Housing Code* SMC—*Standard Mechanical Code* SPC—*Standard Plumbing Code*
International Conference of Building Officials (ICBO)	UBC—*Uniform Building Code*	UFC—*Uniform Fire Code* UHC—*Uniform Housing Code* UMC—*Uniform Mechanical Code* UPC—*Uniform Plumbing Code*

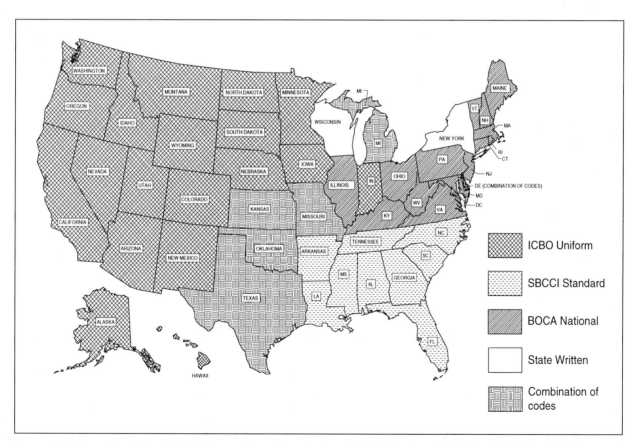

Figure 2.2 Map of model code jurisdictions. *Source: Introduction to Building Codes* published by the National Conference of States on Building Codes and Standards, Inc., 1994.

code's title is taken from the first U.S. building code, which has since been discontinued. The original *National Building Code* was published in 1905; BOCA first published its *Basic Building Code* in 1950. This code is widely adopted throughout the northeastern and mideastern regions of the United States.

The Southern Building Code Congress International (SBCCI) was organized in 1940 and first published the **Standard Building Code** in 1945. SBCCI has grown to include a variety of codes, including the only model gas code. This code is widely adopted throughout the southeastern states.

Organized in 1922, the International Conference of Building Officials (ICBO) first published the **Uniform Building Code** in 1927. Widely adopted in the western region of the United States, the *Uniform Building Code* also enjoys an international reputation, serving as the basis for the national codes of Brazil, Japan, and Saudi Arabia and for the buildings of the U.S. Army, Navy, and Air Force.

Uniformity in code requirements is the prime objective of the Council of American Building Officials (CABO). CABO was established in 1972 by the three nationally recognized model code organizations to further communications with legislative, federal, and industry organizations. CABO publishes the *CABO One and Two Family Dwelling Code*, a landmark document because it reached a consensus among BOCA, ICBO, and SBCCI. As a major step toward a single U.S. building code, in 1992 CABO authorized a Board for the Coordination of Model Codes (BCMC), which developed a code format acceptable to its members.

To determine a code's application to a particular project, two aspects of the building must be known: the use or occupancy and the type of construction. Typical occupancy designations for the three model codes include assembly, business, educational, hazardous, institutional, and residential. The type of construction is determined by the building materials used and the fire resistance rating of the structural elements and other building components. Categories of construction typically include steel and iron, reinforced concrete, and reinforced masonry, among other materials allowed within the jurisdiction.

Building codes can be confusing documents. Frequently, illustrated commentaries are prepared by the model code organizations to help designers understand the contents of the codes. Code commentaries help to clarify the application and intent of the various code provisions. Consultation with the building code officials who have authority in the project's jurisdiction is often required to assure that the code is being interpreted properly.

Fire Codes

Whereas a building department focuses on the enforcement of the building code, the local fire department is often concerned about a construction project's compliance with the fire code. Fire codes are typically performance based and deal primarily with the contents of a building and the preservation of human life. Fire codes differ from building codes in that they make little distinction between different types of construction. The chief of the fire department, the fire marshal, and the department's inspectors are responsible for the enforcement of the fire code. Just as there is no single U.S. building code, there is no universally adopted fire code in the United States.

Four model fire prevention codes are commonly referenced in the United States:

- *National Fire Prevention Code* (sometimes referred to as the *Basic Fire Prevention Code*), which is sponsored by BOCA and was the first fire code issued
- *Uniform Fire Code*, sponsored by ICBO
- *Standard Fire Prevention Code*, sponsored by SBCCI
- NFPA 101 *Life Safety Code*

The National Fire Protection Association **NFPA 101** *Life Safety Code* is the most widely referenced fire code in the United States. Originally used only as an advisory source, the *Life Safety Code* was revised in the 1940s in response to a national demand for fire safety legislation. Many federal agencies, states, and cities have adopted this code in its entirety or reference parts of it in their regulations. It includes requirements for exits (number, capacity, lighting, and their protection against fire and smoke), alarm systems for both occupants and the fire department, and fire drill procedures.

DEVELOPMENT OF FIRE CODES

Many fire codes and flammability standards have been developed as a direct result of significant fires. Work on the NFPA 101 *Life Safety Code* began in 1913 as a result of the Triangle Shirtwaist Company fire in New York City, which claimed the lives of 145 young women (Table 2.3). The initial investigation and the subsequent recommendations focused on the causes of loss of life in fires. In 1942, the Cocoanut Grove night club in Boston went up in flames, claiming 492 lives. Consequently, more stringent requirements for decorations were mandated, and revolving doors were no longer allowed as fire exits.

STANDARDS

Like building codes, the first industrial standards date back thousands of years, defining units of measure to ensure fair commercial transactions. As the Western world turned away from an agricultural-based economy, the standardization of parts and products was essential for industrial growth.

Building codes and fire codes are kept to a workable size by referencing standards, rather than including the detailed descriptions of materials, tests, and rating systems.

Standards are material specifications, practices, or test methods based on technical research and testing by industry experts. Standards are not laws unless they are incorporated by reference in a code. The standards referenced in building codes can be classified as material standards, engi-

TABLE 2.3   GREAT AMERICAN FIRES 1903–1942 AND THE EFFECT ON FIRE CODES

Date	Location	Property Destroyed	Life Loss	Constructive Results
1903	Chicago, Illinois	Iroquois Theatre	602	Improvements in construction of, and fire protection for, theaters
1904	Baltimore, Maryland	80 city blocks	0	Standardization of fire hydrant hose threads
1906	San Francisco, California	28,000 buildings	674	Reinforcement of windows, demonstrated need for auxiliary water towers
1908	Collinwood, Ohio	Lakeview Grammar School	175	Establishment of school fire drills
1911	New York, New York	Triangle Shirtwaist Company	145	Precursor to NFPA 101 Life Safety Code
1937	New London, Texas	Consolidated School	294	Demonstrated need for state laws as safeguards for public buildings not subject to municipal ordinances and inspections
1940	Natchez, Mississippi	Rhythm Club	207	Banning of combustible decorations, improvement of exit facilities, and installation of emergency lighting equipment in nightclubs
1942	Boston, Massachusetts	Cocoanut Grove	492	

Source: Reprinted with permission from *Principles of Fire Protection* by Percy Bugbee, © Copyright 1978, National Fire Protection Association, Quincy, MA 02269.

neering practice standards, and testing standards. Both public and private organizations publish standards.

The **American National Standards Institute** (ANSI) does not develop standards. ANSI coordinates the development of standards by private and government organizations. For example, some organizations prepare voluntary standards focused on their own areas of expertise. Because these standards may not represent a consensus of the industry, the sponsoring organizations often subject their standards to the ANSI consensus process to lend industrywide credibility to them. These standards are issued jointly by the sponsoring organizations and ANSI. The Business and Institutional Furniture Manufacturers Association (BIFMA), The Building Owners and Managers Association (BOMA), NFPA, and Underwriter's Laboratories (UL) are some examples of industry organizations that sponsor ANSI standards.

There are more than 8,000 ANSI standards covering a variety of products that are used in nearly all areas of life. ANSI standards include requirements for bicycle helmets, home appliances, and hospital supplies, to name just a few. ANSI also represents the United States in the International Standards Organization (ISO).

The **American Society for Testing and Materials** (ASTM) develops standards for products and materials used in manufacturing and construction. These cover a wide range of products, including thermal insulations, electrical insulating materials, textiles, building construction, paint, and resilient floor covering. ASTM committee membership is open to all and typically includes manufacturers, consumers, academics, government officials, architects, and interior designers. More than 600 ASTM standards are included by reference in the three model building codes.

The **National Fire Protection Association** (NFPA) is a private, voluntary, tax-exempt organization that serves as a primary source of fire protection information. The association develops standards concerned with the causes and prevention of destructive fires. As discussed earlier, it publishes the NFPA 101 *Life Safety Code*, a widely used fire code. NFPA codes and standards encompass the entire scope of fire prevention, including fire fighting, sprinkler systems, and portable fire extinguishers.

The **Underwriters Laboratory** (UL) was founded in 1894, with its sole objective being the promotion of public safety. Faced with fire hazards at the Palace of Electricity (featuring more than 100,000 incandescent light bulbs) at Chicago's World Columbian Exposition, city fire officials sought to perform tests on these new electrical devices. After the Exposition, with the support of insurance underwriters, the testing laboratory became the Underwriter's Electrical Bureau, later renamed Underwriters Laboratory in 1901.

The term "listed" in UL markings means that sample products have been tested and evaluated with regard to fire, electric shock, and other safety hazards (Figure 2.3). UL's field representatives make unannounced visits to manufacturing facilities to confirm that materials and products continue to comply with UL standards. Each product is listed in one of the product directories, such as the following:

Electrical Appliance and Utilization List
Electrical Construction Materials List
Hazardous Location Equipment List
Fire Protection Equipment List
Building Materials Directory
Gas and Oil Equipment List
Fire Resistance Index
Classified Products List

Figure 2.3 UL listing mark. UL Listing Mark provided by Underwriters Laboratories Inc.

The standardization of fire safety requirements and safety testing in the United States coincided roughly with the widespread introduction of electricity at the end of the nineteenth century. Insurance industry concern over the staggering number of fire-related claims was the driving force behind the development of objective safety standards.

For the most part, the test methods described in flammability standards aim to evaluate the fire resistant properties of a product or material in circumstances similar to those under which they are commonly installed or applied. The variety of flammability tests that apply to fabric provide a good example. There are separate flammability tests depending on whether the fabric is hung as a drapery, backed and applied as a wallcovering, or applied to an upholstered seat cushion (see page 67).

FLAMMABILITY STANDARDS

Most flammability test ratings are based on arbitrary scales and do not represent the actual physical properties of a material. A notable exception is the Radiant Flooring Panel Test, which measures the Critical Radiant Flux (CRF) in watts/cm^2 and establishes the threshold above which flame spread will occur.

Various code authorities, standard-setting organizations, and trade associations may slightly modify a flammability standard, perhaps changing the flame source or altering it so that the test better suits the capability of their testing facilities. Consequently, there are often several flammability standards that are so similar, they are essentially the same.

**Flammability
Standards for
Construction Materials
and Assemblies**

STEINER TUNNEL TEST

Commonly referred to as the "tunnel test," the Steiner Tunnel Test is named after Albert J. Steiner who developed this and many other test methods. Underwriter Laboratories built the first tunnel test chamber in about 1922. It is the oldest test used for interior finishes.

In 1968, through the adoption of a variety of test sample mounting methods, the Steiner Tunnel Test was expanded to include materials other than finishes. Mounting recommendations are included for adhesives, foams, wallcoverings, and heavy textiles. Test results can vary significantly, depending on the mounting method (Figure 2.4).

Figure 2.4 ASTM E 84, the Steiner Tunnel Test. The material to be tested, in this case a wall covering, is mounted using the same method and material that will be used on the project site. Courtesy of the Department of Fire Technology, Southwest Research Institute.

Objective:

To measure the horizontal flame spread and smoke development of interior finishes and building materials. This test simulates a situation in which everything in the room is on fire.

Test methods that are essentially the same:

ASTM E 84 — *Standard Test Method for Surface-Burning Characteristics of Building Materials*

NFPA 255 — *Method of Test of Surface-Burning Characteristics of Building Materials*

UBC 8-1 — *Standard Test Method for Surface-Burning Characteristics of Building Materials*

UL 723 — *Test Method for Surface Burning Characteristics of Building Materials*

Explanation of the Test:

A sample 7.3 m (24 ft) long and 53.3 cm (21 in) wide is mounted to the ceiling of a tunnel 7.6 m (25 ft) long. A gas burner at the end of the tunnel is ignited and allowed to burn for 10 minutes. A draft of air is forced through the test chamber, pulling the flame along the sample about 121.9 cm (4 ft) (Figure 2.5).

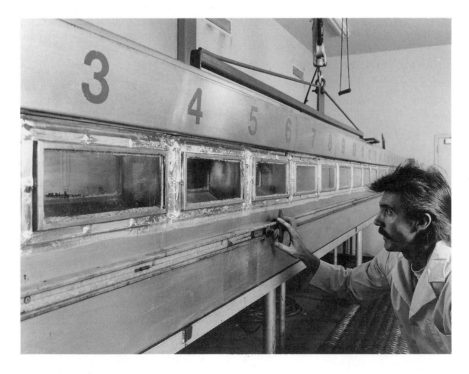

Figure 2.5 The 7.3-m-(24-ft-) long Steiner tunnel. The length the flame travels (referred to as the flame spread) down the sample is monitored through windows in the side of the tunnel test chamber. Courtesy of the Department of Fire Technology, Southwest Research Institute.

TABLE 2.4   FLAME-SPREAD CLASSIFICATIONS OF MODEL CODES

Flame-Spread Index	BOCA (NBC)	SBCCI (SBC)	ICBO (UBC)
0–25	I	A	I
26–75	II	B	II
76–200	III	C	III

Ratings:

The surface-burning characteristics of the test sample are compared with those of standard red oak flooring. This is essentially a test for surface flame spread, but it also provides measurements of smoke density.

The **flame-spread index** measures the maximum distance the flame spreads along the length of the sample. Glass-reinforced cement board (which is noncombustible) is given a flame spread rating of zero, and red oak flooring is arbitrarily given a rating of 100. Products are often described as being rated Class A or Class B in manufacturers' literature, referring to their flame-spread index. However, only one of the three model codes uses A, B, and C as designations (Table 2.4).

The **smoke density index** measures the light absorption properties of the smoke generated by the test. As with the flame-spread index, the smoke developed index for red oak is used as the reference.

Flammability Standards for Floor Coverings

METHENAMINE PILL TEST

Commonly referred to as the "pill test," the Methenamine Pill Test measures the response of carpet to a burning methenamine tablet (or pill). Since 1971, federal regulations have required that all carpet sold in the United States pass this test. Small carpets and rugs must be tested by, but are not required to pass, the pill test. If they do not pass, they must be labeled as flammable.

Objective:

To determine whether a carpet will spread a newly started fire.

Test methods that are essentially the same:

CPSC 16 CFR, Part 1630—*Standard for the Surface Flammability of Carpets and Rugs* (formerly DOC FF-1-70)

CPSC 16 CFR, Part 1631—*Standard for the Surface Flammability of Small Carpets and Rugs* [formerly DOC FF-2-70, for rugs that have no dimension greater than 1.83 m (6 ft) and an area not greater than 2.23 m (24 sq ft)]

ASTM D 2859—*Standard Test Method for Flammability of Finished Textile Floor Covering Materials*

Figure 2.6 The Methenamine Pill Test. A methenamine tablet (referred to as a pill) is centered on a carpet sample and ignited. Courtesy of the The Carpet and Rug Institute.

Explanation of the test:

A 22.9 cm (9 in) carpet square is placed under a metal plate with a 20.3 cm (8 in) diameter hole in the center. A methenamine tablet is placed in the center of the carpet sample and ignited. The flame is about 1.2 cm (1/2 in) in diameter and 2.5 cm (1 in) high. The distance the carpet burns beyond the ignition point is measured. The sample fails if the carpet burns to within 2.5 cm (1 in) of the metal plate (Figure 2.6).

Rating:

Pass or fail.

FLOORING RADIANT PANEL TEST

Floor coverings are not usually regarded as the primary cause of flame spread during a fire. However, flooring material in corridors has been observed to present problems in full-scale tests and actual building fires. In a fully developed fire, the combination of heat, flame, smoke, and gases emanating from burning rooms surrounding a corridor can make a substantial contribution to flame spread.

The Flooring Radiant Panel Test exposes the floor covering sample to radiant heat and igniting flames. This test was designed to simulate more realistic circumstances than the Steiner Tunnel Test, which mounts materials on the ceiling of the test chamber. The Flooring Radiant Panel Test is different from most other flammability test methods because it measures an actual property of the carpet system. It is not based on an arbitrary scale (Figure 2.7).

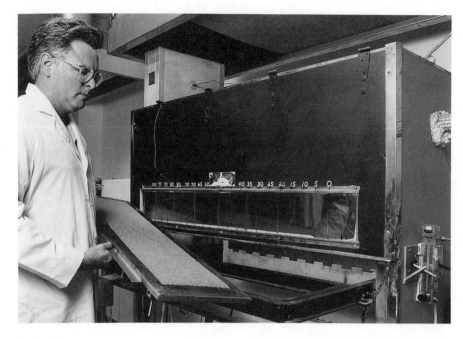

Figure 2.7 The Flooring Radiant Panel Test. The test sample, in this case, a carpet cushion, is mounted in a metal frame and placed in the test chamber. Courtesy of the Department of Fire Technology, Southwest Research Institute.

Objective:

To measure the ability of a floor covering to limit the progression of a fully developed fire through a corridor.

Test methods that are essentially the same:

ASTM E 648 — *Standard Test Method for Critical Radiant Flux of Floor Covering Systems Using a Radiant Heat Energy Source*

NFPA 253 — *Standard Method of Test for Critical Radiant Flux of Floor Covering Systems Using a Radiant Heat Energy Source*

Explanation of the test:

A sample is placed on the floor of the test chamber. It is preheated by a radiant panel, and a gas burner ignites the sample (Figure 2.8).

Figure 2.8 The flooring sample is preheated by a radiant panel and ignited to simulate the performance of flooring in a corridor surrounded by rooms with fully developed fires. Courtesy of the Department of Fire Technology, Southwest Research Institute.

Rating:

The distance the flooring system burns to extinguishment is converted to watts/cm^2 from a calibration graph and is reported as the Critical Radiant Flux (CRF). This value represents the threshold above which flame spread will occur. The higher the Critical Radiant Flux value, the more resistant the material is to flame propagation.

Class I. CRF of not less than 0.45 watts/cm^2 (typically required within corridors and exit ways of hospitals and nursing homes).

Class II. CRF of not less than 0.22 watts/cm^2 (typically required within corridors and exit ways of other occupancies, except one- and two-family dwellings).

ROOM CORNER TEST

Flammability Standards for Wall Finishes

The Room Corner Test for flammability was developed exclusively for textile wallcoverings. It was designed to simulate more realistic circumstances than the Steiner Tunnel Test, which mounts materials on the ceiling of the test chamber. The wall substrate, adhesive, and textile wallcovering to be used are installed in a near full-scale room and tested (Figure 2.9).

Figure 2.9 The Room Corner Test. The wall substrate, adhesive, and textile wall covering are installed and exposed to a flame source. Courtesy of the Department of Fire Technology, Southwest Research Institute.

Objective:

To determine the contribution to a room fire made by a wall finished with a textile wallcovering.

Test methods that are essentially the same:

NFPA 256—*Standard Methods of Fire Tests for Evaluating Room Fire Growth Contribution of Textile Wall Covering*

UBC 42-2—*Standard Test Method for Evaluating Room Fire Growth Contribution of Textile Wall Covering*

SBCCI—*Standard Test Method for Evaluating Room Fire Growth Contribution of Textile Wall Covering*

Explanation of the test:

The textile wallcovering is installed on three wall surfaces in a room that is 2.4 m x 3.7 m x 2.4 m (8 ft x 12 ft x 8 ft). The installation is exposed to a flame source of 40 kW for 5 minutes, which is then increased to 150 kW for 10 minutes (Figure 2.10).

Rating:

Pass or fail based on whether or not flashover occurs.

Figure 2.10 The Room Corner Test is monitored. Courtesy of the Department of Fire Technology, Southwest Research Institute.

WALL OR FLOOR AND CEILING ASSEMBLY TEST

Flammability Standards for Wall and Ceiling or Floor and Ceiling Assemblies

Prior to 1900, fire safety was *prescribed*, meaning certain building materials were required for use in various applications. After the turn of the century, however, innovations in construction technology and materials created a demand for standards that evaluate the fire *performance* of diverse wall, ceiling, and floor types. Thus the use of new materials was encouraged while fire safety was maintained. A fire endurance test was developed to determine an assembly's ability to prevent the travel of fire, heat, and gas. Floor and roof assemblies intended to be load-bearing structures are required to be loaded with weights simulating the mass of an actual structure, to more effectively evaluate the effect of fire on the integrity of structural elements.

Objective:

To evaluate the amount of time a burning assembly will contain a fire, retain its structural integrity, or both.

Test methods that are essentially the same:

ASTM E 119 — *Standard Test Methods for Fire Tests of Building Construction and Materials*

NFPA 251 — *Standard Test Methods for Fire Tests of Building Construction and Materials*

UBC 7-1 — *Fire Tests for Building Construction and Materials*

UL 263 — *Fire Tests for Building Construction and Materials*

Explanation of the test:

A sample of the wall or floor and ceiling assembly is built and tested. In some cases, after the fire test is completed, a fire hose is turned on the burning test sample to determine whether it can withstand fire fighting attempts.

Rating:

The result is reported in the form of an endurance time. Standard ratings are 1-hour, 2-hour, 3-hour, and 4-hour.

DOOR ASSEMBLY TEST

Flammability Standards for Door Assemblies

Separating areas of a building with fire-resistive walls restricts fires to their areas of origin and can limit their spread. Fire door assemblies are used to protect openings in these barriers. Usually, a fire door has a fire protection rating lower than that of the wall in which it is installed. This is allowed, because under normal conditions the area surrounding a door opening is clear, lessening the potential fire exposure in the vicinity of the door.

Objective:

To evaluate the ability of a door and frame to remain in an opening during a fire.

Test methods that are essentially the same:

ASTM E 152 — *Standard Methods of Fire Test of Door Assemblies*
NFPA 252 — *Fire Tests of Door Assemblies*
UBC 7-2 — *Fire Tests of Door Assemblies*
UL 10B — *Fire Tests of Door Assemblies*

Explanation of the test:

Similar to the test for wall or floor and ceiling systems (ASTM E 119) (Figure 2.11).

Rating:

The result is reported in the form of an endurance time. Standard ratings are 20-minute, 30-minute, and 90-minute.

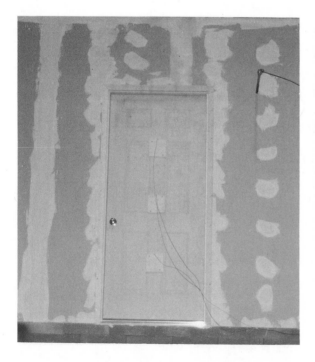

Figure 2.11a A door and frame to be tested are installed in a wall. Sensors are attached to the door to monitor the test. Courtesy of the Department of Fire Technology, Southwest Research Institute.

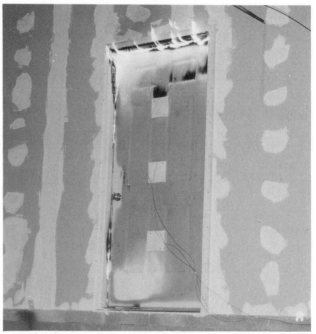

Figure 2.11b The fire rating of a door is based on the amount of time it takes for the flame to penetrate the closed door. Courtesy of the Department of Fire Technology, Southwest Research Institute

CIGARETTE IGNITION RESISTANCE TEST FOR FURNITURE COMPOSITES

Flammability Standards for Furniture

The Cigarette Ignition Resistance Test for Furniture Composites is a composite test. The seating components (the foam, liner, and fabric) to be used in the piece of upholstered furniture are tested together. This test simulates the way in which a seat cushion will respond to a burning cigarette without the expense of destroying an actual chair (Figure 2.12).

Figure 2.12a The Cigarette Ignition Resistance Test of Furniture Composites. Lighted cigarettes are placed on a mockup of the seating components—the foam, liner, and upholstery fabric—simulating a fire that would result from a burning cigarette left on a chair seat. Courtesy of the Department of Fire Technology, Southwest Research Institute.

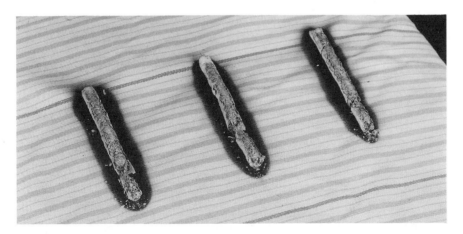

Figure 2.12b The mockup fails the flammability test if the char develops more than 2.5 cm (2 in) in any direction or if it breaks into flames. Courtesy of the Department of Fire Technology, Southwest Research Institute.

Objective:

To determine the resistance to ignition of a piece of upholstered furniture.

Test methods that are essentially the same:

> State of California, Department of Consumer Affairs, Bureau of Home Furnishings and Thermal Insulation, Technical Bulletin 116 — *Requirements, Test Procedure and Apparatus for Testing the Flame Retardance of Upholstered Furniture*
>
> BIFMA F-1 — *First Generation Voluntary Upholstered Furniture Flammability Standard for Business and Institutional Markets*
>
> NFPA 261 — *Standard Method of Test for Determining Resistance of Mock-up Upholstered Furniture Material Assemblies to Ignition by Smoldering Cigarettes*

Explanation of the test:

Three lighted cigarettes are placed on the mock-up. To intensify the heat, the cigarettes are covered with cotton sheeting.

Rating:

The upholstered furniture composite fails the test if the char develops more than 2.5 cm (2 in) in any direction or if there is flaming combustion.

CIGARETTE IGNITION RESISTANCE TEST OF FURNITURE COMPONENTS

The Cigarette Ignition Resistance Test of Furniture Components is a component test. It evaluates the flammability properties of the upholstered furniture materials (fabric and fillings) separately. The filling materials are required to be both flame resistant and cigarette-ignition resistant. In California, all upholstered seating must pass this test.

Objective:

To determine the resistance to flame and cigarette ignition of individual upholstered furniture materials.

Test methods that are essentially the same:

> UFAC *Fabric Standard Classification Test Method*
>
> NFPA 260 — *Standard Method of Test and Classification System for Cigarette Ignition Resistance of Components of Upholstered Furniture*

Test method that is similar:

State of California, Department of Consumer Affairs, Bureau of Home Furnishings and Thermal Insulation, Technical Bulletin 117—*Requirements, Test Procedure and Apparatus for Testing the Flame Retardance of Resilient Filling Materials Used in Upholstered Furniture*

Explanation of the test:

Upholstery materials, resilient cellular materials, expanded polystyrene beads, non-man-made filling materials, feathers and down, and man-made fiber filling materials are tested separately for a variety of fire test response characteristics including flame spread, cigarette resistance, and smoldering resistance.

Rating:

Pass or fail.

FULL SEATING TEST

The most stringent flammability test available for seating in commercial interiors is commonly referred to as "Cal Tech 133," after the original test method (see Appendix D). Compliance with this test is required in some jurisdictions for commercial interiors with high-risk occupancies, such as jails, nursing homes, health care facilities, auditoriums, and hotels.

Component tests do not measure the effects of combinations of different materials, the geometry of the chair, or toxic fumes generated during a fire. This test, however, takes all these factors into account. Because an actual chair (sometimes a prototype) is tested, a seating unit is destroyed in the process.

Most manufacturers can modify their seating to comply with the standards measured by this test. Compliance is typically achieved by adding an aramid underliner (fire-barrier fabric) or another flame-retardant fabric between the cushion and upholstery materials. Fire-resistant thread, typically fiberglass, must be used to sew the fabrics. When exposed to fire, the barrier decomposes into ash, extinguishing the surface flames and sealing the filling materials against exposure to air and heat. Compliance with Cal Tech 133 can also be achieved with the use of special flame-retardant cushions. Talc or clay is added to these foams to fill the air pockets that support combustion. The abrasive action of these fillers can break down the foam, reducing the life of the seating unit.

Objective:

To determine the fire performance characteristics of seating exposed to an open flame, for example, an arson attempt, as opposed to a burning cigarette.

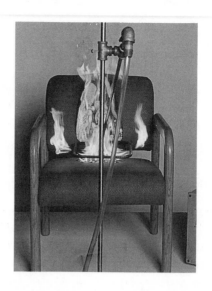

Figure 2.13a *California Technical Bulletin 133*. Compliance with *California Technical Bulletin 133* is typically achieved by adding a fire-blocker fabric between the cushion and the upholstery fabric. A chair is exposed to a flame source. Photo courtesy of the Du Pont Company.

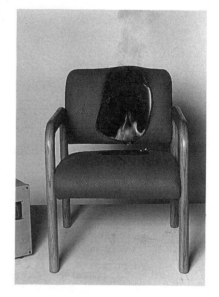

Figure 2.13b, c Chair with a fire-blocker fabric liner self-extinguishes after the flame source is removed. Photo courtesy of the Du Pont Company.

Figure 2.13d, e Chair without a fire-blocker fabric liner bursts into flames. Photo courtesy of the Du Pont Company.

Test methods that are essentially the same:

State of California, Department of Consumer Affairs, Bureau of Home Furnishings and Thermal Insulation, Technical Bulletin 133 — *Flammability Test Procedure for Seating Furniture for Use in Public Occupancies*

NFPA 266 — *Standard Method of Test for Fire Characteristics of Upholstered Furniture Exposed to Flaming*

BFD IX-10 — *Boston Fire Department Chair Test*

UL 1056 — *Fire Test of Upholstery Furniture*

ASTM E 1537 — *Test Method for Fire Testing of Real Scale Upholstered Furniture Item*

Explanation of the test:

A large flame is held 2.5 cm (1 in) above the seat and 5 cm (2 in) from the seat back for 80 seconds. Various measurements are taken until the burning stops. (Figure 2.13).

Rating:

Pass or fail. Rate of heat release, smoke obscuration, and carbon monoxide are measured.

VERTICAL IGNITION TEST

Flammability Standards for Furnishings

NFPA 701 defines two tests used for hanging fabrics and some window treatments: small-scale and large-scale. Fabrics may be required to pass the small-scale test, large-scale test, or both, depending on the intended use. This standard is currently being revised to include multiple layers of fabrics, for example, lined draperies. The model codes do not usually require fire retardance of free-hanging materials such as draperies. Requirements for these applications are often covered by the city or state fire marshall and depend on the type of occupancy.

Objective of small-scale test:

To determine the ignition resistance of fabrics restrained in a vertical position to a 38 mm (1½ in) flame.

Objective of large-scale test:

To determine the ignition resistance of fabric hung in a vertical position to a 280 mm (11 in) flame. This test simulates drapery and hospital cubicle curtain applications.

Test methods:

NFPA 701 — *Standard Methods of Fire Tests for Flame-Resistant Textiles and Films*

UL 214 — *Test for Flame Propagation of Fabrics and Films*

Figure 2.14 NFPA 701, the Vertical Ignition Test. A flame is held in contact with the fabric to be tested. Courtesy of the Department of Fire Technology, Southwest Research Institute.

Explanation of the tests:

For the small-scale test, fabric samples are restrained vertically in a metal frame. A 50 x 250 mm (2 x 10 in) section of the fabric remains exposed. A flame is held in contact with the sample for 12 seconds. The resulting after flame, flaming drip, weight loss, and char length are measured.

The large-scale test describes two different options for preparing fabric samples. The fabric is hung in folds or in a single sheet, whichever more closely approximates its end use, and is exposed to a flame for 2 minutes. The after flame, drip burn, and char length are measured (Figure 2.14).

Rating:

Pass or fail.

MATTRESSES AND MATTRESS PADS

Since 1972, a test for mattresses and mattress pads has been required by federal law. It was the first flammability test required for furniture.

Objective:

To measure the resistance to cigarette ignition of a mattress and pad.

Test methods that are essentially the same:

CPSC 16 CFR, Part 1632—*Standard for the Flammability of Mattresses and Mattress Pads* (formerly DOC FF-4-72)

State of California, Department of Consumer Affairs, Bureau of Home Furnishings and Thermal Insulation, Technical Bulletin 106, California Administrative Code Title 4, Chapter 3, Section 1371— *Requirements, Test Procedures and Apparatus for Testing the Resistance of a Mattress or Mattress Pad to Combustion Which May Result from a Smoldering Cigarette*

Explanation of the test:

Eighteen lighted cigarettes are placed on the surface of the mattress. Half are covered with cotton sheeting to intensify the heat. The other half remain uncovered. After the cigarettes burn out, the mattress is then turned over, and the bottom surface is tested.

Rating:

Pass or fail.

SMOKE DENSITY

Smoke generated by fire inhibits vision and breathing, making escape more difficult. The smoke density test measures the density of smoke that affects visibility during egress from a fire. It does not measure the effect of eye irritants, which can significantly limit the visual range. The transmission of light through smoke generated from a cube of solid material is measured. The first smoke density chamber was developed at the National Institute for Standards and Technology (formerly NBS) in 1967.

Objective:

To measure the amount of smoke given off by a flaming or smoldering material.

Test methods that are essentially the same:

ASTM E 662—*Standard Test Method for Specific Optical Density of Smoke Generated by Solid Materials*

NFPA 258—*Standard Research Test Method for Determining Smoke Generation of Solid Materials*

Explanation of the test:

A test sample is exposed to a heat source in an airtight chamber for a two-part test. During part one, smoke during the smoldering state is measured. A flame source is added, and smoke during the flaming state is measured. A smoke-density value is determined (Figures 2.15).

Figure 2.15a The Smoke Density Test. A test sample, foam insulation in this case, is mounted in a frame. Courtesy of the Department of Fire Technology, Southwest Research Institute.

Figure 2.15b The sample is placed in the airtight smoke density chamber and exposed to a smoldering heat source. Courtesy of the Department of Fire Technology, Southwest Research Institute.

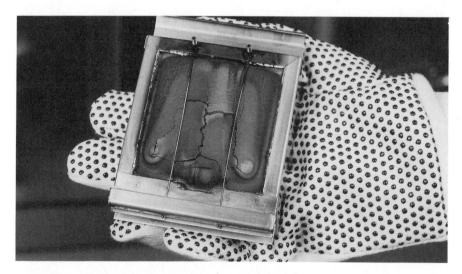

Figure 2.15c The foam insulation test sample after completion of the Smoke Density Test. Courtesy of the Department of Fire Technology, Southwest Research Institute.

Rating:

Smoke-density is reported in terms of maximum optical density based on an arbitrary scale of zero to 800. Most jurisdictions require a smoke-density rating of 450 or less.

Fabric can be used as a wallcovering, draperies, upholstery material, or floor covering. The appropriate test for fabric flammability depends on its application. Table 2.5 lists the applicable flammability tests described earlier for a variety of fabric applications.

Flammability Standards for Fabric

TABLE 2.5   FABRIC APPLICATION AND FLAMMABILITY REQUIREMENTS

Application	Applicable Flammability Tests	Refer to Page
Attached to a Wall		
Stretched fabric wall systems Freestanding furniture panels Tackboards Acoustic panels	Steiner Tunnel Test	54
Wall coverings	Room Corner Test	55
Free Hanging		
Window treatments Banners and flags	Vertical Ignition Test	63
Seating		
Upholstery	Cigarette Ignition Resistance Test of Furniture Components	60
Floor Covering		
Carpet Carpet tile	Flooring Radiant Panel Test	53
Rugs	Methenamine Pill Test	52

Materials

METALS

Metals are generally categorized by their iron content (Table 3.1). **Ferrous** (from the Latin *ferrum,* meaning "iron") metals consist mostly of iron. Steel, for example, is a ferrous metal. **Nonferrous** metals contain little or no iron, generally have good corrosion resistance, and are nonmagnetic. Nonferrous metals include copper and aluminum. Desirable properties of different metals can often be combined by mixing metals together to form **alloys**.

The production techniques used to achieve various metal shapes are dependent on the properties of the metal. **Cast** metal products are produced by pouring molten material into a mold. **Extruded** shapes are produced by forcing semimolten material through a die. Long linear shapes are produced by extrusion. **Forged** shapes are hammered, pressed, or rolled into the desired configuration. **Wrought** metal shapes are formed by rolling the metal into sheets and then punching or cutting out the required flat shape.

Dissimilar Metals

When dissimilar metals are connected by an electrolyte, a current, called a galvanic current, flows from one to the other. An **electrolyte** is any liquid that conducts electricity, for example, water. The current causes one

TABLE 3.1   METALS

Ferrous (contain iron)	Nonferrous (contain little or no iron)
Steel	Copper
Stainless Steel	Aluminum
	Tin
	Magnesium

TABLE 3.2   GALVANIC SCALE

CORRODED (ANODIC) END/MORE NOBLE

Zinc
Aluminum
Galvanized Steel
Cadmium
Mild Steel, Wrought Iron
Cast Iron
Stainless Steel, Types 304 and 316 (active)
Lead-Tin Solder
Lead
Brass, Bronze
Copper
Stainless Steel, Types 304 and 316 (passive)

PROTECTED (CATHODIC) END/LESS NOBLE

Source: SMACNA *Architectural Sheet Metal Manual*, 5th ed., 1993, with permission.

of the metals to deteriorate, and this reaction is called **galvanic corrosion**. The threat of galvanic corrosion is greatest in exterior applications where materials are exposed to rain or high humidity. However, even in interior applications galvanic corrosion is of concern. Dissimilar metals in contact with each other, including nails, screws, and bolts, must be coated with or separated by a nonabsorbent, nonconductive material.

Metals that are higher on the galvanic scale (see Table 3.2) will corrode when electrolytically connected to metals that are lower on the scale. The metal that is more anodic will corrode, or lose material to, the metal that is more cathodic. The farther apart metals are on the scale, the more rapid the corrosion.

In addition to the dissimilarity of metals, the amount of metal also plays a part in galvanic corrosion (see Table 3.3). The less noble (inactive or inert) metal will more likely corrode severely if its surface area is small in comparison with the more noble metal. For example, aluminum (more noble) screws used to fasten a sheet of stainless steel (less noble) to a wall would present a serious corrosion problem in the presence of an electrolyte. But stainless steel screws in an aluminum sheet would give an acceptable performance.

Metal Finishes

There are two primary references for metal finishes—one for metal sheets and shapes and one specifically for hardware. Metal finishing for aluminum, copper alloys, stainless steel, carbon steel, and iron is described in the *Metal Finishes Manual* published by the Architectural Metal Products Division (AMP) of the National Association of Architectural Metal Manufacturers (NAAMM). The Builders Hardware Manufacturers Association (BHMA) sponsors ANSI A156.18 *American National Standard for Materials and Finishes,* which establishes finishes for metal hardware.

TABLE 3.3   GUIDELINES FOR SELECTION OF FASTENERS BASED ON GALVANIC ACTION

Fastener Metal ——————→ ↓ Base Metal ↓	Zinc and Galvanized Steel	Aluminum and Aluminum Alloys	Steel and Cast Iron	Brasses, Copper, Bronzes, Monel	Martensitic Stainless Type 410	Austenitic Stainless Types 302/304, 303, 305
Zinc and Galvanized Steel	A	B	B	C	C	C
Aluminum and Aluminum Alloys	A	A	B	C	Not Recommended	B
Steel and Cast Iron	AD	A	A	C	C	B
Terne (Lead-Tin) Plated Steel Sheets	ADE	AE	AE	C	C	B
Brasses, Copper, Bronzes, Monel	ADE	AE	AE	A	A	B
Ferritic Stainless Steel (Type 430)	ADE	AE	AE	A	A	A
Austenitic Stainless Steel (Type 302/304)	ADE	AE	AE	AE	A	A

Key: A. The corrosion of the base metal is not increased by the fastener.
 B. The corrosion of the base metal is marginally increased by the fastener.
 C. The corrosion of the base metal may be markedly increased by the fastener material.

 D. The plating on the fastener is rapidly consumed, leaving the bare fastener metal.
 E. The corrosion of the fastener is increased by the base metal.
 Note: Surface treatment and environment can change activity.

Source: Nickel Development Institute, *Design Guidelines for the Selection and Use of Stainless Steel,* Toronto, Ontario, 1991, p. 51.

There is a third reference for metal finishes that some manufacturers still use. The Department of Commerce, Commercial Standard CS22-40, used the designation "US" to define metal finishes. However, this standard was discontinued after World War II. For easy comparison, ANSI A156.18 lists the nearest US equivalents to the BHMA designation (Table 3.4).

FINISHING PROCESSES

AMP 500 *Introduction to Metal Finishing* describes the three basic finish types—mechanical, chemical, and coating—for various metals (Table 3.5). **Mechanical finishes** are accomplished by buffing, grinding, polishing, or otherwise texturing the metal surface for a specific appearance. **Chemical finishes** involve the reaction of various solutions on the metal surface. These finishes may or may not have an effect on the performance of a metal surface. **Coatings** are either materials applied to the metal or formed by the metal itself through a chemical or electrochemical process.

All three finish types are used extensively on aluminum. Coatings are far more important in carbon steel and iron finishes. Copper alloys are commonly finished with both mechanical and chemical methods. Stainless steel is most frequently finished by mechanical means.

TABLE 3.4   BHMA FINISH DESIGNATIONS (PARTIAL LIST)

BHMA Code No.	Description	U.S. Designation
FINISHES FOR ALUMINUM HARDWARE		
627	Satin aluminum, clear coated	US27
628	Satin aluminum, clear anodized	US28
666	Bright brass plated, clear coated	US3
667	Satin brass plated, clear coated	US4
668	Satin bronze plated, clear coated	US10
671	Flat black coated	US19
672	Bright chromium plated	US26
FINISHES FOR STAINLESS STEEL HARDWARE		
629	Bright stainless steel, 300 Series	US32
630	Satin stainless steel, 300 Series	US32D
FINISHES FOR CARBON STEEL HARDWARE		
631	Flat black coated	US19
633	Satin brass plated, clear coated	US4
637	Bright bronze plated, clear coated	US9
639	Satin bronze plated, clear coated	US10
640	Oxidized satin bronze plated, oil rubbed	US10B
649	Light oxidized statuary bronze plated, clear coated	US20
650	Dark oxidized statuary bronze plated, clear coated	US20A
651	Bright chromium plated	US26
652	Satin chromium plated	US26D
FINISHES FOR BRASS AND BRONZE HARDWARE		
605	Bright brass, clear coated	US3
606	Satin brass, clear coated	US4
611	Bright bronze, clear coated	US9
612	Satin bronze, clear coated	US10
613	Dark oxidized satin bronze, oil rubbed	US10B
622	Flat black coated	US19
623	Light oxidized statuary bronze, clear coated	US20
624	Dark oxidized statuary bronze, clear coated	US20A
625	Bright chromium plated	US26
626	Satin chromium plated	US26D
632	Bright brass plated, clear coated	US3

ALUMINUM

Nonferrous Metals

Aluminum is truly a modern material. Although it was first detected as a mineral in the early 1800s, it was not until the end of that century that the processing technique was developed that gave birth to the modern aluminum industry. About 8% of the earth's crust is composed of aluminum, making it the world's most plentiful metal. Unlike the ores of gold

TABLE 3.5   COMPARATIVE APPLICABILITY OF THE VARIOUS FINISHES FOR ARCHITECTURAL APPLICATIONS

Type of Finish or Treatment	Metal			
	Aluminum	Copper Alloys	Stainless Steel	Carbon Steel and Iron
MECHANICAL FINISHES				
As Fabricated	——————————— Common to All of the Metals ——————————— *(produced by hot rolling, cold rolling, extruding, or casting)*			
Bright Rolled	——————— commonly used ——————— *(produced by cold rolling)*			Not used
Directional Grit Textured	——————— commonly used ——————— *(produced by polishing, buffing, hand rubbing or cold rolling)*			Rarely used
Non-Directional Matte Textured	——————— commonly used ——————— *(produced by sand or shot blasting)*			Rarely used
Bright Polished	——————— commonly used ——————— *(produced by polishing and buffing)*			Not used
Patterned	——————— available in light sheet gages of all metals ———————			
CHEMICAL FINISHES				
Nonetch Cleaning	——————— Commonly Used on All of the Metals ———————			
Matte Finish	Etched finishes Widely used	Seldom used	Not used	Not used
Bright Finish	Limited uses	Rarely used	Not used	Not used
Conversion Coatings	Widely used as pretreatment for painting	Widely used to provide added color variations	Not used	Widely used as pretreatment for painting
COATINGS				
Anodic	Most important type of finish	Not used	Not used	Not used
Organic	Widely used	Opaque types rarely used; transparent types common	Sometimes used	Most important type of finish
Vitreous	Widely used	Limited use	Not used	Widely used
Metallic	Rarely used	Limited use	Limited use	Widely used
Laminated	Substantial uses	Limited use	Not used	Substantial uses

Source: Introduction to Metal Finishing, AMP 500, p. 3. Reprinted with permission of the National Association of Architectural Metal Manufacturers (NAAMM), Chicago, IL, 1988.

and silver, aluminum ore is not found free in nature. It is always chemically combined with other elements and must therefore be extracted.

A unique combination of properties make aluminum the most versatile metal. Aluminum is soft and flexible, allowing it to be easily fabricated. It is light in weight and yet remarkably strong. Some aluminum alloys have a greater strength than structural steel. Unlike steel, it is highly resistant to corrosion. Aluminum is an excellent thermal and electrical conductor; electrical wiring is often made of aluminum. Aluminum is used for door frames and hardware, interior window frames, horizontal louver blind slats, and contemporary furniture.

Aluminum Finishes

Because it is inherently corrosion resistant, aluminum often requires no special finish. A protective oxide film forms rapidly and naturally on the surface when exposed to air. Aluminum is, however, susceptible to attack by alkaline chemicals such as those found in concrete and masonry mortar.

Finishes are frequently applied to aluminum for decorative purposes (Table 3.6). Conversion coatings are generally used to prepare the metal for painting, but can also be used as final finishes. Because aluminum's natural oxide film does not always provide a good bonding surface for

TABLE 3.6   SUMMARY OF STANDARD DESIGNATIONS FOR ALUMINUM FINISHES

All designations are to be preceded by the letters AA, to identify them as Aluminum Association designations. Finishes printed in **boldface** type are those most frequently used on architectural work.

MECHANICAL FINISHES (M)

As Fabricated	Buffed	Directional Textured	Non-Directional Textured
M10—Unspecified	M20—Unspecified	M30—Unspecified	M40—Unspecified
M11—Specular as fabricated	**M21—Smooth specular**	M31—Fine satin	M41—Extra fine matte
M12—Non-specular as fabricated	M22—Specular	**M32—Medium satin**	**M42—Fine matte**
M1x—Other	M2x—Other	M33—Coarse satin	**M43—Medium matte**
		M34—Hand rubbed	**M44—Coarse matte**
		M35—Brushed	M45—Fine shot blast
		M3x—Other	**M46—Medium shot blast**
			M47—Coarse shot blast
			M4x—Other

CHEMICAL FINISHES (C)

Non-Etched Cleaned	Etched	Brightened	Conversion Coatings
C10—Unspecified	C20—Unspecified	C30—Unspecified	C40—Unspecified
C11—Degreased	C21—Fine matte	C31—Highly specular	C41—Acid chromate-fluoride
C12—Chemically cleaned	**C22—Medium matte**	C32—Diffuse bright	C42—Acid chromate-fluoride-phosphate
C1x—Other	C23—Coarse matte	C3x—Other	C43—Alkaline chromate
	C2x—Other		C44—Non-chromate
			C45—Non-rinsed chromate
			C4x—Other

COATINGS—ANODIC (A)

General	Protective and Decorative	Architectural Class II	Architectural Class I
A10—Unspecified anodic coating	A21*—Clear (natural)	**A31—Clear (natural)**	**A41—Clear (natural)**
A11—Preparation for other applied coatings	A22*—Integral color	**A32—Integral color**	**A42—Integral color**
A12—Chromic acid anodic coating	A23*—Impregnated color	**A33—Impregnated color**	**A43—Impregnated color**
	A24—Electrolytically deposited color	**A34—Electrolytically deposited color**	**A44—Electrolytically deposited color**
	A2x—Other	A3x—Other	A4x—Other
A13—Hard coating			
A1x—Other	*Third digit (1, 2, or 3) added to designate min. thickness in $\frac{1}{10}$ mils.		

For example, AA-M12C22A31 specifies a nonspecular mechanical finish as fabricated; an etched, medium matte, chemical finish; with a clear anodic coating 0.01 mm (0.4 mil) or thicker.

Note: The Aluminum Association (AA) and NAAMM use the same designation system for aluminum and its alloys.

Source: Finishes for Aluminum, AMP 501, page 16. Reprinted with permission of the National Association of Architectural Metal Manufacturers (NAAMM), Chicago, IL. 1988.

coatings, the surface is "converted" to one with improved adhesion if a coating is desired.

The most common finish that is applied principally to aluminum and its alloys is the anodic coating. **Anodizing** involves passing an electrical current across a solution (most commonly sulfuric acid) in which the aluminum is immersed. The process is called anodizing, because the metal itself serves as the anode (the electrode at which oxidation [build-up] occurs, as opposed to the cathode, the electrode at which reduction [corrosion] occurs). The resulting coating is much thicker than the naturally formed aluminum oxide coating—as thick as 0.030 mm (0.0012 in) —as opposed to the oxide film of less than a millionth of a millimeter thick. The thicker anodized coating provides increased corrosion resistance. Anodized coatings can be transparent, translucent, or opaque and can increase surface abrasion resistance without changing the surface texture.

COPPER

Copper is readily available, easily fabricated, and corrosion resistant under a wide range of conditions. Copper is not affected by alkaline chemicals and so is often used where metal to masonry contact is required.

Prolonged exposure of an untreated copper surface results in a brown and, eventually, green patina. A **patina** is a thin layer of corrosion resulting from oxidation. Copper's appearance can be restored by polishing the surface to remove the oxide film. The metallic surface can also be preserved by the application of a transparent coating.

Copper can be made harder and stronger by adding small amounts of tin. **Bronze** was originally a copper-tin alloy, but the term today is used to identify other alloys with a bronze color. **Brass**, a copper-zinc alloy, is commonly used for door hardware and upholstered furniture tacks.

In interior applications, the greatest use of copper is in electrical wiring; it has the second highest conductivity of any material (silver's is only slightly higher). Copper is also popular for use in plumbing supply pipes and fittings.

Copper Finishes
The Copper Development Association (CDA) and NAAMM use the same designation system for copper and its alloys (Table 3.7).

Ferrous Metals

IRON

About 5% of the earth's crust is composed of iron. **Wrought iron** is made from iron ore that is heated until it is soft but not melted. **Cast iron** contains a large amount of carbon, making it so hard and brittle that it cannot be worked into the required shape but must be cast into molds. Plumbing drainage pipes and ornamental rails for exterior applications are often made from cast iron.

TABLE 3.7   SUMMARY OF STANDARD DESIGNATIONS FOR COPPER ALLOY FINISHES

In this listing, those finishes that are printed in **boldface** type are the ones most frequently used for general architectural work; those marked * are commonly used for hardware items.

MECHANICAL FINISHES (M)

As Fabricated	Buffed	Directional Textured	Non-directional Textured
M10—Unspecified	M20—Unspecified	M30—Unspecified	M40—Unspecified
M11—Specular as fabricated	M21—Smooth specular*	M31—Fine satin*	M41—(Unassigned)
M12—Matte finish as fabricated	M22—Specular*	**M32—Medium satin**	**M42—Fine matte***
M1x—Other (to be specified)	M2x—Other (to be specified)	**M33—Coarse satin**	M43—Medium matte
		M34—Hand rubbed	M44—Coarse matte
		M35—Brushed*	M45—Fine shot blast
		M36—Uniform	M46—Medium shot blast
		M3x—Other (to be specified)	M47—Coarse shot blast
			M4x—Other (to be specified)

CHEMICAL FINISHES (C)

Non-Etched Cleaned	Conversion Coatings	
C10—Unspecified	**C50—Ammonium chloride**	(patina)
C11—Degreased	**C51—Cuprous chloride— hydrochloric acid**	(patina)
C12—Cleaned	**C52—Ammonium sulfate**	(patina)
C1x—Other (to be specified)	C53—Carbonate	(patina)
	C54—Oxide	(statuary)
	C55—Sulfide*	(statuary)
	C56—Selenide	(statuary)
	C5x—Other (to be specified)	

COATINGS—CLEAR ORGANIC (O)

Air Dry (Gen'l arch'l work)	Thermoset (Hardware)	Chemical Cure
060—Unspecified	070—Unspecified	080—Unspecified
06x—Other (to be specified)	07x—Other (to be specified)	08x—Other (to be specified)

COATINGS—LAMINATED (L)

L90—Unspecified
L91—Clear Polyvinyl Fluoride
L9x—Other (to be specified)

COATINGS—VITREOUS AND METALLIC

Since the use of these finishes in architectural work is rather infrequent, it is recommended that they be specified in full, rather than being identified by number.

COATINGS—OILS AND WAXES

These applied coatings are primarily used for maintenance purposes on-site. Because of the broad range of materials in common use, it is recommended that, where desired, such coatings be specified in full.

Source: Finishes for the Copper Alloys, AMP 502, page 12. Reprinted with permission of the National Association of Architectural Metal Manufacturers (NAAMM), Chicago, IL. 1988.

STEEL

Steel comprises the various alloys of iron and carbon. More than 90% of the steel manufactured into finished products is carbon steel. **Carbon steel** contains up to 1.20% carbon. Generally, no other alloying elements are added. It is reasonably strong but has poor resistance to corrosion. **Galvanizing** is the application of zinc to the surface of cast iron, steel, or steel alloys to prevent corrosion. The coating can be applied in one of two ways: it can be hot dipped or electroplated. Carbon steel is popular for use in structural steel beams, concrete reinforcing bars, and door hardware.

STAINLESS STEEL

Stainless steel is an iron alloy that is inherently corrosion resistant because of the addition of chromium. The self-healing chromium-oxide forms a transparent film on the surface of the steel, preventing oxidation (rust). Stainless steel alloys contain at least 50% iron and 10.5% chromium.

Stainless steel is not affected by mortar or concrete and does not stain adjacent surfaces. It is popular for use in commercial interiors as column covers and railings. Its finish retention capability also makes it useful in food preparation and surgical equipment, kitchen sinks, and fine eating utensils.

The American Iron and Steel Institute (AISI) originated the designation system that indicates the chemical composition and the manufacturing process of stainless steel. Today, the Iron and Steel Society (ISS), the Nickel Development Association (NDA), and NAAMM use the same designations for stainless steel finishes (Table 3.8). The 200 series alloys contain magnesium in addition to chromium and nickel. The 200 and 300 series alloys are **austenitic** (normally nonmagnetic). Austenitizing, the process of heating steel above a certain temperature to cause certain components to transform to austenite, is named after Sir William Roberts-Austen, who invented the process. The 300 series is more corrosion resistant and is easier to fabricate and weld than any other type of stainless steel. Series 400 does not contain nickel and is therefore less corrosion resistant (see Table 3.9).

Although stainless steel is available in approximately 60 different alloys, Types 302 and 304 are by far the most often used for both interior and exterior architectural applications. Sometimes referred to as *18-8*, these alloys contain approximately 18% chromium and 8% nickel. Types 302 and 304 are very similar in performance and appearance. The specification of Type 302/304 indicates that either alloy is acceptable.

WOOD

Tree species are divided into two classes, softwood and hardwood (Table 3.10). These terms do not describe a wood's hardness or density. Basswood, for example, is classified as a hardwood but is actually relatively easy to cut or scratch. **Softwoods** are defined as coniferous trees, evergreens which have needles instead of leaves. Softwoods, by far the more widely used type of wood, are used as framing lumber and in decorative

TABLE 3.8   STANDARD DESIGNATIONS FOR STAINLESS STEEL FINISHES

Finish Designation	Definition	Typical Uses
UNPOLISHED OR ROLLED FINISHES		
No. 1	A rough, dull surface that results from hot rolling to the specified thickness, followed by annealing and descaling.	Furnace stacks, kiln liners
No. 2D	A dull finish that results from cold rolling, followed by annealing and descaling, and perhaps a final light roll pass through unpolished rolls. A 2D finish is used where appearance is of no concern.	Institutional kitchen equipment, furnace parts
No. 2B	A bright, cold-rolled finish resulting from the same process used for a No. 2D finish, except that the annealed and descaled sheet receives a final light roll pass through polished rolls. This is the general-purpose cold-rolled finish that can be used as is, or as a preliminary step to polishing.	Cookware, flatware
POLISHED FINISHES		
No. 3	An intermediate polished surface obtained by finishing with a 100-grit abrasive. Generally used where a semifinished polished surface is required. A No. 3 finish usually receives additional polishing during fabrication.	Institutional kitchen equipment
No. 4	A polished surface obtained by finishing with a 120-150 mesh abrasive, following initial grinding with coarser abrasives. This is a general-purpose bright finish with a visible "grain" that prevents mirror reflection.	Column covers, wall panels, furniture, sinks, storefronts
No. 6	A dull satin finish having lower reflectivity than a No. 4 finish. It is produced by Tampico brushing a No. 4 finish in a medium abrasive and oil. It is used for architectural applications and ornamentation where a high luster is undesirable, and to contrast with brighter finishes.	Furniture (finish not generally available from stainless steel producers, but can be obtained from metal finishers and may be applied to a product after manufacturing.)
No. 7	A highly reflective finish that is obtained by buffing finely ground surfaces, but not to the extent of completely removing the "grit" lines. It is used chiefly for architectural and ornamental purposes.	Furniture (finish not generally available from stainless steel producers, but can be obtained from metal finishers and may be applied to a product after manufacturing.)
No. 8	The most reflective surface, which is obtained by polishing with successively finer abrasives and buffing extensively until all grit lines from preliminary grinding operations are removed. It is used for applications such as mirrors and reflectors.	Furniture (finish not generally available from stainless steel producers, but can be obtained from metal finishers and may be applied to a product after manufacturing.)

Source: *Finishes for Stainless Steel, AMP 503*, page 5. Reprinted with permission of National Association of Architectural Metal Manufacturers (NAAMM), Chicago, IL. 1988.

moldings. **Hardwoods** are from deciduous trees, which have broad leaves that are shed each winter. These include fruit and nut trees (Figure 3.1). Hardwoods are often used as flooring and furniture components.

There are several different wood products available for use in interior construction and furniture manufacturing. The traditional solid wood is giving way to the consistency and affordability of a variety of wood composite panels such as particleboard, medium-density fiberboard, and hardboard.

TABLE 3.9   STAINLESS STEEL ALLOYS

Series Designation	Structure	Alloying Elements
400	Martensitic (hardenable by heat treatment; ferromagnetic)	12% to 18% Chromium
	Ferritic (nonhardenable; ferromagnetic)	12% to 27% Chromium
300	Austenitic (hardenable by cold working; nonmagnetic)	16% to 26% Chromium and 6% to 22% Nickel
200	Austenitic (hardenable by cold working; nonmagnetic)	16% to 19% Chromium, 3.5% to 6% Nickel, and 5.5% to 10% Manganese

TABLE 3.10   HARDWOODS AND SOFTWOODS

Species	Softwood	Hardwood	Hardness
Ash		●	Hard
Basswood		●	Soft
Beech		●	Hard
Birch, Yellow		●	Hard
Cedar, Western Red	●		Soft
Cherry, American Black		●	Hard
Fir, Douglas	●		Medium
Hickory		●	Very hard
Maple, Hard		●	Very hard
Maple, Soft — "Natural"		●	Medium
Oak, English Brown		●	Hard
Oak, Red		●	Hard
Oak, White		●	Hard
Pecan		●	Hard
Pine, Ponderosa	●		Medium
Pine, Southern Yellow	●		Medium
Redwood	●		Soft
Teak		●	Hard
Walnut, American Black		●	Hard

Source: AWI, Architectural Woodwork Institute, 1952 Isaac Newton Square, Reston, VA 22090.

Solid Wood

Solid wood is used where durability and strength are of concern, for example, in countertop or table edges and chair legs. Unlike veneers or plastic laminates, which must be replaced when damaged, solid wood can be sanded down and refinished. The method by which wood is sawed affects its appearance and usability (Figure 3.2).

Plain sawn is the most common type of sawn lumber. It produces the least waste and requires the least labor. The cuts are made tangentially to the annual growth rings, which, when viewed from the end of the board, are 30 degrees or less to the face of the board.

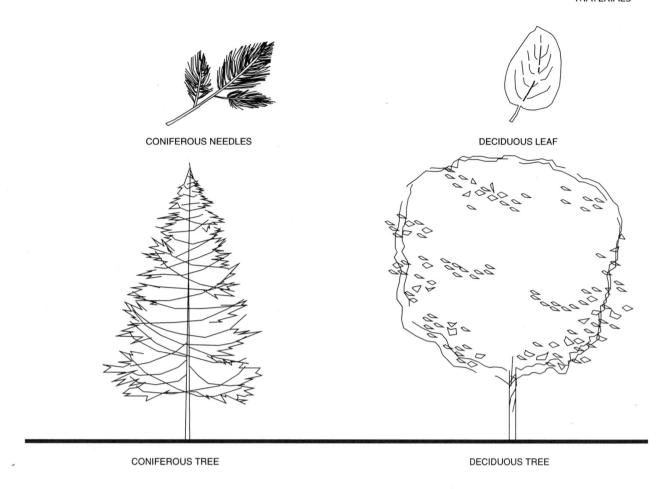

CONIFEROUS NEEDLES

DECIDUOUS LEAF

CONIFEROUS TREE

DECIDUOUS TREE

Figure 3.1 Coniferous (hardwood) and deciduous (softwood) trees.

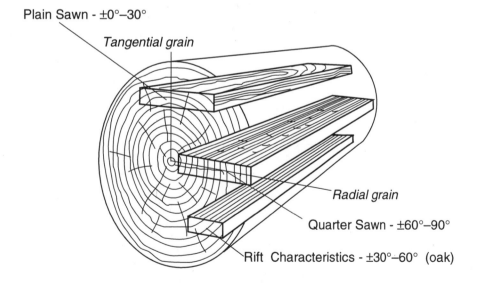

Plain Sawn - ±0°–30°

Tangential grain

Radial grain

Quarter Sawn - ±60°–90°

Rift Characteristics - ±30°–60° (oak)

Figure 3.2 Methods of sawing wood. AWI, Architectural Woodwork Institute, 1952 Isaac Newton Square, Reston, VA 22090.

Quarter sawn lumber, available in certain species, is more costly to produce than plain sawn. The growth rings, when viewed from the end of the board, are 60 to 90 degrees to the face of the board. Quarter sawn lumber is often preferred for wood flooring; because of its uniform surface, it tends to wear more evenly.

Rift sawn lumber is cut with the growth rings at 30 to 60 degrees to the face of the board. In certain species, primarily oak, rift sawing produces flecks on the surface of the board.

Wood Composite Panels

Decreasing supplies of prime timber may continue to increase the popularity of wood composition boards. These boards are known not for their appearance, but for their performance and affordability (Figure 3.3).

PLYWOOD

Plywood is a sandwich of wood or wood products between two layers of wood veneer, top and bottom. Particleboard and medium density fiberboard (MDF) are commonly used as a core for plywood. Layers of wood veneer or solid lumber can also be used (Figure 3.4). There are generally two categories of plywood: that which is faced with hardwood and used for decorative purposes and that which is used for underlayment or other concealed construction applications.

Construction grade plywood is graded and marked according to product standard PS 1 – *Construction and Industrial Plywood.* This standard is promulgated by the U.S. Department of Commerce, National Institute of Standards and Technology (NIST), in cooperation with the American Plywood Association (APA). Construction grade plywood is rated and marked according to application, exposure (whether appropriate for interior or exterior use), and thickness (Figure 3.5).

Figure 3.3 Various wood board products. From left to right, MDF, a shaped particleboard sample, hardboard, and oriented strand board (lower right corner).

Figure 3.4 Plywood types.

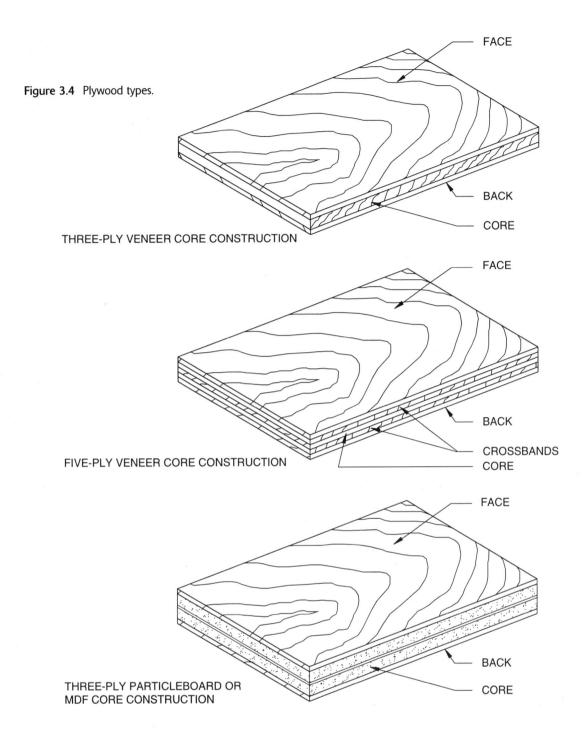

FACE

BACK

CORE

THREE-PLY VENEER CORE CONSTRUCTION

FACE

BACK

CROSSBANDS

CORE

FIVE-PLY VENEER CORE CONSTRUCTION

FACE

BACK

CORE

THREE-PLY PARTICLEBOARD OR
MDF CORE CONSTRUCTION

Figure 3.5 APA trademark.
APA — The Engineered Wood
Association.

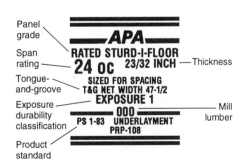

Panel grade

Span rating

Tongue-and-groove

Exposure durability classification

Product standard

APA
RATED STURD-I-FLOOR
24 OC   **23/32 INCH**
SIZED FOR SPACING
T&G NET WIDTH 47-1/2
EXPOSURE 1
000
PS 1-83   UNDERLAYMENT
PRP-108

Thickness

Mill lumber

Hardwood veneer plywood is used extensively in the manufacturing of furniture and decorative wall paneling. The Hardwood Plywood Manufacturers Association (HPMA) sponsors ANSI HP-1 *Hardwood and Decorative Plywood.* This standard classifies hardwood veneer plywood by species, grade of veneers, type of plywood, composition of the plywood panel, and size and thickness (Table 3.11).

PARTICLEBOARD

Particleboard is manufactured from wood particles or fibers, which are bonded under heat and pressure with an adhesive resin (Table 3.12). The wood particles can easily be seen by examining a piece of particleboard. Its surface is relatively smooth and hard and can hold a shaped edge fair-

TABLE 3.11   ANSI HP CLASSIFICATION CATEGORIES FOR HARDWOOD AND DECORATIVE PLYWOOD

SPECIES

Seventy-one species are classified in 4 categories (A, B, C, and D), based primarily on their modulus of elasticity and specific gravity.

GRADES OF VENEERS

Face Grades (Grade AA permits the fewest number of natural characteristics; more and larger flaws are permitted in each successive grade.)	Grades AA, A, B, C, D, E
Specialty Grade	SP
Back Grades	1,2,3, and 4
Inner Ply Grades	J,K,L, and M

TYPES OF PLYWOOD

(Listed in descending order of the bond water-resistance.)
Technical (Exterior)
Type 1 (Exterior)
Type 2 (Interior)

CONSTRUCTIONS (BASED ON THE KIND OF CORE)

Hardwood veneer core
Softwood veneer core
Hardwood lumber core
Softwood lumber core
Particleboard core
Medium density fiberboard (MDF) core
Hardboard core
Special core

TABLE 3.12   PARTICLEBOARD INTERIOR APPLICATIONS

Application	Grade (ANSI A208.1)	Product References
Floor Underlayment	M-1	ICBO, SBCCI, BOCA, One- and Two-Family Dwelling Code
Shelving	M-1	
	M-2	
	M-3	
Countertops	M-2	ANSI A161.1
	M-3	
Kitchen Cabinets	M-S	ANSI A161.1
	M-2	
Door Cores	LD-1	NWWDA Industry Series IS 1 (Wood Flush Doors)
Stair Treads	M-3	HUD/FHA UM 70a
Moldings	M-3	WWMMP Standard WM 2

Source: National Particleboard Association, *Buyer's and Specifiers Guide to Particleboard and MDF* 1994–95.

ly well. It is one of the most dimensionally stable of the cellulosic boards. Exposed particleboard edges are usually covered, often with a solid wood edging, to improve their appearance. The edges offer poor screw holding capability.

Particleboard is the most commonly specified substrate for decorative laminates. It is also popular for use as kitchen cabinet shelving and as a flooring underlayment. ANSI A 208.1, sponsored by the National Particleboard Association (NPA), establishes the minimum performance requirements for particleboard (Table 3.13).

MEDIUM DENSITY FIBERBOARD (MDF)

Medium density fiberboard (MDF) is manufactured by breaking down wood particles into fibers through the use of steam pressure. The resulting fibers are mixed with an adhesive resin and pressed into MDF panels. The fineness of the fibers used in MDF give it a homogeneous appearance and a very smooth surface (Figure 3.6). The panel edge allows intricate machining, and the face can be embossed to produce three-dimensional cabinet door fronts and moldings. MDF is also used as a substrate for decorative laminates.

ANSI A 208.2 *Medium Density Fiberboard,* sponsored by the NPA, describes the requirements for the strength and dimensional stability of MDF. MDF is available in different thicknesses and is classified by density and use (interior or exterior). There are four product grades: high density; two medium densities, one for thicknesses greater than 21 mm (⅞ in) and another for those of 21 mm (⅞ in) or less; and low density. As much as 95% of the MDF manufactured in the United States is medium density grade.

TABLE 3.13   PARTIAL LIST OF REQUIREMENTS IN ANSI A 208.1 *WOOD PARTICLEBOARD*

Grade	Hardness	General Uses
Requirements for Grades of Type 1 Wood Particleboard (for Interior Applications)		
1-H-1	500	High-density industrial products
1-H-2	1000	
1-H-3	1500	
1-M-1	500	Underlayment, commercial
1-M-2	500	Industrial
1-M-3	500	Industrial
1-M-S	500	Commercial, industrial
1-LD-1	NS	Door core
1-LD-2	NS	Door core
Requirements for Grades of Type 2 Wood Particleboard (for Exterior Applications)		
2-H-1	500	High-density exterior industrial products
2-H-2	1800	
2-M-1	500	Siding
2-M-2	500	Siding, sheathing, flooring, exterior industrial uses
2-M-3	500	Siding, sheathing, flooring, exterior industrial uses
2-M-W	500	Siding, sheathing, flooring

H—High nominal density [above 240 kg/sq m (50 lb/sq ft)]
M—Medium nominal density [200 to 240 kg/sq m (40 to 50 lb/sq ft)]
LD—Lower nominal density [less than 240 kg/sq m (40 lb/sq ft)]
W—Made from wafers

Figure 3.6 MDF (medium density fiberboard). Photo credit: Michael E. Dolan.

Figure 3.7 Hardboard. Photo credit: Michael E. Dolan.

Figure 3.8 Oriented strand board. Photo credit: Michael E. Dolan.

HARDBOARD

Hardboard is essentially a high density fiberboard. It is made from the same type of fibers used in MDF but is bonded under higher pressure, often without an adhesive (Figure 3.7). Hardboard is commonly known by the trade name Masonite. The familiar pegboard is made of hardboard. Two types of hardboard are available: smooth on one side or smooth on both sides. ANSI A 135.4 *Basic Hardboard*, sponsored by the American Hardboard Association (AHA), defines five classes of hardboard (Table 3.14). Class 4 Service panels are recommended as underlayment for resilient flooring.

ORIENTED STRAND BOARD (OSB)

Oriented strand board (OSB) is made from thin, narrow strands of both hardwood and softwood, which are blended with adhesive and formed into a multilayered panel (Figure 3.8). The core strands are perpendicular to the surface strands, which are parallel to the long direction of the panel. Performance requirements for OSB are addressed in product standard PS 2—*Wood Based Structural Use Panels*. This standard is promulgated by the U.S. Department of Commerce, National Institute of Standards and Technology (NIST), in cooperation with the APA.

TABLE 3.14   CLASSIFICATION AND MARKING OF HARDBOARD IN ANSI A 135.4 *BASIC HARDBOARD*

Class Number	Name	Marking (number and color of stripes on board's edge)
1	Tempered	1 red
2	Standard	2 red
3	Service tempered	1 green
4	Service	2 green
5	Industrialite	1 blue

Wood Veneer

Veneers are slices of wood about .9 to .7 mm (1/28 to 1/36 in) thick (Figure 3.9). They provide far more surfacing material than sawn lumber, making the use of exotic woods affordable because of the smaller amounts required. Because they are adhered under pressure to a stable substrate, usually particleboard or MDF, warping is not a problem with veneers as it can be with solid wood. The wood slices can also be adhered to a flexible fabric backing for wood veneer wall covering.

The individual veneer slices cut from a log section are called **leaves**. The term *flitch* can refer to the section of log ready to be sliced into leaves or to the bundle of leaves stacked in sequence after slicing (Figure 3.10). The slicing sequence is preserved so that the leaves can be matched to form the rich, familiar patterns associated with wood veneer. The designer may visit the veneer supplier, select a flitch and reserve it, making sure there is enough to accommodate the requirements of the project. Because of blemishes in the wood and the trimming required to get the desired match, the veneer used from a flitch may be only a third of the yield from the raw log. If the yield of the flitch is not correctly calculated, it may not be possible to finish a project with matching wood.

Wood species, veneer slicing, and veneer matching are the three key considerations in selecting a veneer.

Figure 3.9 Paper thin wood veneers. Photo credit: Michael E. Dolan.

Figure 3.10 Flitch. Photo from Woody Vaughn, *personal archive of the former L. Vaughn Co.*

VENEER SLICING

Plain, or flat, slicing is done parallel to a line through the center of the log, producing a slightly wavy grain pattern (Figure 3.11). Plain slicing is most often used for the best quality veneers.

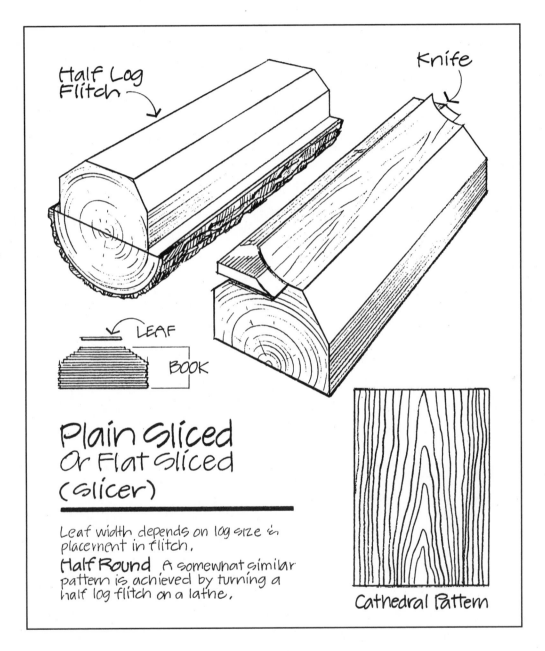

Half Log Flitch

Knife

LEAF

BOOK

Plain Sliced
Or Flat Sliced
(slicer)

Leaf width depends on log size & placement in flitch.

Half Round A somewhat similar pattern is achieved by turning a half log flitch on a lathe.

Cathedral Pattern

Figure 3.11 Plain sliced or flat sliced veneer. Illustrations from the booklet *Understanding Veneer*, copyright April 1991 by Saunders Wood Specialties, Park Falls, WI.

Quarter slicing is similar to the quarter sawing process for lumber, producing a series of striped veneer panels (Figure 3.12). The term *quarter* refers to the log segment that forms the basis of the flitch.

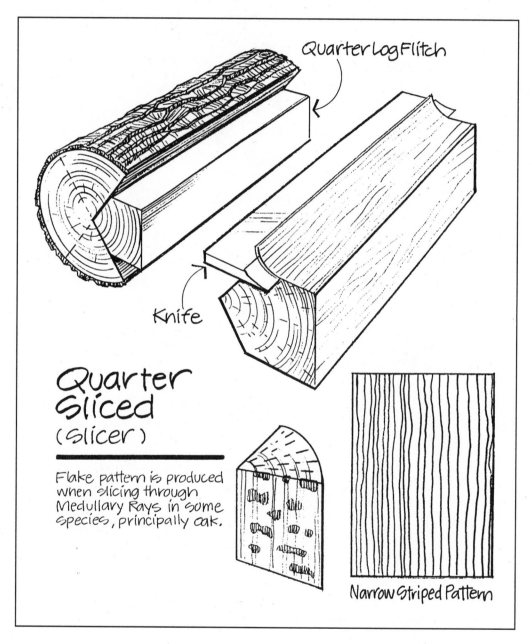

Quarter Log Flitch

Knife

Quarter Sliced (Slicer)

Flake pattern is produced when slicing through Medullary Rays in some species, principally oak.

Narrow Striped Pattern

Figure 3.12 Quarter sliced veneer. Illustrations from the booklet *Understanding Veneer,* copyright April 1991 by Saunders Wood Specialties, Park Falls, WI.

Rift cutting is not usually done with any species other than oak. The rift cut is curvilinear, producing a very narrow striped grain (Figure 3.13). Rift cutting can also produce a **comb grain** veneer. Comb grain is available only in oak and produces a very narrow, very straight, striped grain resembling the pattern a wide-toothed comb might make.

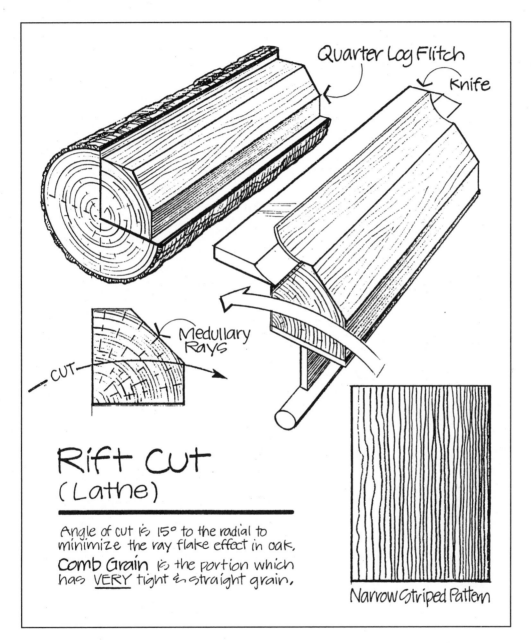

Figure 3.13 Rift cut veneer. Illustrations from the booklet *Understanding Veneer*, copyright April 1991 by Saunders Wood Specialties, Park Falls, WI.

Rotary cutting produces wide sheets of veneer and is popular for use in less expensive veneer applications. The log is mounted on a lathe and the veneer is sliced off as the log spins around (Figure 3.14). Softwood veneers are usually rotary sliced.

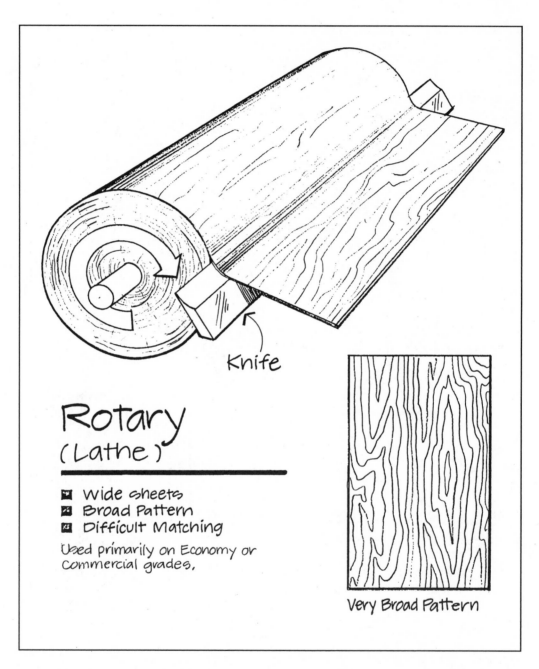

Knife

Rotary
(Lathe)

☑ Wide Sheets
☑ Broad Pattern
☑ Difficult Matching

Used primarily on Economy or Commercial grades.

Very Broad Pattern

Figure 3.14 Rotary cut veneer. Illustrations from the booklet *Understanding Veneer,* copyright April 1991 by Saunders Wood Specialties, Park Falls, WI.

VENEER MATCHING

Veneer leaves may be arranged in different sequences to form various patterns and effects. Because the progression through the depth of the annual rings is lost in rotary cut veneers, they are very hard to match.

Book Match

Like pages in an open book, adjacent leaves in the flitch are laid side by side. The back of the top leaf is matched to the face of the lower leaf, creating a mirror image and a continuity in grain (Figure 3.15). This is the most commonly used veneer match.

Slip Match

Adjacent leaves are laid side by side in sequence, in a repeating pattern with less continuity in grain (Figure 3.16). This type of matching is common in quarter sliced and rift cut veneers.

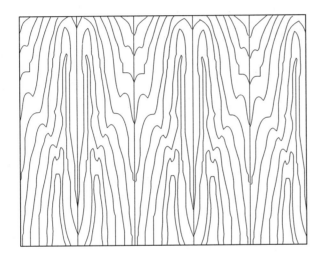

Figure 3.15 Book match veneer. AWI, Architectural Woodwork Institute, 1952 Isaac Newton Square, Reston, VA 22090.

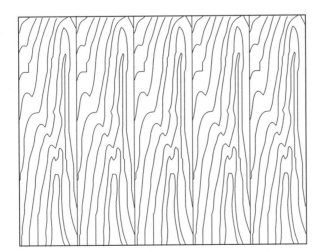

Figure 3.16 Slip match. AWI, Architectural Woodwork Institute, 1952 Isaac Newton Square, Reston, VA 22090.

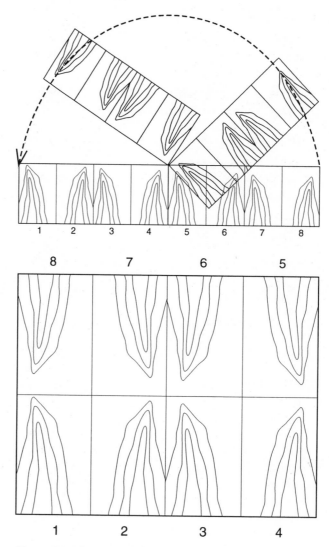

Figure 3.17 Panel end match. AWI, Architectural Woodwork Institute, 1952 Isaac Newton Square, Reston, VA 22090.

End Match
Veneers are book or slip matched, and then the ends of the sheets are matched, creating a long and wide matching veneer piece (Figure 3.17).

Wood Finishing

Finishing operations include the application of stains, if they are used, and the application of a protective top coat. Finishing protects the wood surface from permanent staining by sealing the pores. It enhances the beauty of the wood grain and color and guards against damage to the wood surface caused by heat, dirt, and spills.

STAINS

Stains are transparent or opaque coatings that penetrate and color a wood surface without masking its inherent grain. Stains can be used to change the color of a piece of wood. For example, mahogany is usually stained a deep red-brown to modify its natural light orange color. Sometimes wood is stained to resemble a different species.

LACQUERS

Laquers dry by the evaporation of their strong solvents. The solvents evaporate so fast that laquers are typically spray applied, rather than brushed on. Lacquers may or may not contain pigments and are the most popular commercial furniture and casework finishes. Acrylic and vinyl laquers are available, which do not have a nitrocellulose base as do noncatalyzed and catalyzed laquers.

Standard, or noncatalyzed, laquers can easily be touched up or recoated, because the solvent in each coat slightly dissolves the previous coat, forming a monolithic finish. Standard laquers are easy to apply, recoat, and repair using conventional equipment. They are the most popular furniture finishes.

Catalyzed laquers, like noncatalyzed laquers, contain nitrocellulose. They dry faster than standard laquers, so dust is even less likely to settle on the curing coat and contaminate the finish. Catalyzed laquers are harder than standard laquers and are moderately easy to touch up. They are very hard and brittle, and tend to splinter and spider web.

VARNISHES

Varnishes cure by evaporation of the solvents, oxidation of the oil, or both. Polyurethane, added to make varnish resistant to water and alcohol, is popular as a wood floor finish. **Conversion varnishes**, like the laquers, are very durable and fast drying forming thick coats. They have superb resistance to a variety of common chemicals.

POLYESTER AND POLYURETHANE FINISHES

The contemporary, high-tech polyester and polyurethane coatings are known for their excellent chemical resistance and incredibly durable, dense, and smooth finishes. When pigmented, they resemble high pressure decorative laminates in appearance. They require special skill and equipment for application and are expensive. Spectacularly shiny gloss levels can be achieved with these coatings. Polyesters are basically 100% solids when applied and are extremely difficult to touch-up. Like polyesters, polyurethanes exhibit hardness and excellent resistance to chemicals but are much easier to apply.

PLASTICS

Plastics comprise a widely diverse group of materials; there are about 15,000 different plastic formulas available worldwide. Like metals, plastics can be alloyed (mixed) with other such materials to improve performance characteristics. Many plastics have long, multisyllable chemical titles, and manufacturers often devise trade names for better marketability. For example, polytetrafluoroethylene is best known by the trade name *Teflon*.

All plastics share three common traits. First, with few exceptions (silicone is one), plastics are based on the carbon atom. Second, plastics are derived from petrochemicals (Figure 3.18). Third, all plastics are polymers. **Polymers** are giant molecules, composed of up to millions of relatively light, simple molecules. **Polymerization**, the formation of these giant chains, is basic to the formation of plastics. Polymers are characterized by high molecular weight, outstanding stability, and a strength of intermolecular force that prevents easy destruction.

Our constructed environments are filled with this thoroughly modern material: plastic laminates are the standard for countertops; vinyl flooring or nylon carpet is included in practically every interiors project; today's paints are typically alkyds or latexes; and many furniture components are either made of plastic or coated with it.

The Components of Plastics

Resin (like *polymer*, an alternative term used for *plastic*) is the basic ingredient of plastic. Resins are combined with fillers, stabilizers, plasticizers, pigments, and other components to form plastics. **Fillers** are added to impart a certain characteristic property, such as durability or heat resistance. Some fillers, called extenders, may be added to decrease the amount of relatively expensive plastic required and to increase the mass of the product. **Stabilizers** lend protection against degradation of the plastic resulting from exposure to environmental conditions such as ultraviolet rays and even oxygen. **Plasticizers** are mixed with the resin to increase flexibility, resiliency, and impact resistance. The addition of plasticizers lend the required flexibility to sheet vinyl so that it can be rolled without cracking.

Plastics are commonly categorized as either thermoplastic or thermosetting materials. **Thermoplastics** become soft when heated and can be remolded repeatedly without affecting the properties of the plastic. Thermoplastics harden when cooled and require the addition of plasticizers to increase their flexibility. **Thermoset** plastics are permanently hardened after undergoing an irreversible chemical change during processing. Once they are set, they cannot be softened and remolded.

Thermoplastics

Thermoplastics generally offer higher impact strength, easier processing, and better adaptability to complex designs than thermosets. Thermoplastics commonly used in construction materials and furniture include acrylonitrile-butadiene-styrene, acrylics, cellulosics, fluoroplastics, nylons, polyolefins, polystyrenes, and vinyls.

ACRYLONITRILE-BUTADIENE-STYRENE (ABS)

Introduced in the late 1940s, acrylonitrile-butadiene-styrene (ABS) is very tough, but not brittle, and is resistant to chemicals and to impact. ABS is used in construction for plumbing drain, waste, and vent pipes. Outdoor furniture, drawer liners, and chair shells are common furniture applications for ABS (Figure 3.19).

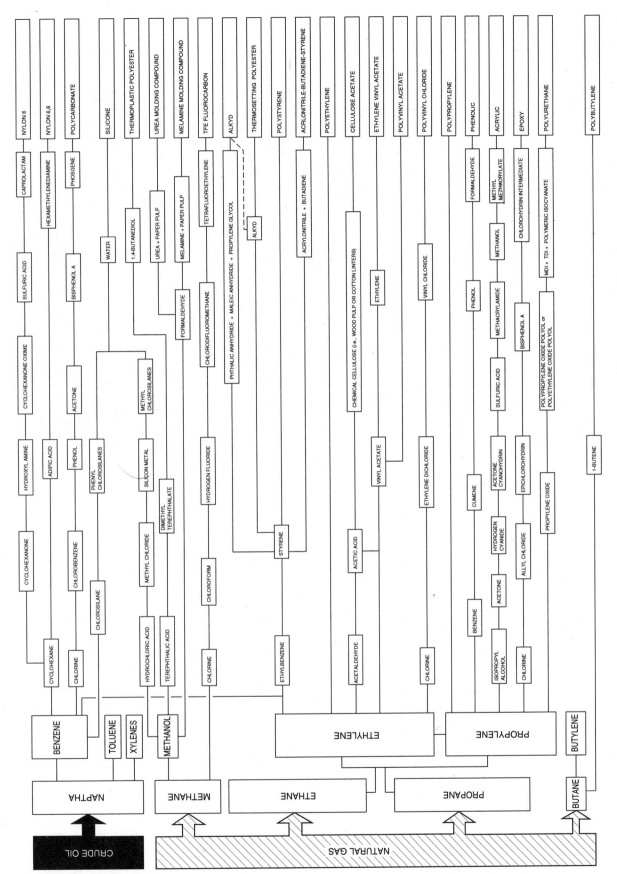

Figure 3.18 Flow chart of major plastic resins and how they are derived. *Source: Plastics* published by Van Nostrand Reinhold 1974 by John DuBois.

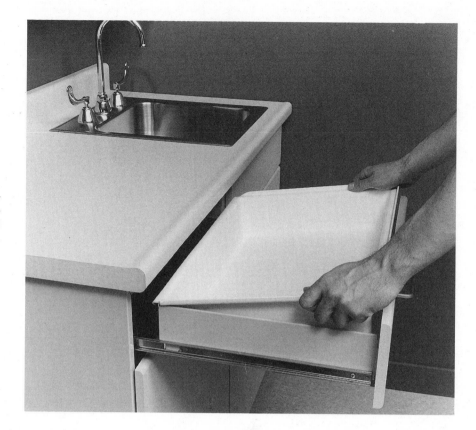

Figure 3.19 This drawer liner, made of vacuum-formed ABS, is removable for easy cleaning in this healthcare application. Steelcase.

ACRYLICS

Acrylics have the clarity of glass, good weatherability, surface hardness, and chemical resistance. This material is lightweight and colorfast; it does not yellow with age. Acrylics are used for skylight glazing, safety glazing, and paint resins. Lucite and Plexiglas are popular trade names.

CELLULOSICS

Developed in 1868, cellulose nitrate was the first synthetic plastic material. One of its first uses, in response to an ivory shortage, was in hair combs and billiard balls. Celluloid (photographic film) and cellophane (packaging material) are in the cellulosic family of plastics. The breakage resistance of cellulosics makes them ideal for table edging, venetian blind wands, signage, and store fixtures.

FLUOROPLASTICS

Common characteristics of fluoroplastics are outstanding chemical resistance, resistance to temperatures from −220°C (−425°F) to 260°C (500°F), low coefficient of friction, and practically no moisture absorption. Polyvinyl fluoride (PVF) and polytetrafluoroethylene (commonly known by the trade name *Teflon*) are the most commonly used fluoroplastics in architectural applications.

NYLON

Nylon was originally developed by Du Pont in the 1930s and was first used as a high-strength fiber for women's stockings. Nylons offer high strength, toughness at low temperatures, and good wear and abrasion resistance. Nylon is probably best known as an extruded fiber in textiles and carpet. It is commonly used for chair caster rollers and drawer glides because of its low friction characteristic.

POLYOLEFINS

The family of polyolefins includes many popular plastics used in commercial interiors products, such as polybutylenes, polyethylenes, and polypropylenes.

Polybutylenes (PB) exhibit good retention of mechanical properties at elevated temperatures and high tensile strength. The largest markets for PB are plumbing supply pipe, hot-melt adhesives, and sealants.

Polyethylenes are known for their strength and flexibility. They are tough materials, have excellent chemical resistance, offer a low coefficient of friction, and are easy to process. Polyethylene is commonly used for electrical wire insulation. In clear sheet form, it is used as a vapor barrier. It is also used as molded seating, drawer glides, and door tracks.

Polypropylenes are among the most versatile plastics and are employed in many fabrication methods. They are semitranslucent or milky white in color and have excellent colorability and chemical resistance, a high melting point, and are moderately priced. Fiber is a major market for polypropylenes. They are commonly used in upholstery fabric, carpet backing, and indoor/outdoor carpet fiber.

POLYSTYRENES

Polystyrenes are inexpensive and easy to process. They are noted for their sparkling clarity, hardness, and extreme ease of processing. They have excellent colorability and are widely used for disposable fast food packaging and cups. In the construction industry, polystyrenes are used for light fixture diffusers in sheet form and as the core material for doors in foamed, or expanded, form. For furniture, they are commonly used for wood-grain-patterned chair parts and mirror frames.

VINYLS

Vinyls encompass a large group of plastics, including polyvinyl chloride (PVC) and polyvinyl butyral (PVB). PVC has good impact resistance and dimensional stability and may be best known for its application as plumbing pipe. PVCs constitute perhaps the largest volume of plastics consumed worldwide.

Since 1938, PVB has been used as an interlayer in safety glass; it is also popular for use as a textile coating. Within the interiors industry, materials such as floor coverings, window blinds, upholstery material, and wall coverings are largely made of vinyl.

Thermosets

Thermosets generally resist higher temperatures and provide greater dimensional stability than thermoplastics. Thermosets include alkyds, epoxies, furans, melamines, thermoset polyesters, and polyurethanes.

ALKYDS

Alkyds are classified as polyesters. Alkyd plastics are actually by-products of the alkyd coating industry. Offering moderately high heat resistance, alkyds have a rapid cure cycle and good mold flow characteristics, which allow them to be molded into relatively complicated shapes. Their most prevalent use in commercial interiors is as a paint coating.

EPOXIES

Epoxy resins react with curing agents or hardeners to form an exceptionally durable plastic. Epoxies have superior adhesion and excellent resistance to chemicals and corrosion. Their application in the construction industry is mainly as adhesives or protective coatings for floors and walls. Epoxy ester coatings are often used in floor and gymnasium finishes. Powder coatings, based on heat-cured epoxy resins, are increasingly popular as metal furniture finishes. Epoxies are an important component of solid surfacing materials such as Corian.

FURANS

Furan resins are naturally dark in color and turn black when catalyzed to cure. Their most common use is in corrosion-resistant cements and grouts. The floors and walls of such structures as manholes and processing tanks can be protected by furan cement.

MELAMINES

Hardness, clarity, and stain resistance characterize the melamine family of plastics. Melamine surfaces are difficult to scratch or cut and they do not yellow with age. Most laminating resins for both low and high pressure laminates are melamines. **Thermoset decorative laminates**, sometimes referred to as low pressure laminates, are made by impregnating laminating paper with melamine resin and then applying it to a substrate (usually particleboard) under low pressure and low heat. The substrate is cut to the required size and shape, and the thermoset decorative laminate is applied, effectively sealing in the substrate (Figure 3.20). Polyester-impregnated paper is also used on thermoset decorative laminates. These panels are often used as interior panels and shelves in casework (Figure 3.21). They are not as durable as high pressure decorative laminates, but they are far less expensive.

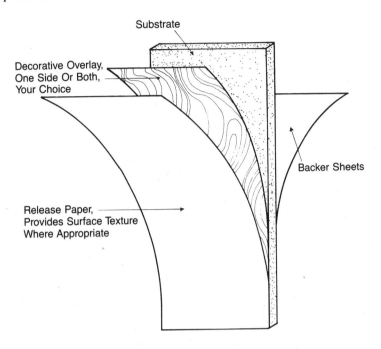

Figure 3.20 Elements of a thermoset decorative panel before pressing. AWI, Architectural Woodwork Institute, 1952 Isaac Newton Square, Reston, VA 22090.

Figure 3.21 Thermoset decorative panels are used on the inside face of this cabinet door. Steelcase.

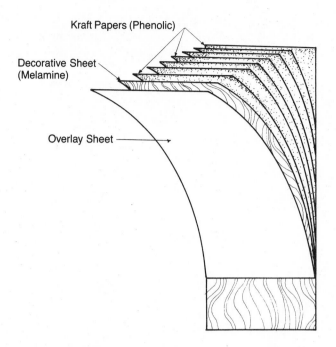

Kraft Papers (Phenolic)

Decorative Sheet (Melamine)

Overlay Sheet

Figure 3.22 Elements of a high-pressure decorative laminate (HPDL) sheet before pressing. AWI, Architectural Woodwork Institute, 1952 Isaac Newton Square, Reston, VA 22090.

High pressure decorative laminates (HPDL) consist of a sandwich of melamine-impregnated overlay and decorative surface papers, over phenolic resin-impregnated papers (Figure 3.22). These layers are pressed under temperatures exceeding 130°C (265°F) and high pressure. HPDLs are known by the common trade name Formica. Unlike thermoset decorative laminates, sheets of HPDLs are adhered to the surface of substrates, such as particleboard, which can then be trimmed and edge banded.

The National Electrical Manufacturers Association (NEMA) publishes the standard for HPDLs—NEMA LD 3 *High Pressure Decorative Laminates*. Before World War II, laminates were produced primarily for electrical insulation. Although HPDLs today are used in a much greater variety of decorative applications, NEMA still promulgates the standard. The four most common types of HPDL sheets are as follows:

GP—General Purpose. Used for most horizontal surfaces, e.g., countertops

CL—Cabinet Liner. A thin sheet used for vertical applications, typically inside casework, that will not need to withstand heavy wear

BK—Backer. Economical, nondecorative sheets used on the side of the substrate hidden from view to prevent warping as a result of changes in temperature or humidity

PF—Postforming. Used for tightly radiused curves, e.g., at the edge of a formed countertop

These designations are typically followed by the sheets' thickness in hundredths of an inch. For example, *GP50* means General Purpose type HPDL that is 0.050 in thick.

POLYESTERS

Thermoset polyesters include a vary large family of plastics. Polyester is commonly used with glass fibers to form **fiberglass**. **Alkyds**, used in paints and other coatings, are oil modified polyesters. A **gel coat** is a pigmented polyester coating that is applied to the inside surface of a mold and becomes an integral part of the finished piece. Cultured marble countertops are fabricated with a polyester gel coat.

POLYURETHANES

Polyurethanes are available in a multitude of forms with an extensive variety of physical properties. Rigid polyurethane foam is widely used as a building insulation material. However, the most common application of polyurethane is for cushioning in seating and mattresses. Polyurethane foam can be molded for a preformed chair seat or back, or foam slabs can be cut into the desired shape.

SILICONES

Silicones are unique among plastics because they are based on the silicon atom, rather than the carbon atom. The raw material for silicone is one of the most abundant on the earth's surface—sand (quartzite). Silicone is still obtained by a process developed by General Electric in the 1940s. Similar to the way in which iron is reduced from iron ore, silicone is obtained by the reduction of silicon dioxide in a furnace. Silicones are known for their stability through a wide range of temperatures, ultraviolet radiation, and harsh weather. They are used in commercial interior applications as water-repellent fabric finishes and joint sealants.

GLASS

Glass is used for windows in interior partitions and doors, as decorative wall tiles, and as tabletops—a variety of applications, each with very different performance requirements. Although glass has been made for thousands of years, developments in production processes in this century have made it a truly modern material.

Glass is considered a liquid, even though it is rigid and behaves like a solid. As is characteristic of a liquid, the atoms in a sheet of glass are randomly arranged. They are frozen in place by rapid cooling during manufacturing. In most other mineral solids, the atoms are arranged in a recognizable geometric pattern and have a crystalline structure.

Float Glass

More than 95% of the glass manufactured in the United States is float glass. Float glass is the primary glass for most other glass types. The process is relatively new, having been developed in 1955 by the Pilkington Glass Company in the United Kingdom. Molten glass is floated on a bed of molten tin. Because the molten metal is denser than the glass, the two liquids do not mix together. The glass surfaces become flat and parallel.

After forming, the glass is cooled by a controlled process called annealing. **Annealing** relieves internal strains that may have developed during the manufacturing process. It ensures that the glass does not cool and contract at different rates across its surface. If glass is not annealed, it may fracture from differential stresses throughout the sheet when it reaches room temperature. The requirements for float glass are defined in ASTM C 1036 *Specification for Flat Glass.*

Heat-Treated Glass

There are two types of glass that utilize heat processes to increase the strength of float glass: fully tempered and heat-strengthened (Table 3.15).

FULLY TEMPERED GLASS

Glass is fully tempered by heating float glass and then suddenly cooling it with special blowers. The outer surface cools quickly and contracts, constraining the hot inner core as it continues to cool. The surface and edges of fully tempered glass are in compression, while the inner core is in tension. Fully tempered glass is three to five times more resistant to impact, applied pressure, and bending stresses than annealed glass, because the surface tension must be overcome before the glass can be broken. The tempering process is defined by ASTM C 1048 *Specification for Heat-Treated Flat Glass—Kind HS, Kind FT Coated and Uncoated Glass.*

Cutting or drilling fully tempered glass will destroy the integrity of the skin's compressive strength and will likely cause breakage. This is why fully tempered glass cannot be field cut. Fully tempered glass must be fabricat-

TABLE 3.15 GLASS TYPES

	Annealed (regular float glass)	Fully Tempered	Heat Strengthened (partially tempered)	Laminated	Wired
Safety glass	No	Yes	No	Yes	Yes (in some applications)
Can be field cut or drilled	Yes	No	Not recommended	Depends on glass type laminated	Yes
Shatter pattern	Shards	Small cubes	Shards	Pieces adhere to interlayer	Pieces held in place by wire
For use in Fire-rated assemblies	No	No	No	No	Yes

ed, with the required holes or cutouts. It is available in thicknesses from 3 mm to 25 mm (⅛ in to 1 in).

HEAT-STRENGTHENED GLASS

The manufacturing process for heat-strengthened glass is similar to that of fully tempered, except that the glass is only partially tempered. Annealed glass is heated and cooled in a manner similar to that for fully tempered glass; however, lower surface stresses are produced. Heat-strengthened glass is about twice as resistant to breakage as float glass.

Safety Glass

Safety glass is glazing material that, if shattered, breaks in such a way that reduces the likelihood of cutting and piercing injuries. Fully tempered glass and laminated glass qualify as safety glass types. Unlike annealed and heat strengthened glass, which breaks into shards, fully tempered glass breaks into small cubical pieces. If laminated glass is shattered, the broken glass adheres to the interlayer.

The requirements for safety glass are defined by two very similar standards: CPSC 16 CFR Part 1201 *Safety Standard for Architectural Glazing Materials* and ANSI Z97.1 *Safety Glazing Materials Used in Buildings – Safety Performance Specifications and Methods of Test.* These standards use the same test procedures, with the exception that the Consumer Product Safety Commission (CPSC) standard uses a greater impact load. Although wired glass does not pass the tests for safety glass described in CPSC 16 CFR Part 1201, it is granted an exemption because it is the only glass type that performs successfully in fire tests.

Wired Glass

Wired glass has wire mesh or parallel wires rolled into the center of the glass sheet. If breakage occurs, the wire helps to hold glass fragments in the opening, thus preventing personal injuries. This is the only glass type suitable for use in fire-rated doors or partition assemblies, because, if excessive heat cracks the glass, it will remain in place.

Laminated Glass

Laminated glass consists of two or more layers of glass and an interlayer material sandwiched together to form a single sheet. There are two types of interlayers: polyvinyl butyral (PVB) sheets that are bonded under heat and pressure, and urethane acrylate resin, a liquid that is cured under ultraviolet light. PVB interlayers can be colored or patterned and can be combined for a decorative effect. Rice paper and other ornamental sheets can also be used in the lamination process. Cast resin interlayers are clear.

Annealed, fully tempered, heat-strengthened, and wire glass types can be laminated. Security glass (bulletproof or burglar resistant) and acoustical glass are types of laminated glass using thicker interlayers. If laminated glass is broken, the glass remains bonded to the interlayer, offering protection from injury, which makes it popular for use in skylights. The standard for laminated glass is ASTM C 1172 *Specification for Laminated Architectural Flat Glass.*

TEXTILES AND LEATHER

The immensity of the textile industry is reflected in the vast number of uses of textiles in commercial interiors projects. Fabric is used on walls as wall coverings, stretched fabric wall and ceiling systems, wall-mounted panels, and systems furniture panels; as vertical hangings for draperies, banners, and vertical louver blinds; as upholstery for seating; and as floor coverings, including carpet and rugs. Leather is commonly used as a luxury upholstery material, but can be used as a floor tile as well.

Fibers

Textiles are any fabrics made of fibers, whether woven, knitted, felted, or manufactured by some other means. The fiber is the basic element of the textile. A **fiber** is the fine, hairlike strand that forms the basis of a yarn. Fibers are found in nature or manufactured (synthetic) and are categorized by their length (Table 3.16). **Staple fibers** are short, typically measured in centimeters or inches. All natural fibers except silk are staple fibers. **Filament fibers**, measured in meters or yards, are long and continuous. Because synthetic fibers are produced by extruding chemical solutions through a shower-head-like device called a spinerette, they are filament fibers. However, they can be cut to staple fiber lengths.

Natural fibers are from animal, plant, or mineral sources. Plant- and animal-based fibers are produced seasonally and are susceptible to the forces of nature—wounds, insects, and too much water or the lack of it. **Synthetic fibers** are man-made and thoroughly modern, most having been developed in the twentieth century. Although centuries ago the method by which silkworms extruded silk was noted as a technique that could possibly be adopted for synthetic fiber production, rayon—the first synthetic fiber—began commercial production in 1939. Most synthetic fibers are thermoplastic, meaning that they soften and melt when heated (see "Plastics" earlier in this chapter).

Yarns are formed by twisting fibers together to create a continuous strand. Yarns are classified in two types: *spun* and *filament*. **Spun** yarns are composed of staple fibers twisted together. **Filament** yarns are composed of continuous strands made from either a spinerette generated synthetic fiber or from silk. These are commonly referred to as **bulked continuous filament (BCF)** and are typical of nylon and polypropylene fibers. BCF yarns are continuous strands of synthetic fiber that are formed into yarn bundles without the need for spinning, which is required for all natural and staple synthetic fibers. BCF generally offers better wear, but staple fibers provide the much-sought-after "wool-like" appearance.

Because yarns are sold by weight, yarn designations express the relationship between length and weight. The denier system is used for filament yarns, and the yarn count system is used for spun yarns. **Denier** is a unit of yarn measurement equal to the weight in grams of 9000 meters of the yarn. The higher the denier, the heavier the yarn and generally the better the strength, resiliency, and abrasion resistance. Heavier filament yarns are designated by higher denier numbers. For example, a 15-denier yarn would be suitable for sheer hosiery; a 2200-denier yarn would be suitable for carpet. The **yarn count** system is a relative gauge of a spun yarn's weight. Heavier yarns are designated by lower yarn count numbers. For example, a 70-count yarn is quite fine, whereas a 10-count yarn is thick and heavy.

TABLE 3.16 TEXTILE FIBERS

General Chemical Type	Natural			Man-Made	
	Generic Term	Source		Generic Term	Source
Cellulose (Plant)	Cotton	Seed	Cotton plant	Rayon	Wood and cotton
	Kapok		Kapok tree	Acetate	
	Hemp	Stem	Hemp plant	Triacetate	
	Jute		Jute plant		
	Flax (linen)		Flax plant		
	Ramie (China grass)		Ramie shrub		
	Sisal	Leaf	Agave plant		
	Pina		Pineapple plant		
	Coir	Nut husk	Coconut		
Protein (Animal)	Silk	Silkworm secretion	Moth larvae		
	Wool	Hair	Sheep		
	Mohair		Angora goat		
	Angora		Angora rabbit		
	Horsehair		Horse mane and tail		
	Alpaca		Alpaca		
	Camel hair		Bactrian camel		
	Cashmere		Cashmere goat		
	Llama		Llama		
	Vicuna		Vicuna		
Mineral	Asbestos	Asbestos rock fibers		Glass	Silica, sand, and limestone
				Metallics	Various metals
Elastomers	Rubber	Rubber tree sap		Synthetic rubber	Chemicals
				Spandex	
Synthesized				Acrylic	Petroleum (manufactured polymers)
				Aramids	
				Modacrylic	
				Nylon	
				Olefin	
				Polyester	
				Saran	
				Vinal	
				Vinyon	

Source: D. Jackman and M. Dixon, *The Guide to Textiles for Interior Designers,* Winnipeg, MB, Peguis Publishers Limited, 1983, p. 20.

NATURAL FIBERS

Cotton

The most widely used plant fiber is cotton. It is a cellulosic fiber that covers the seeds of the cotton plant. Its fibers are fairly uniform in width—more so than other natural fibers. Staple fiber lengths vary from 6 mm to 60 mm (¼ in to 2 ½ in).

In the mid-1800s, a calico printer named John Mercer developed a process to give cotton a silky finish. **Mercerized cotton** is produced by treating cotton yarn under tension to increase its strength and reduce shrinkage. The process causes the fiber to swell slightly, making it appear rounder and smoother. The smoother surface increases the light reflection off the fiber surface thus giving a more lustrous appearance.

Cotton fiber (unlike cotton fabric) is relatively dimensionally stable but, like other cellulosic fibers, has low elasticity and resiliency. It is also one of the densest fibers. Known for comfort, cotton wicks away moisture along the fiber and through the fabric. Flammable and easily wrinkled, this fabric is used more in the apparel industry than in commercial interiors.

Kapok

Like cotton, kapok is derived from a seed. It is taken from the seed pod of the Java kapok tree. Too brittle to be spun into fiber but soft enough to be used as cushioning, kapok was once used extensively for stuffing pillows and seat cushions. It is very lightweight and nonabsorbent, making it popular as a stuffing for personal flotation devices, because kapok can support about 30 times its weight in water.

Jute

Jute is made from the stem and stalk of the jute plant. It is harsh, brittle, lints badly, and wrinkles easily, limiting its use primarily to carpet and linoleum backing. Burlap is a fabric that is often made from jute. Jute reacts to chemicals similarly to flax and cotton. It has excellent resistance to microorganisms and insects.

Flax

Probably the oldest fiber ever woven into fabric, flax was used for mummy wrappings in ancient Egypt. Flax is a bast fiber, which means it is derived from the stalk of the plant. The flax plant grows to a height of .6 m to 1.2 m (2 ft to 4 ft). The final fiber length is about 300 mm to 600 mm (12 in to 24 in).

Linen, which is made from flax, is less soft and absorbent than cotton but more resistant to mildew. It is extremely strong, virtually nonelastic, and tends to be brittle. Linen does not lint and resists fraying and seam slippage. One of the major disadvantages of linen is that it wrinkles and creases readily.

Ramie

Sometimes called China grass, ramie is produced from a perennial shrub. It is an exceptionally strong fiber and has a natural luster comparable to that of silk. Ramie fabrics can resemble fine linen if the fiber is thin, or they can be heavy, like canvas, if the fiber is bulky and coarse. Ramie tends to be nonelastic and brittle. Because of its stiffness, ramie is often blended with softer fibers such as cotton and rayon.

Sisal

Stiff and inflexible, sisal (pronounced *sigh-soul*) is a leaf fiber. Named after Sisal, a Mexican town in the Yucatan peninsula where it is grown, it is also farmed in Africa and South America. It tends to stain and crush easily. Sisal is used for floor mats, rugs, and rope.

Silk

The strongest natural fiber, silk varies in length from 900 m to 1550 m (1000 yd to 1700 yd) or longer and is more wrinkle resistant than the natural cellulosic fibers. Like wool, silk is not degraded by cleaning solvents. However, silk deteriorates under UV radiation (sunlight) and is comparatively more expensive than other fibers.

Sericulture is the growth of silk moths for their silk production. The process is quite labor-intensive, which accounts for the expense of the fiber. Mulberry leaves are the sole source of nutrients for the silkworm. Liquid silk is excreted from the head of the silkworm to form a cocoon around its body. Cocoons are dried in an oven, killing the pupae inside while preserving the integrity of the cocoons. The silk is then carefully unwrapped and treated for use as a fiber.

Wool

Wool fiber is sheared from domesticated animals, primarily sheep. Wool, like other animal hair, contains excess amounts of oil (lanolin), which is removed during the fiber processing. Its resiliency and elasticity are exceptional, making it an excellent fiber for use in carpets. Wool carpet remains the standard by which synthetic fiber carpets are judged. Its flexibility is also very good; wool can be reshaped by steaming or pressing.

Wool burns slowly and is self-extinguishing; it stops burning when the flame source is removed. Cigarette burns are quickly extinguished with minimal noticeable damage. Wool carpet is often preferred in the public areas of luxurious hospitality facilities, such as hotel and casino lobbies.

Wool is susceptible to damage by insects; however, treatments are available to make the wool fabric unpalatable to moths. The wool fiber has almost no resistance to alkalies, which are ingredients in most detergents. For this reason, wool usually must be dry cleaned.

The Wool Products Labeling Act was enacted to assist the consumer in understanding the origin of the wool in a fiber or fabric. Fiber labeled *wool* may contain unused wool yarn that has been recovered and reconstructed into new yarns. **Virgin wool** is the designation for wool made into yarn for the first time. **Lamb's wool** is sheared from animals under 8 months of age.

Asbestos

The only natural mineral found in fiber form, asbestos is completely fireproof and was used for many years in firefighters' apparel, in ironing board covers, and in other hazardous industry applications. Some asbestos fibers are insoluble and have barbed edges. When inhaled, they become lodged in the lungs and cannot be expelled by coughing. Because lung cancer and other serious diseases have been associated with exposure to asbestos, its use in most applications is no longer legal.

Natural Rubber

Rubber in fiber form dates from the 1920s, when it was discovered that latex (liquid rubber) could be extruded into fiber. Rubber is unique among the natural fibers. It is highly elastic, flexible, and impermeable to water and air. It tends to lose its strength through age and deteriorates in sunlight. Synthetic rubbers, such as spandex, also have a few of these drawbacks.

SYNTHETIC FIBERS

Rayon

The first synthetic fiber, rayon, was made by emulating the excretion method of the silkworm. Known originally as "artificial silk," rayon is made principally from wood pulp. There are two processes used in the production of rayon, the cuprammonium and the viscose methods. The viscose method is the major method used today. Viscose rayon blends well with other fibers, is absorbent and therefore dyes readily, and is economical to produce. It can be made to resemble cotton, linen, silk, or wool. However, it is not particularly strong and loses strength when wet. Rayon has a low resiliency, and so it wrinkles easily.

Acetate and Triacetate

Although acetate and triacetate have similar chemical compositions, they behave differently as fibers. For example, acetate has poor resiliency whereas triacetate has good resiliency. Acetate fibers are flexible, resulting in fabric with excellent draping qualities. This is a thermoplastic fiber, easily damaged by heat and easily wrinkled. Triacetate is processed differently than acetate, resulting in a fiber of greater stability and abrasion resistance. It can be heat treated to prevent the heat sensitivity inherent to acetate. Permanent pleats can be set in triacetate.

Acrylic

First introduced in 1950 under the trade name Orlon, acrylic fiber can be cut into staple length and then mechanically bulked for an insulative, fluffy, wool-like effect. It can also be made to emulate the look and feel of silk in filament form. It is exceptionally light, providing bulk without weight, and blends well with other fibers. Acrylic fibers accept dyes well, providing a good selection of colors. Some acrylics pill easily.

Aramids

Among the various modern synthetic fibers, aramids have unique properties. Alkalies, acids, and solvents have virtually no effect on them. Aramids are marketed under the trade names Nomex and Kevlar. Nomex is a high-temperature-resistant fiber used mostly in apparel such as firefighters' clothing and space suits. Kevlar is also a high-temperature-resistant fiber and is incredibly strong—stronger than comparably sized steel. It is used as a barrier fabric between the upholstery cushion and fabric in seating that complies with California Technical Bulletin 133. It is also used in bullet-resistant vests. A .38 caliber bullet fired from 3 m (10 ft) will bounce off a Kevlar fabric. Aramids are difficult to dye, but because they are not used for decorative purposes, this is not usually considered a drawback.

Nylon

Nylon, classified as a polymide, is one of the strongest synthetic fibers. It is highly elastic with good elongation and recovery properties. Its great strength, high resiliency, and good abrasion resistance makes it the most popular carpet fiber. Compared with that of natural fibers, nylon's moisture absorbency is low, so it dries quickly. However, its low moisture absorption also makes it prone to the build-up of static electricity.

Nylon is available in many formulations. Nylon 6,6 is a type of nylon that has 6 carbon atoms per individual molecule in each of the two chemicals (hexamethylene diamine and adipic acid) used to make it. Nylon 6,6 is the most widely used type and includes fibers marketed under the popular trade names of Antron and Celanese. (Table 3.17)

Olefin (Polypropylene and Polyethylene)

Olefin is relatively inexpensive and very popular for use as a carpet fiber. Today, the most widely used olefin fiber is polypropylene. Polyethylene was the first olefin fiber to reach commercial importance, being used as upholstery for airplane seats for many years. Olefin is one of the lightest synthetic fibers and has excellent elastic recovery. Because of its outstand-

TABLE 3.17   FIBERS USED IN COMMERCIAL INTERIORS

Trade Name or Trade Mark	Use	Manufacturer
ARAMID		
Kevlar	Fire blocker liner for seating	Du Pont
NYLON		
Anso	Carpet	AlliedSignal
Antron	Carpet	Du Pont
Capalana	Upholstery, wall panels	AlliedSignal
Cordura	Upholstery	Du Pont
Ultron	Carpet	Monsanto
Zeftron	Carpet and upholstery	BASF
OLEFIN		
Marquessa Lana	Carpet	Amoco Fabrics & Fibers
Marvess	Carpet	Amoco Fabrics & Fibers
Tyvek	Nonwoven air barrier	Du Pont
POLYESTER		
Dacron	Upholstery	Du Pont
Micromattique	Draperies	Du Pont
Trevira	Upholstery, cubicle curtains	Hoechst Celanese

ing resistance to stains and crushing and its lack of static generation, olefin continues to increase in popularity as a carpet fiber. The familiar air barrier Tyvek, manufactured by Du Pont, is made of olefin fibers.

Polyester

The initial research by Du Pont that led to the discovery of nylon also led to the invention of polyester. Polyesters today encompass a large family of fibers with unmatched performance. Among the many outstanding characteristics of polyester is its low moisture absorbency, wrinkle resistance, high strength and resiliency, abrasion resistance, and dimensional stability. Polyester also has excellent crease resistance and is easy to maintain. It is frequently blended with other fibers to enhance their performance. Hospital cubicle curtains are often made of polyester. Dacron, Fortrel, Kodel, and Trevira are all popular trade names for different types of polyester.

Glass

Although glass has been used for centuries, it was not until the mid-1800s that it was first produced in fiber form. One of the most important characteristics of glass fiber is that it is unaffected by fire. Glass fiber thread is sometimes used to stitch upholstery fabrics for seating that complies with California Technical Bulletin 133 (see "Flammability Standards" in Chapter 2). Sheer casements are popular applications for fabrics made of glass fibers. Glass has a very low abrasion resistance. Some draperies made of glass fibers show wear if, when they are drawn, they drag against a window sill or floor. Owens-Corning's trade name for its glass fiber product is Fiberglas.

Fabric Construction

Most textiles used for commercial interiors are woven; there are very limited uses for knitted and other nonwoven types of fabrics. Woven fabrics are made by interlacing yarns at right angles to each other on a loom. The lengthwise yarns are called the **warps**, or ends, and the widthwise yarns are called the **wefts**, or filling yarns (Figure 3.23). The lengthwise edges of the fabric are called **selvages**. There are three basic weaves, plain, twill, and satin. Variations and combinations of these types form other weaves.

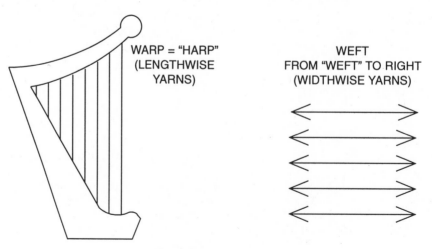

WARP = "HARP"
(LENGTHWISE
YARNS)

WEFT
FROM "WEFT" TO RIGHT
(WIDTHWISE YARNS)

Figure 3.23 Warp and weft.

PLAIN WEAVE

Each warp yarn passes over and then under the weft yarns. This results in no particular surface pattern or texture, making plain weaves ideal backgrounds for printed fabrics. Plain weaves wear well but tend to wrinkle (Figure 3.24).

TWILL WEAVE

Each warp yarn passes over and then under the weft yarns as in the plain weave, but the sequence is started slightly higher (or lower) on each successive yarn. A diagonal pattern is created. Denim and gabardine are twill weaves (Figures 3.25, 3.26, and 3.27).

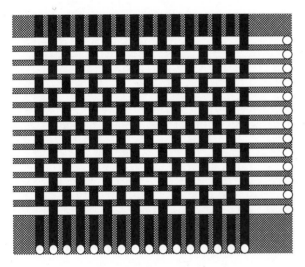

Figure 3.24 Plain weave.

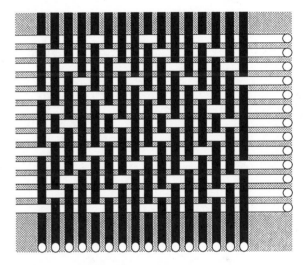

Figure 3.25 Herringbone weave.

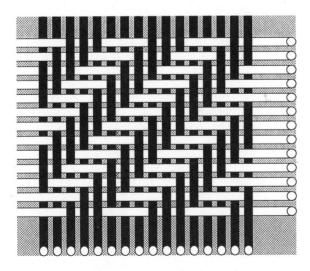

Figure 3.26 3/3 Twill weave.

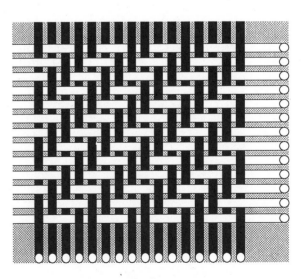

Figure 3.27 2/2 Twill weave.

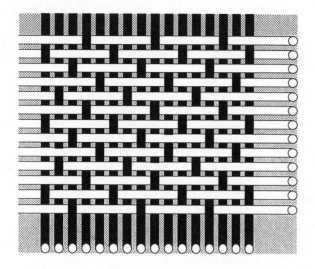

Figure 3.28 Five-thread satin weave.

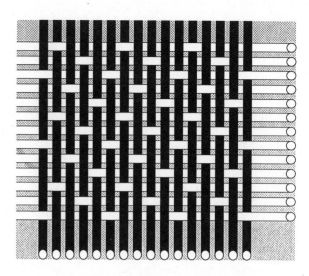

Figure 3.29 Five-thread sateen weave.

SATIN WEAVE

Each yarn floats over at least four yarns creating a smooth, lustrous surface. Because there are such long lengths of yarn on the surface of the textile, snagging is a problem. Sateen is a form of satin weave (Figures 3.28 and 3.29).

Specific types of weaving equipment are required to achieve detailed woven patterns. The **jacquard loom**—named for its French inventor, Joseph Marie Jacquard—is used for tapestries, brocades, and damask weaves. Jacquard weaving uses a series of punched cards. As in a player piano, in which each card perforation controls the striking of a key, each hole in a jacquard card controls the action of one warp yarn. The jacquard mechanism controls thousands of warp yarns in this manner. Setting up a jacquard loom is labor-intensive making this the most expensive weave type. It is used chiefly for upholstery materials.

Fabric Wear Resistance

The wear resistance of fabric is affected by many factors, such as the type and length of the fiber; the structure of the yarn; the construction of the fabric; and the type, kind, and amount of finishing material added to the fibers, yarns, or fabric (Table 3.18). Although abrasion resistance is associated with durability, the ability of a fabric to withstand deterioration varies with the application. Abrasion test results are helpful when they are used for purposes of comparison but are not a reliable prediction of actual wear-life.

Abrasion resistance for fabric is often stated in terms of the number of cycles it can endure on a specified machine. The Oscillatory Cylinder Method, commonly called the "Wyzenbeek test" after the man who developed the testing equipment, is the traditional test for abrasion resistance. The Taber Abraser test is sometimes used for fabric but is most often used for testing carpet and is discussed in Chapter 4, "Carpet," page 197.

TABLE 3.18 PROPERTIES OF MAJOR TEXTILES

Properties	Cotton	Flax	Wool	Silk	Acetate	Viscose Rayon	Triacetate	Acrylic	Glass	Nylon	Olefin	Polyester
Abrasion Resistance	Good	Fair	Fair	Fair	Poor	Fair	Poor	Fair	Poor	Excellent	Excellent	Good
Absorbency (% M.R.)	8½	12	13½	11	6½	11	3½	1½	0	4½	0.1	1
Drapability	Fair	Poor	Good	Excellent	Excellent	Good	Excellent	Good	Poor	Good	Fair	Fair
Wash or Dry Clean	Either	Either	DC	Either	DC	Either	Either	Either	Hand wash	Either	Either	Either
Sunlight Resistance	Fair	Good	Good	Poor	Good	Fair	Good	Excellent	Excellent	Poor	Good	Good
Hand	Good	Good	Fair–Excellent	Excellent	Excellent	Good	Excellent	Good	Poor	Fair	Fair	Fair
Pilling Resistance	Good	Good	Fair	Good	Good	Good	Good	Fair	Excellent	Poor	Good	Very poor
Resiliency	Poor	Poor	Good	Fair	Fair	Poor	Good	Good	Excellent	Good	Excellent	Excellent
Static Resistance	Good	Good	Fair	Fair	Fair	Good	Fair	Poor	Excellent	Poor	Good	Very poor
Strength (Grams/Denier)	3.0–5.0 Good	6.6–8.4 Excellent	0.8–2.0 Poor	3.9–4.5 Good	0.8–1.5 Poor	0.7–6.0 Poor-Good	0.8–1.4 Poor	1.8–3.5 Fair	6.0–7.0 Excellent	2.5–7.5 Excellent	4.8–7.0 Good	2.5–9.5 Excellent
Thermoplastic	No	No	No	No	Yes	No	Yes	Yes	Yes	Yes	Yes	Yes

Source: A. Cohen, *Beyond Basic Textiles*, New York, Fairchilds Publications, 1982, p.5.

ASTM D 4157 *Standard Test Method for Abrasion Resistance of Textile Fabrics (Oscillatory Cylinder Method)* describes the procedures for the Wyzenbeek Test. In this test, a sample is stretched taught and held against a curved, rotating cylinder with an abrasive surface. The results of the test are typically reported in terms of number of cycles required before there is a noticeable change in the fabric. Some manufacturers use the following criteria to rate the durability of upholstery material: 3,000 cycles for light duty; 9,000 cycles for medium duty; and 15,000 cycles for heavy duty. For example, a fabric that shows no noticeable wear at 9,000 cycles but is worn through at 15,000 cycles would be classified as medium duty. The cycles represent the number of double rubs applied to the test sample.

Fabric Finishing

Fabrics can be selected for their look and modified by a variety of processes to achieve the required performance. A soft fabric with a luxurious hand, or feel, can be transformed into a stiff wall covering with the application of an acrylic or paper backing. A textile woven from an easily stained fiber can be coated with a thin layer of vinyl and thus converted for use on restaurant seating. Extra strength and durability can be added to a loose-weave fabric with the application of a fabric backing, making it usable for application as an upholstery fabric. Any type of treatment can change the nature of a fabric, such as the color, dimensional stability, hand, luster, or stiffness. Therefore, samples of the fabric with all specified treatments applied should be required so that the final effect can be judged by the user.

FLAME-RESISTANT TREATMENTS

To comply with building code requirements, fabrics must sometimes be treated with flame-resistant chemicals. There are two types of flame-resistant treatments: polymers and salines.

A **polymer flame-resistant treatment** is applied through an immersion process. The fabric is rolled off the bolt and submerged in a chemical bath. The polymer solution is then heat set into the fabric. Shrinkage can occur as a result of such a treatment. Fabric finishers usually anticipate this and require up to 5% more fabric than is needed for the project. In some fabrics, there will be a noticeable change in color or stiffness. Most polymer flame-resistant treatments are quite durable but will eventually wash out if the fabric is dry cleaned more than 20 times.

A **saline flame-resistant treatment** is less expensive than a polymer solution, but does have some drawbacks. The salt solution has a corrosive effect on metals, such as upholstery tacks and staples. Saline treatments are not as durable as polymer treatments and have a tendency to leach out, discoloring the treated fabric. These treatments also increase a fabric's ability to absorb moisture. For long fabric lengths (e.g., curtains for a story-high window), the cumulative effect can be noticeable dimensional fluctuations as the humidity changes.

FLAME-RESISTANT BACKINGS

Flame-resistant backings can be used in applications where the most stringent flammability requirement for seating—California Technical Bulletin 133—is required (see "Flammability Standards" in Chapter 2). Flame-resistant backings provide far more protection against the spread of fire than flame-resistant treatments. Aramid fabrics, such as Du Pont's Kevlar, are laminated to the back of upholstery fabric. Lamination reduces the amount of labor involved in applying the barrier fabric between the seat cushion and the finish fabric. Instead of being upholstered twice, first with the aramid and then with the upholstery fabric, the seat is upholstered only once with the laminated fabric.

STAIN-RESISTANT TREATMENTS

Stain-resistant treatments make most fabrics resistant to oil- and water-based stains. These treatments are usually spray applied and rarely have an effect on flame-resistant treatments applied to the same fabric. Fluids bead up on the surface of the treated fabric, do not spread, and can be easily removed. These finishes are odorless, harmless, and do not alter the hand of the fabric. Teflon, manufactured by Du Pont, and Scotchguard, by 3M, are trade names for popular stain-resistant treatments. Both chemicals are members of the fluoroplastics family (see "Plastics" earlier in this chapter).

Leather

Leather is processed animal skin, mostly that of cattle. It is expensive for several reasons: such processing is labor-intensive, aniline dyes are costly, and there is a high rejection rate of the finished hides (Figure 3.30). **Cattle hide** is the skin of a fully grown cow. Such skins are large hides, ranging from 4.6 sq m to 5.5 sq m (50 sq ft to 60 sq ft) (Figure 3.31). The center portion of the hide, called **bend**, yields the best quality hide. **Calfskin** is the hide of a young animal and is considerably smaller, about 2.3 sq m to 3.2 sq m (25 sq ft to 35 sq ft) (Figure 3.32). Calfskin is characterized by its softness, suppleness, and fine grain. Leather is categorized by the surface imperfections and how it is processed.

In calculating the yield of a hide, a waste factor of about 10% to 15% is typically factored in. Each 0.9 m (yard) of 900-mm-wide (36-in-wide) fabric requires about 1.4 sq m (16 sq ft) of leather. Each 0.9 m (yard) of 1370-mm-wide (54-in-wide) fabric requires 1.7 sq m (18 sq ft) of leather.

Full-grain leather (or full-top-grain leather, as it is sometimes called) possesses the genuine original grain of the hide. The surface is not embossed or altered in any way; it is the full, natural hide. Full-grain leathers have the least amount of surface imperfections. These constitute the most expensive type of hides.

In **top-grain** leather the original surface pattern, including scars from barbed wire or brands, is removed by abrasion. This skinless surface is embossed with a pattern, typically resembling the grain of the skin that was removed.

Figure 3.30 Leather upholstery material being marked for cutting. Steelcase.

Split leathers are made by slicing the hide into two or three thin layers to give uniform thickness to the grain side of the hide. The inside layer is often finished as suede. Inexpensive leathers may be pigmented split leathers with an embossed imitation grain.

There are basically two steps in transforming a hide into a piece of leather suitable for use as an upholstery material: tanning and finishing. First, the leather is tanned to preserve the hide. Tanning puts the life back into a leather hide by replacing the natural gelatinous materials found in the skin with tanning solutions. Tanning makes the leather strong, supple, and enduring. There are three primary tanning agents: mineral, vegetable, and a combination of the two.

Mineral tanning. The tanning solution is based on chromium salts. Mineral tanned hides accept dyes well, including rich, vibrant colors. About 90% of leather today is tanned by this method.

Vegetable tanning. Tree bark, typically oak, and water form the basis of this tanning solution. The hides are submerged in the solution, and tannins (tanning materials) from the bark swell the hides. Vegetable-tanned hides have a heavier feel and a distinct smell. They are often left undyed. Vegetable-tanned hides become pliable when wet, yet will retain their shape when dry.

Combination tanning. This tanning method produces a hide that is quite supple, with a limited acceptance of dyes.

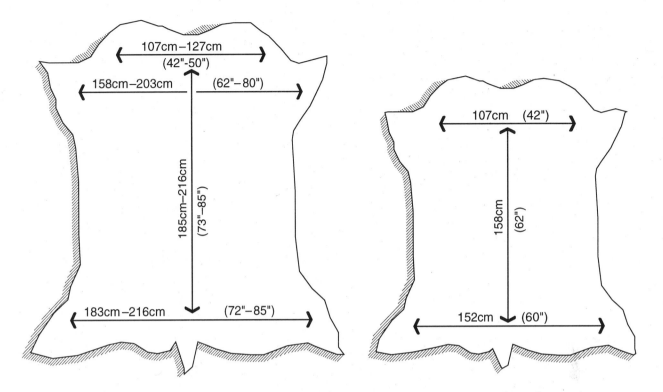

Figure 3.31 Cattle hide. *Source: Edelman Leather Handbook,* Teddy & Arthur Edelman, Ltd., Hawleyville, CT.

Figure 3.32 Calf hide. *Source: Edelman Leather Handbook,* Teddy & Arthur Edelman, Ltd., Hawleyville, CT.

The final step in preparing leather for use is finishing. Finishes can color the leather and help to protect it from hard wear. Dyeing, embossing, and water- or stain-proofing may be part of the finishing process.

Comparable to stains for wood that do not contain opaque pigments, **aniline dyes** are translucent. They do not obscure the natural grain pattern and surface imperfections. The best-quality upholstery leathers are aniline dyed. The dye penetrates through the depth of the hide completely so that as the leather wears, the color remains the same. **Semianiline dyes** contain some pigments. The normal variation from one dyed hide to another can be quite noticeable. The use of semianiline dyes helps to ensure uniformity in color among many hides.

CHAPTER 4

Construction Materials

WALL FINISHES

Walls define space and provide a palette on which a finish is applied. They also serve as complex systems, concealing the building services — elevators, power, communications, HVAC, and plumbing — within them. Walls perform as separators from visual and acoustic distractions, and from fire. In most commercial interiors, light-gauge steel studs form a frame supporting a substrate finished with paint, wallcovering, tile, paneling, or an upholstered system.

Gypsum board is the wall substrate of choice for commercial interior wall finishes. The contemporary child of lath and plaster, gypsum board is inexpensive and easy to handle and install. The standard size for gypsum board is 1220 mm by 2440 mm (4 ft by 8 ft). However, many manufacturers are producing gypsum board in a true metric size of 1200 mm by 3600 mm.

Gypsum board, sometimes referred to as *wallboard*, *drywall*, or *sheet rock*, is a panel consisting of a noncombustible gypsum core with a paper surface (Figure 4.1). Wallboard can be scored and bent around curves. It is easy to repair and inexpensive to replace. It performs well as a substrate for all types of decorative and performance finishes, such as wall covering and paint.

Gypsum board is available for a wide variety of specialty applications. Type X wallboard is manufactured to achieve fire resistance ratings. According to ASTM C 36, a wall constructed of a single layer of Type X gypsum board on either side of load-bearing wood studs must provide at least a one-hour fire resistance rating for 16 mm- (⅝ in-) thick board, or a ¾-hour rating for 12.7 mm- (½ in-) thick gypsum board. Fire-resistance ratings for walls are described in Chapter 2, "Flammability Standards," page 57.

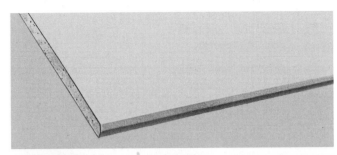

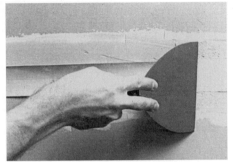

Figure 4.1 Gypsum board. Photo courtesy of National Gypsum Co.

Figure 4.2 Gypsum board is screwed to a furring channel. Photo courtesy of National Gypsum Co.

Figure 4.3 The gypsum board intersections are taped and spackled. Photo courtesy of National Gypsum Co.

Other specialty applications include:

Moisture-resistant gypsum board is sometimes called "green board" because of its pale lime green color. It has a water-repellant paper face and a moisture-resistant core. Moisture-resistant gypsum board is used as a backing for ceramic tile and in wet areas. It is available with a Type X core.

Foil-backed board has a layer of aluminum foil laminated to its backside. The foil surface provides an effective vapor retarder.

Gypsum board plaster base is used as a substrate for veneer plaster and is erected in the same manner as regular gypsum board. It is often referred to as "blue board," because of the color of its absorptive paper face, designed for a strong bond with plaster materials.

Prefinished gypsum board is covered with decorative vinyl- or textile-surfaced faces. It is often used in prefabricated demountable partition systems.

Gypsum shaft wall systems are lighter in weight and easier to install than traditional masonry shaft walls. Shaft walls surround multistory vertical chases for elevator or mechanical enclosures. To prevent a fire from quickly spreading to other floors, shaft walls are required to be fire resistance rated. Gypsum shaft wall systems typically consist of floor and ceiling tracks, special studs, special gypsum panels, and Type X gypsum panels.

Wallboard is installed by screwing (and sometimes nailing) it to studs or furring channels (Figure 4.2). The edges of the wallboard are tapered to accept a paper reinforcing tape or a self-adhering fiberglass tape and joint compound (Figure 4.3).

Annotated Specification Checklist
for Gypsum Board

PART 1 GENERAL

PROJECT CONDITIONS

Environmental Requirements: ASTM C 840.

PART 2 PRODUCTS

MATERIALS

Gypsum Board: ASTM C 36.

Fire-Rated Gypsum Board: ASTM C 36, Type X.

Moisture-Resistant Backing Board: ASTM C 630.

Thickness: 16 mm- (⅝ in-) thick gypsum board is typical for interior wall construction. 6.4 mm- (¼ in-), 12.7 mm- (½ in-), or 9.5 mm- (⅜ in-) thick gypsum board is also available. For tight curves, thinner gypsum board may be required. For acoustic barriers, thicker board may be preferred.

ACCESSORIES

Corner Bead

Control Joint

Acoustic Sealant (See "Acoustic Ceilings" on page 147.)

PART 3 EXECUTION

INSTALLATION

Installation: ASTM C 840.

Paints and Coatings

Paint remains the most economical decorative finish available to designers. It protects and preserves while adding color and sheen to a space. The technology of paint composition and formulation is constantly evolving. Better performing, easier-to-apply coatings are constantly in development in response to government regulations, environmental concerns, and the demands of the market.

Beyond decorating and protecting, specialty coatings are available that can significantly modify the performance of the substrate to which they are applied. Epoxy coatings can create an impermeable, chemical-resistant surface of superior durability. Fire-retardant intumescent coatings can be applied to combustible materials, such as wood, to achieve a required flame spread rating. And multicolor coatings offer improved scratch resistance over regular paint as well as a distinctive appearance.

PAINT INGREDIENTS

There are three basic ingredients in paint: pigments, thinner, and resin. Paint formulations also include a variety of additives to provide desirable performance characteristics. The thinner and resin constitute the liquid portion of the paint, also referred to as the vehicle. The **vehicle** is so called because it conveys the ingredients that remain on the substrate surface after the paint has dried.

Pigments are often the most expensive paint ingredient and are primarily responsible for a paint's opacity, color, and sheen. Opacity is the ability to hide or obscure a substrate. Several pigments are typically combined to achieve the desired paint color. Extender (also called *inert*) pigments do not provide opacity but are added for sheen, as well as their leveling and adhesion properties.

The volume of pigments in a paint solution controls the sheen by determining the texture of the cured paint film (Figure 4.4). By varying the amount of pigment, different sheens are produced. A larger volume of resin encases the pigment and creates a more reflective, or glossy, surface. A larger volume of pigment particles produces a rougher-textured, less-reflective, flatter appearance. The large volume of pigments in flat paints makes them unsuitable for areas subject to hard wear or rigorous cleaning. The protruding pigment particles have a tendency to break off when abraded, creating shiny areas.

Sheen must be considered when a paint is selected. Because sheen is a function of the reflectivity of the coated surface, it affects perception of the paint color. Terms to describe sheen are not standardized among paint manufacturers. Table 4.1 lists commonly used terms and their distinguishing characteristics.

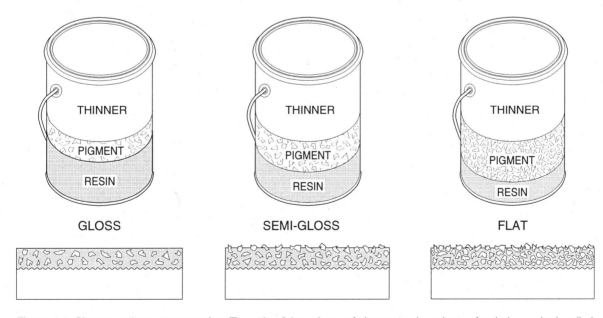

Figure 4.4 Pigment volume concentration. The ratio of the volume of pigment to the volume of resin in a paint is called the pigment volume concentration (PVC). Light reflects off a cured paint film with a low PVC for a glossy appearance. Light is diffused by a high PVC paint for a flat finish.

TABLE 4.1 PAINT SHEENS

Sheen	Description	Pigment Volume Concentration (PVC)	Applications
Flat	Dull, matte surface, free from reflection.	High. Particles protrude from paint film surface.	Low-wear surfaces that require low glare and that do not require scrubbing.
Eggshell (also called satin)	This term refers to the modest gloss of a clean egg and is used to describe a variety of finishes ranging from flat to semigloss.	Medium.	Areas requiring moderate washability.
Semigloss	Surface with some reflectivity.	Medium. Pigment particles mostly contained within the paint film.	Areas requiring wear resistance and washability.
Gloss	Highly reflective, very shiny surface.	Low. Pigment particles contained within the paint film with no protrusions.	Smooth substrate required because surface imperfections are more likely to show.

The **thinner** is the volatile (readily evaporating) portion of a paint. It does not become part of the cured paint film. The thinner reduces the paint solution to the proper viscosity so that it is not too thick and sticky to be applied. It enables the paint to flow and level itself on the substrate. For oil-based paints, the thinner is a solvent, which dissolves the resin and the pigments. The most common solvent for oil-based paints is mineral spirits. For water-based paints, the thinner is water, which dilutes the paint, dispersing the resin and pigments in a solution until it is applied (Figure 4.5).

Figure 4.5 Paints and stains. Benjamin Moore & Co., Inc.

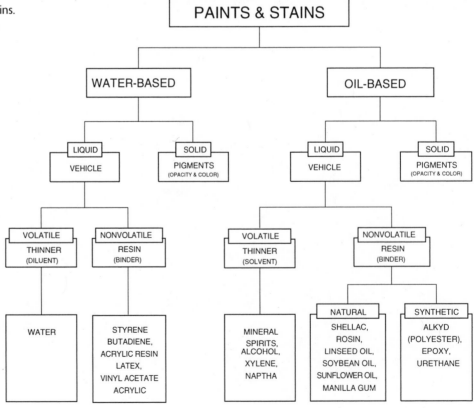

The thinner (especially if it is water) is the least expensive ingredient of paint. An inexpensive, inferior-quality paint will contain more thinner in proportion to the resin or pigment, and it will take several times as much paint to achieve the same finish as a better quality paint.

Additives enhance the properties of the vehicle or the pigment, providing, for instance, quicker drying time or improved resistance to fading (Table 4.2). Additives also help with paint application. For example, wetting agents help break down the foam generated during stirring and anti-settling agents reduce the settling of the pigments during storage. Preservatives and fungicides destroy organisms that would otherwise thrive in the dark, moist interior of a paint can.

The **resin** is the nonvolatile (not readily evaporating) portion of the paint that binds the pigments together, forming the cured paint film. For this reason, it is called the *binder* or *film former*. The resin is responsible for some of the most important performance attributes of a paint. This component gives the dried paint film its continuity, abrasion resistance, and stain resistance. It also enhances the hardness and strength of the paint film. The resin is such an important ingredient that paints are often identified by their resins.

There are two basic categories of resins: those that are dissolved in a solvent-based solution and those that are dispersed in a water-based solution. Oil and alkyd paints are solvent based, and latex paints are water based. The three most popular types of resins for interior applications are oil, alkyd, and latex.

Solvent-Based Resins

Most solvent-based paints dry and harden through the chemical process of oxidation. The thinner evaporates as the resins, reacting with the oxygen in the air, are oxidized to form a cured paint film. Solvent-based paints have better adhesion, a smoother film appearance, and dry much harder than water-based paints. The most common types of solvent-based resin paints for commercial interiors are oils and alkyds.

TABLE 4.2   COMMON PAINT ADDITIVES

Additive	Purpose
Antiskinning	Prevents skin from forming in can prior to use
Biocides	Prevents spoilage resulting from bacterial growth
Coalescent	Aids in formation of continuous film in latex paint
Defoamer	Eliminates air from paint or reduces bubbling upon application
Driers	Accelerate conversion of solvent paints from liquid to solid state
Freeze-Thaw Stabilizers	Lower latex paint freezing point
Mildewcide	Resists growth of mildew
Surfactant	Stabilizes mixtures of resins or pigments in solvents or water
Thickeners	Increase consistency of paint and prevent separation of pigment in oil- and water-based paints

Source: Courtesy of Benjamin Moore and Co., Inc.

Solvent-based coatings may not be allowed in locations with stringent **volatile organic compound (VOC)** restrictions. VOCs are increasingly being restricted because of their adverse effects on human health and the environment. VOCs are released into the air while paint dries. In the presence of sunlight, VOCs mix with nitrogen oxide in the atmosphere and form ozone, which is unhealthy for plants, animals, and human beings. VOCs are measured in grams of organic solvent in a liter of paint, or g/l (lb/gal).

Each state, as well as many counties and cities, have air pollution control agencies that determine the local VOC requirements, although not all jurisdictions have implemented VOC regulations. These regulations are changing so rapidly that they might be modified between the time a paint is specified and the time the application of the paint begins. The regional office of the Environmental Protection Agency (EPA) should be contacted for current information on VOC regulations.

Oil-Based Paint. Oil is the oldest solvent-based resin still available today. Linseed oil has long been the most commonly used resin; however, more recently, the less expensive soybean oil has become quite popular. Oil paints contain both natural and synthetic resins.

Alkyd Paint. Most solvent-based paints today are alkyds. Alkyd resins, which are oil-modified polyesters (see "Plastics" in Chapter 3), have been used as an alternative to oil or in conjunction with oil since their introduction in the 1930s. The term *alkyd* is derived from *alcid*, a combination and contraction of two primary ingredients found in this resin type, alcohol (*al*) and acid (*cid*).

Alkyds are faster drying, harder, more durable, and have better color retention properties than unmodified oil-based paints. They are easy to apply and have outstanding washability and scrubbability characteristics. Alkyds also have less odor than most other solvent-based paints. However, they have poor resistance to alkaline surfaces, such as masonry, and should not be used unless these substrates are properly primed. Like oil-based paints, alkyd paints cure by means of oxidation.

It is possible to determine whether an existing paint finish is an alkyd by leaving a solution of 30 ml (two tablespoons) lye crystals and 0.24 liter (one cup) warm water on the surface for 10 minutes. If the finish is an alkyd, it will blister.

Water-Based Resins

Water-thinned, or emulsion, paints dry and harden through evaporation. Coalescing agents in the paint ensure that the resin particles fuse together as they dry to form a continuous film. Most water-based paints are referred to as latex paints, even if they do not contain latex.

Water-based paints are inherently lower in VOCs than solvent-based paints because the thinner is water. However, they are not necessarily VOC-free. VOCs for water-based paints are determined in a slightly different manner than for solvent-based paints. The water content of the paint is not included in the mass (weight). For example, if a quarter of a liter of latex paint is water, the number of grams of VOC would be calculated on the liter minus the amount of water, or three-quarters of a liter of paint.

Latex Paint. First introduced in the 1940s by Glidden, latex paints are often preferred for commercial interior applications. They have very little odor and a fast drying time. They are water thinned, which makes them easy to apply, clean up, and discard. Latex paints have the additional advantage of being somewhat porous, allowing the evaporation of moisture from beneath the surface of the paint film. This helps to prevent the build-up of migrating moisture under the paint surface, which can cause an adhesion failure. Latex paints contain only synthetic resins.

It is possible to determine whether an existing surface has been coated with latex paint; the paint pigment will rub off slightly with the application of isopropyl alcohol.

EPOXY COATINGS

Epoxy coatings are known as high-performance coatings because of their superior durability. They are used where impermeability, resistance to chemical corrosion, or abrasion resistance is required. They are also appropriate for use on surfaces subjected to frequent scrubbing, harsh chemicals, or severe moisture.

Although they are unmatched in resistance to abuse, epoxy coatings have several drawbacks. They are relatively expensive and require a much better quality surface preparation than regular paint. Special skill is often required for their application. The strong solvents in epoxy coatings make habitation within a freshly painted space impossible. Adequate ventilation must be provided during and after application.

Catalyzed epoxies come in two parts, resin and catalyst, that must be mixed just before they are applied. There are three types of catalyzed epoxies commonly used in commercial interiors: polyesters, polyamides, and urethanes. Polyester epoxies produce a tough, glossy surface. Polyamide epoxies provide a flexible but durable film. Urethane epoxies are the most versatile of the epoxy coatings.

FIRE-RETARDANT AND FIRE-RESISTANT COATINGS

Flame-retardant paints slow the rate at which a fire spreads by delaying the ignition of the surface that has been coated. They are designed to sacrifice themselves to protect the substrate. Considerably more expensive and less durable than regular paints, they are commonly used on combustible materials, such as wood, to achieve the required flame spread rating (see "Flammability Standards" in Chapter 2). These paints can delay, but cannot prevent, a fire from spreading.

Most fire-retardant coatings are **intumescent**, which means that they swell, forming a charred layer of blisters when exposed to extremely high heat (Figure 4.6). This foamlike material insulates the substrate from the fire. Proper application of intumescent paint is crucial, because the fire rating is based on the number of coats applied at the prescribed thickness. Intumescent coating manufacturers certify painters to ensure that their products are correctly applied. Intumescent paints can be water based or solvent based.

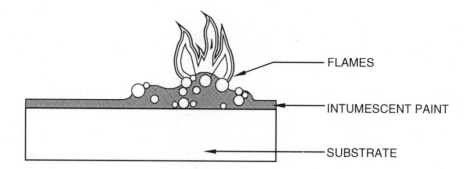

FLAMES

INTUMESCENT PAINT

SUBSTRATE

Figure 4.6 Intumescent paint bubbles and swells when exposed to high heat. The paint film forms a charred layer of blisters, insulating the substrate from fire.

Fire-resistant paints differ from fire-retardant paints in that they resist the spread of fire by not contributing to the flame. They are not as effective at controlling the spread of fire as fire-retardant paints.

MULTICOLOR COATINGS

Invented by Dr. John C. Zola in the late 1940s, the first multicolor coating technique was used in Hollywood in the burgeoning film industry. Zolatone, as the product would come to be called, replaced a hand-mottling technique used to add a three-dimensional character to black-and-white movie sets. Dr. Zola's innovation lives on and is now produced under different product names by several coating manufacturers.

Today, multicolors are selected for their distinctive effect or to mimic the look of hand-sponged finishes or fine-grained stones, such as granite and marble (Figure 4.7). Beyond their unique design statement, they also offer substantial durability and scratch resistance.

Figure 4.7 The fine-grained look of a multicolor coating. Courtesy Surface Protection Industries.

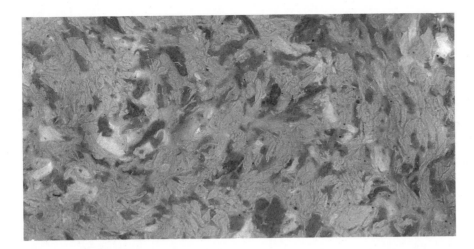

Figure 4.8 Water-based multicolor coating formulations suspend colored flakes in a latex solution. Courtesy Surface Protection Industries.

Multicolor coatings are unique among paint finishes in their composition. Traditional solvent-based multicolors are composed of tiny bubbles of different sizes, and colors suspended in a nonpigmented solution. The little beads of pigment remain separate until they are applied. These pigment beads burst upon impact with the surface to be coated, creating small splashes of various colors. Low VOC multicolor formulations suspend colored flakes in an aqueous solution (Figure 4.8) that is spray-applied.

Because solvent-based multicolors depend on the pigment beads being broken to achieve the splattered effect, multicolors must be spray applied. The relative size of the different color splashes can be adjusted in one of two ways. Changing the size of the pigment bead results in a larger or smaller amount of that color on the finish surface. However, not all manufacturers offer this option. By changing the air pressure of the spray equipment, the pigment beads can be ruptured as they leave the nozzle, dispersing the pigment into smaller fragments; the higher the air pressure, the finer the color particles.

Multicolor coating application involves two coats, background and finish. The background coat is almost monochromatic, achieved by increasing the air pressure on the spray applicator. This acts as an undercoat of sorts, ensuring proper coverage and protection of the wall surface. After the application of the base coat, the air pressure on the spray equipment is adjusted and the finish coat is sprayed on.

PAINT AND COATING PERFORMANCE

Determining the quality of a paint or coating is difficult. There is no industry standard by which various paints can be compared. Some experts recommend basing product comparisons on the percentage of volume solids; the higher the percentage, the better. However, the volume solids content alone is insufficient to determine quality. A variety of tests have been

TABLE 4.3   PERFORMANCE TESTS FOR PAINTS AND COATINGS

Property	ASTM Test Method
Specular gloss and gloss retention	D 523
Dry film hardness	D 3363
Dry film adhesion, wet film adhesion, boiling water adhesion	D 3359
Impact resistance	D 2794
Abrasion resistance	D 968
Muriatic acid resistance	D 1308
Detergent resistance	D 2248
Humidity resistance	D 2247 and B 117
Color retention	D 2244
Chalk resistance	D 523

developed by the American Society for Testing and Materials (ASTM) to assist in the comparison of the appearance and performance of painted finishes; these are listed in Table 4.3.

SUBSTRATE PREPARATION

Paint rarely fails because the coating is bad. Coating failure usually occurs for one or both of the following reasons:

1. *The surfaces to be coated have not been properly prepared.* Proper substrate preparation is vital to the performance of a coating. A paint finish is only as good as the surface to which it is applied. Not even the highest-quality paint can survive a poorly prepared substrate. If paint is applied over an incompatible material, adhesion will eventually fail, causing peeling, blistering, cracking, or flaking. All of the products that will be coated, such as patching compounds, sealants, primers, sealers, paints, and other coatings, must be compatible. The paint manufacturer should be consulted for the proper combination of products to ensure a successful finish surface.

2. *Coatings have not been properly applied.* Proper application is especially important for catalyzed epoxy coatings and other two-part formulations that must be mixed on the project site just before they are applied. Paint manufacturers specify how much paint should be applied by giving an application rate or a dry film thickness. The **application rate** is given as the area of substrate in square feet that should be covered by a gallon of paint, or *sq ft/gal*. For example, an intumescent paint may have to be applied at a rate of 190 sq ft/gal to achieve the required coating thickness, whereas a regular paint may have an application rate of 300 sq ft/gal. The **dry film thickness (DFT)**, the thickness of the cured paint finish, is measured in *mils*, which is equal to 0.0254 mm ($1/1000$ in). The wet film thickness is sometimes also given because it is easier and less damaging to measure.

Annotated Specification Checklist
for Paints and Coatings

Part 1 GENERAL

SUBMITTALS

Product Data: Application rate and manufacturer's instructions for thinning.

Samples: 300-mm-square (12-in-square) step sample on foam core board, showing progressive layers of coating system. *During contract administration this information may be helpful as the work in progress is observed.*

QUALITY ASSURANCE

Installer Qualifications: Certified by coating manufacturer. *A qualified Installer is required only for intumescent paint or other involved applications where skill is crucial to the performance of the finish.*

Regulatory Requirements: _____. *Include this for intumescent paint only. The flame spread ratings required by the building code should be included here.*

Mock-Ups: Full-size on 1.2 m x 2.4 m (4 ft × 8 ft) gypsum wallboard, in space where paint is specified and with final operational lighting configuration. Up to three mock-ups may be required. *The perception of color is affected by reflections from other surfaces, the angle of the surfaces, time of day, exposure of the space to daylight, and lighting, among other influences. A full-size sample in the actual location is the only way to evaluate a paint color selection. Requiring three mock-ups, provides a couple more chances to verify other color selections if the paint specified is not what is desired.*

PROJECT CONDITIONS

Environmental Requirements: Comply with manufacturer's recommendations. *Unlike exteriors, interior applications are usually done in an enclosed and conditioned spaces. Optimal temperature conditions for the application of most paints is between 10°C (50°F) and 32°C (90°F). However, because the climatic conditions under which the paint is applied are crucial to the performance of the coating, it is always best to defer to the manufacturer's requirements.*

MAINTENANCE

Extra Materials: Labeled and sealed 19-liter (5-gallon) containers for each color and sheen. *Even though the paint finish will fade or the color will change with soil or cleaning, it is worth ordering extra paint, especially for custom colors. When touch-up is required, specify that the entire wall surface, from corner to corner, be painted rather than just a small portion of it.*

PART 2 PRODUCTS

MANUFACTURERS

Materials: Factory-fresh manufacturer's recommended coating system, including primer, sealer, or other type of undercoat, and finish coat that is compatible with substrate. *The paint manufacturer is the final authority on the compatibility of substrate, undercoats, and top coat. Incompatibility of coatings ultimately results in failure of the coating.*

PART 3 EXECUTION

EXAMINATION

Verification of Conditions: Verify that substrates are in compliance with paint manufacturer's requirements before paint is applied. *A paint is only as good as the surface to which it is applied.*

PREPARATION

Protection: Protect adjacent surfaces from paint.

Surface Preparation: Prime or seal substrate as recommended by paint manufacturer. Prepare substrate so that it is clean, dry, and smooth.

APPLICATION

Apply in compliance with paint manufacturer's written recommendations at application rate required. *By requiring written recommendations, possible confusion over what a paint manufacturer's representative may have said is avoided.*

FIELD QUALITY CONTROL

Test: Measure dry film thickness (DFT) to verify application rate. *Include this requirement when proper paint thickness is essential, for example, for intumescent paint.*

PROTECTION

Indicate freshly painted surfaces with "Wet Paint" signs. *The Contractor is obligated by the requirements included in Division 1 to protect the finished work until the project is turned over to the Owner. This requirement helps to prevent inadvertent damage by someone other than the Contractor.*

SCHEDULES

The schedule of paint colors and sheens is usually provided on a finish schedule, included either in the specifications or, more commonly, on the drawings.

Wallcoverings

Wallcoverings offer improved durability over ordinary paint finishes while providing texture and pattern to the wall surface. The most popular wallcoverings for commercial use are the vinyls, favored for the practical, affordable, and durable solutions they offer to protecting and decorating. With the application of a wallcovering, the warmth of wood paneling can be affordably achieved (with wood veneer wallcovering) or a room can be wrapped in the richness and beauty of fabric (with backed textile wallcoverings). With properties ranging from the fragility of wallpaper to the strength of woven fiberglass, wallcoverings continue to expand both performance and design possibilities.

For commercial applications, durability is usually an important consideration in the selection of a wallcovering. There is a classification system

TABLE 4.4   ASTM F 793 DEFINITIONS OF SIX WALL COVERING CATEGORIES BASED ON PERFORMANCE

Category I, Decorative Only—Wall covering manufactured for decorative purposes that can be hung without damage in accordance with the manufacturer's instructions.

Category II, Decorative with Medium Serviceability—Wall covering primarily decorative but more washable and colorfast than Category I wall covering.

Category III, Decorative with High Serviceability—Wall covering manufactured for medium use, where abrasion resistance, stain resistance, scrubbability, and increased colorfastness are necessary. Category III wall covering must also meet breaking strength and crocking resistance criteria.

Category IV, Type I Commercial Serviceability—Wall covering manufactured for use where higher abrasion resistance, stain resistance, and scrubbability are necessary in heavy consumer and light commercial use. Category IV wall covering must also meet crocking resistance, tear resistance, cold cracking resistance, heat aging resistance, and breaking strength criteria. Wall covering meets Type I performance criteria as defined by Fed. Spec. CCCW-408C.

Category V, Type II Commercial Serviceability—Wall covering manufactured for use where better wearing qualities are required and exposure to wear is greater than normal. Category V wall covering must meet high abrasion resistance, stain resistance, and colorfastness criteria, in addition to higher crocking resistance, tear resistance and breaking strength criteria, than Categories I through IV. Blocking resistance, cold cracking resistance, coating adhesion, and heat aging resistance tests also apply. Wall covering meets Type II performance criteria as defined by Fed. Spec. CCCW-408C.

Category VI, Type III Commercial Serviceability—Wall covering manufactured for use in heavy traffic areas. Category VI wall covering must meet highest abrasion resistance, stain resistance, tear resistance, colorfastness, crocking resistance, and breaking strength criteria. Blocking resistance, coating adhesion, cold cracking resistance, and heat aging resistance tests also apply. Wall covering meets Type III performance criteria as defined by Fed. Spec. CCCW-408C.

available for all types of wallcovering, although not all manufacturers reference it. ASTM F 793 *Standard Classification of Wallcoverings by Durability Characteristics* may be helpful in comparing the performance of various wallcovering types (Tables 4.4 and 4.5).

VINYL WALLCOVERING

Vinyl wallcovering is second only to paint as the most popular choice for commercial interior wall surfaces. Vinyl wallcoverings are durable, easy to maintain, and provide a wide variety of decorative effects in a myriad of patterns, textures, and colors.

Manufacturing Processes

There are two vinyl wallcovering manufacturing processes: the calendering method and the plastisol method. The **calendering** method (Figure 4.9) squeezes liquid vinyl over a series of hot metal rollers, flattening the compound into a sheet. The vinyl sheet is then laminated under heat and pressure to a backing material. In this process, the vinyl is the consistency of dough (Figure 4.10), creating a harder, tougher vinyl surface that is usu-

TABLE 4.5 ASTM F 793 CLASSIFICATION CRITERIA

Property	Category I—Decorative Only	Category II—Decorative with Medium Serviceability	Category III—Decorative with High Serviceability	Category IV—Type I Commercial Serviceability	Category V—Type II Commercial Serviceability	Category VI—Type III Commercial Serviceability
Minimum colorfastness		23 h	46 h	200 h	200 h	200 h
Minimum washability		100 cycles	100 cycles	100 cycles	100 cycles	100 cycles
Minimum scrubbability			50 cycles	200 cycles	300 cycles	500 cycles
Minimum abrasion resistance				200 cycles (220 grit)	300 cycles (220 grit)	1000 cycles (220 grit)
Minimum breaking strength						
MD (machine direction)				40 lb (178 N)	50 lb (222 N)	100 lb (445 N)
CMD (cross machine direction)				30 lb (133 N)	55 lb (245 N)	95 lb (423 N)
Minimum crocking resistance			Good	Good	Good	Good
Minimum stain resistance*			Reagents 1 to 9	Reagents 1 to 9	Reagents 1 to 12	Reagents 1 to 12
Minimum tear resistance				12	25	50
Maximum blocking resistance				2	2	2
Minimum coating adhesion				2 lb/in (17.8 N/5 cm)	3 lb/in (26.7 N/5 cm)	3 lb/in (26.7 N/5 cm)
Minimum cold cracking				No change	No change	No change
Minimum heat aging resistance				Pass	Pass	Pass
Maximum flame spread		25	25	25	25	25
Maximum smoke developed		50	50	50	50	50
Maximum shrinkage						
MD (machine direction)				2	2	2
CMD (cross machine direction)				1	1	1.5

*Reagents:
(1) Distilled water, 65° to 75 °F
(2) Distilled water, 115° to 125°F
(3) Ethyl alcohol
(4) Vinegar, 3% acetic
(5) Alkali solution
(6) Hydrochloride, 5%
(7) Soup solution
(8) Detergent solution
(9) Pure orange juice
(10) Butter
(11) Catsup
(12) Tea

Figure 4.9 Calendaring produces smooth vinyl film. Columbus Coated Fabrics, Borden Decorative Products Group.

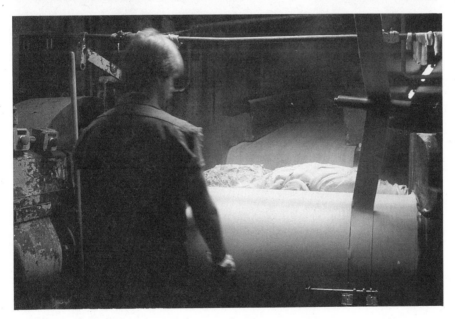

Figure 4.10 The doughlike mixture becomes vinyl film. Columbus Coated Fabrics, Borden Decorative Products Group.

ally much thicker than wallcovering manufactured by the plastisol method. The **plastisol** method spreads liquid vinyl onto a backing material as it is rolled by. The materials are fused together under high temperatures. Plastisol technology is used primarily for residential wallcoverings.

Backing Material

The backing material, sometimes called the substrate, is the major component in determining a wallcovering's strength and dimensional stability. There are four common backing materials:

Scrim (Figures 4.11a and 4.11b). A loosely woven fabric backing that lacks dimensional stability and is used in Type I wallcoverings

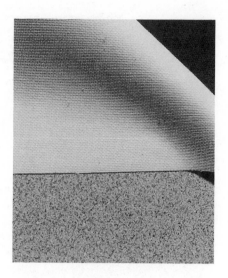

Figure 4.11a Backing materials for vinyl wallcovering. Scrim. Photo credit: Michael E. Dolan.

Figure 4.11b Type I vinyl wall covering with scrim backing. Photo credit: Michael E. Dolan.

Osnaburg (Figures 4.12a and 4.12b). A loose, open-weave fabric used in Type II wallcoverings

Drill (Figures 4.13a and 4.13b). A dense, woven fabric with good dimensional stability used in vinyl wallcovering Types II and III

Nonwoven. A paperlike backing used primarily for Type I wallcoverings

The Chemical Fabrics and Film Association (CFFA) authors a standard that is similar to the Federal Specification (FS) for vinyl wallcovering. CFFA-W-101-A, *CFFA Quality Standard for Vinyl Coated Fabric Wallcoverings* and FS CCCW-408C, *Wall Covering, Vinyl-Coated,* define three grades of wallcovering using the same criteria:

Type I, light duty wallcoverings have a minimum total weight of 7 oz/sq yd (0.237 kg/sq m) and a minimum coating weight of 5 oz/sq yd (0.170 kg/sq m).

Type II, medium duty wallcoverings have a minimum total weight of 13 oz/sq yd (0.442 kg/sq m) and a minimum coating weight of 7 oz/sq yd (0.237 kg/sq m).

Type III, heavy duty wallcoverings have a minimum total weight of 22 oz/sq yd (0.748 kg/sq m) and a minimum coating weight of 12 oz/sq yd (0.407 kg/sq m).

Type I wallcoverings can be considered in areas where paint would be suitable. These wallcoverings provide moderate surface protection and are appropriate for private offices, hotel guest rooms, and other areas not subject to unusual wear or traffic.

Type II is the most widely used type of vinyl wallcovering for commercial applications. These provide protection from traffic and abrasion in public spaces such as busy reception areas, dining rooms, and public corridors.

Figure 4.12a Osnaburg. Photo credit: Michael E. Dolan.

Figure 4.12b Type II vinyl wall covering with Osnaburg backing. Photo credit: Michael E. Dolan.

Figure 4.13a Drill. Photo credit: Michael E. Dolan.

Figure 4.13b Type III vinyl wall covering with drill backing. Photo credit: Michael E. Dolan.

Because Type III vinyl wallcoverings are typically manufactured on order, they are relatively expensive and usually require a long lead time. They are rarely specified because the affordability, availability, and performance of Type II wallcoverings satisfy the requirements of most commercial interior applications. Applications appropriate for Type III vinyl wallcoverings include areas that require wall protection, such as hospital and foodservice corridors.

Mildew Resistance

Impermeable wallcoverings such as vinyl can act as vapor barriers under specific climatic conditions. Mildew is a particular problem in warm, humid climates. Moisture migrating through a wall is trapped behind the wallcovering. Gypsum wallboard can become saturated with the condensation, fostering fungal growth. Perforated vinyl or woven fiberglass wallcoverings can be specified to increase the breathability of the wall. Mildew inhibitors can also be added to the vinyl.

Where mildew resistance is required, the wallcovering should have achieved a rating of 0 or 1 when tested by ASTM G 21 *Practice for Determining Resistance of Synthetic Polymeric Materials to Fungi.* A 0 rating means no fungal growth was observed on a wallcovering sample inoculated with spores and incubated for at least 21 days; a 1 rating means less than 10% of the sample surface area was covered with fungal growth.

WOOD VENEER WALLCOVERING

Wood veneer wallcovering is made by bonding veneer slices, about 0.39 mm (1/64 in) thick, to a woven backing material. The resulting wallcovering is thin enough to be pliable along the grain lines but too thick to be flexible in the horizontal direction (perpendicular to the wood grain) (Figure 4.14). There are three major concerns because of this thinness: finishing operations after installation, proper substrate preparation, and moisture. Wood veneer wallcovering is too thin to be sanded; therefore, care must be taken during installation so that the surface is not stained or damaged.

Wall surface imperfections tend to telegraph through the thin veneer.

Figure 4.14 Sheets of wood veneer wallcovering. Flexwood ®.

In areas where the substrate cannot be prepared to a smooth, level surface, veneered plywood panels are a better choice. Buckling and warpage caused by moisture can be a significant problem for this kind of wallcovering. For this reason, it is not recommended that wood veneer wallcovering be applied to the interior surface of an exterior wall unless the finish face of the wall is furred out and damp-proofed.

Wood veneer wallcoverings are available prefinished or unfinished. Unfinished veneers must be stained and finished after they are installed. Some finishes, for example, penetrating oils, can have an adverse effect on the wallcovering adhesive. Coatings applied to the surface of installed wood veneer should be approved by the wallcovering manufacturer.

The installation of wood veneer wallcovering is similar to the installation of other types of wallcovering; however, the sheets must be butted together and cannot be overlapped and trimmed.

TEXTILE WALLCOVERINGS

The warmth, richness, and beauty of fabric-covered walls cannot be matched by other wall finishes. However, the selection of this wallcovering type must be carefully considered. Not all textiles are suitable for use as wallcoverings. Moreover, textile wallcoverings are not appropriate in applications where wear resistance is a concern.

Most textiles must be back coated to be installed as wallcovering. The backing provides a barrier to prevent adhesive from bleeding through and ruining the finish face of the fabric. Backings also provide the dimensional stability required for a textile to withstand the stretching and smoothing operations of wallcovering installation.

There are two types of back coating treatments: paper backing and acrylic latex backing. The **paper backing** process involves laminating paper to the reverse side of the textile. This process stiffens the textile for easier installation. The textile assumes properties similar to those of wallpaper. The **latex coating** process involves stretching the textile in a frame and applying a latex compound. The textile retains some of its inherent flexibility and is much less dimensionally stable than paper-backed textiles. Latex backings can also improve ravel resistance and seam slippage.

The use of latex-coated textile wallcoverings may increase installation costs. Often, this wallcovering's lack of rigidity requires that the adhesive be applied to the wall, rather than to the back of the wallcovering in the standard manner. This process is more labor-intensive and requires a higher degree of skill.

FIBERGLASS WALLCOVERINGS

Fiberglass is the newest material to be made into a wallcovering. Fiberglass yarns are woven into a fabric that is applied to a backing. This wallcovering type was developed in Europe in response to a need for a wallcovering that could reinforce fragile or deteriorating wall surfaces. Fiberglass wallcoverings can be applied over small holes and cracks, thus reducing the amount of time required to prepare the surface.

The distinguishing characteristic of fiberglass wallcovering is its permeability. This intrinsic mold- and mildew-resistant property makes it a good choice for hot and humid climates and coastal regions where moisture control is a primary consideration.

Fiberglass wallcoverings are installed like other wallcoverings, with one important distinction — they must be painted after they are installed. This wallcovering type provides a textured wall pattern only, not a color (Figure 4.15). Typically, a latex paint is selected so as to maintain the breathability of the wall.

Fiberglass is inherently durable. However, the standard test methods for abrasion resistance, tear resistance, crocking resistance, and breaking strength used to categorize vinyl wallcoverings do not apply to woven fiberglass.

Figure 4.15 Woven fiberglass wallcovering. Photograph courtesy of Tasso.

WALLPAPER

Because of its fragility and poor wear resistance, wallpaper is commonly restricted to residential use. Most wallpapers meet the requirements of *Category I, Decorative Only*, as defined by ASTM F 793. However, the scratch, stain, and abrasion resistance of wallpaper can be improved by requiring that the finish face be coated with a clear vinyl film.

WALL PREPARATION

There are four traditional ways to prepare a wall surface for a wallcovering: seal, size, prime, or apply a wall liner.

Sealers are usually oil based, made either of an alkyd or a shellac. They provide stain-sealing properties. For example, walls that have suffered water damage must typically be sealed before they can be finished with either paint or a wallcovering. Sealers also promote strippability without damage to the wall surface. In areas where moisture can present problems including mildew and long drying times for adhesives, sealers can provide an effective moisture barrier.

Sizing a wall surface lowers the absorbency of the wall by reducing the penetration of the paste. However, sizes do not necessarily improve the bond between the adhesive and the wall surface.

Primers assure proper adhesion and are the most commonly required wall preparation for commercial installations.

Wall liners are nonwoven sheets; their installation is similar to that of wallcovering. They are sometimes required where wall surfaces cannot be prepared by conventional means. Wall liners can be used to prevent cracks, holes, and gaps from telegraphing through the wallcovering. However, they cannot smooth over an existing wall texture.

Annotated Specification Checklist
for Wallcovering

Part 1 GENERAL

SUBMITTALS

Shop Drawings: Show seams. *Include this requirement when seam placement might be highlighted by a wall sconce or signage.*

Samples: 300 mm (12 in) square. *If the wallcovering has a pattern that must be matched, require that the sample be sized to show a complete pattern repeat. If the wallcovering is a textile, require that the top and face of the material be labeled. The face of a textile is not always apparent, depending upon the type of weave and nature of the pattern.*

QUALITY ASSURANCE

Regulatory Requirements: Flame spread of 25 or less; smoke developed, 450 or less. *The flame spread rating required by the building code should be included here. A Class A or I rating (a flame spread of 25 or less) is the most commonly required.*

PROJECT CONDITIONS

Environmental Requirements: Comply with manufacturer's written requirements. *Temperatures lower than about 16°C (60°F) can affect the performance of wallcovering adhesives. Wallcovering should not be installed until after the relative humidity and temperature in a space are at the levels at which they will be maintained during the installation and after occupancy.*

MAINTENANCE

Extra Materials: Packaged and labeled, full-width rolls. *Be specific about how many rolls will be required and where they are to be stored.*

PART 2 PRODUCTS

MATERIALS

*Wallcovering Manufacturer:*_____.

    Pattern: _____. *Specify the manufacturer's designation for the wallcovering pattern.*
    Color: _____. *The same wallcovering pattern may be produced in a variety of colors, called colorways.*
    Width: _____.
    Total Weight: _____. *Specify the weight of the wallcovering because it affects durability and performance. Total weight does not include performance coatings.*

Wallcovering: ASTM F 793, Category _____. *Not all manufacturers use this system to categorize the durability of their wallcoverings. However, if it served as a basis for selection, it should be included here.*

Vinyl Wallcovering: CFFA-W-101-A, Type _____.

Backing: _____. *If the durability of the wallcovering or the backing material served as a basis for selection, it should be included here.*

Special Coating: _____. *Stain-resistant coatings can improve the cleanability of a wallcovering significantly.*

Adhesives: Comply with the manufacturer's written requirements for a strippable adhesive that is compatible with the substrate. *Because adhesive compatibility is crucial to the success of a wallcovering installation, it is best to defer to the manufacturer's recommendations.*

PART 3 EXECUTION

PREPARATION

Acclimatize materials. Wallcovering and adhesives should be at room temperature before installation begins, to avoid problems with thermal expansion and contraction of the material.

INSTALLATION

Match pattern at 1.5 m (5 ft) above the finish floor. *If the wallcovering has a pattern, it should be matched at eye level. Furniture may partially conceal a pattern that is not matched on the lower portion of the wall.*

Center wallcovering strips at signage. *Certain graphic features or wall-mounted light fixtures may attract attention to carelessly placed wallcovering seams. By requiring that the wallcovering strip be centered, the seams will be as far away from the item of interest as possible.*

SCHEDULES

The schedule of wallcoverings is usually given on a finish schedule, included either in the specifications or on the drawings.

Upholstered Wall Systems

Upholstered wall systems combine the luxuriousness of textile wallcoverings and the practicality of a tackable or acoustically absorptive wall surface. **Upholstered wall systems** are site-constructed coverings that stretch fabric taut over a frame and infill material (Figure 4.16). They can also be used in ceiling installations.

The framing material is typically either a plastic extrusion or a wood frame. An extrusion system holds the fabric in place by friction (Figure 4.17) or with concealed fasteners (Figure 4.18), sometimes aided by an adhesive. Concealed fasteners are used with a wood frame system (Figures 4.19a, 4.19b, and 4.19c). The infill material can serve a variety of functions. Acoustic batting (polyester or fiberglass) can be specified for a soft, upholstered appearance or for acoustic insulation. Plywood can be used as an infill material where a nailable or acoustically reflective surface is required. Mineral fiberboard will provide a tackable or acoustically absorptive upholstered wall surface.

Figure 4.16 Upholstered wall systems are site constructed. Fabric is stretched taut over a frame and infill material. Stretchwall.

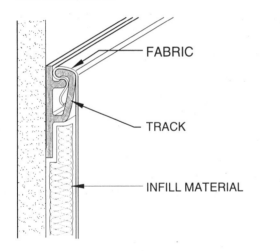

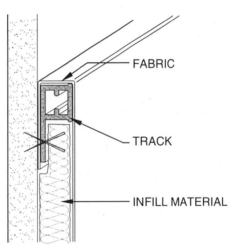

Figure 4.17 Crimped fitting upholstered wall system.

Figure 4.18 Concealed fastener upholstered wall system.

Upholstered wall systems require the selection of a highly stable fabric (see Table 4.6). Upholstery-weight fabrics are good choices. The fabric should be hydrophobic (does not readily absorb moisture); otherwise, seasonal changes in relative humidity may cause sagging and rippling. A fabric that contains more than 30% rayon or viscose, or 10% nylon fibers is typically not suitable for use in upholstered wall systems. If the wall system is to perform as a tackable or nailable surface, the selected fabric should be self-healing and snag resistant. For a seamless appearance, fabrics up to 3050 mm (120 inches) wide can be specified and installed horizontally (sometimes referred to as *railroading*).

Figure 4.19a An upholstered wall system installation. Batt insulation is selected for the infill material in this trading room ceiling because it is acoustically absorptive. The insulation is installed flush with the light fixture junction boxes and the upholstered system frame. Stretchwall.

Figure 4.19b Upholstery-weight fabric is stretched in place over the insulation. Stretchwall.

Figure 4.19c Indirect lighting fixtures are installed over the completed upholstered ceiling system. Stretchwall.

TABLE 4.6   FABRIC SELECTION CONSIDERATIONS FOR UPHOLSTERED
WALL SYSTEMS

SEAMS

Seams can be emphasized or deemphasized, depending on fabric weave and color. Seams disappear in fabric that is vertically directional, yet tend to read as butt joints when the predominant direction of the grain is horizontal. In a nondirectional fabric, seams tend to be more apparent with light colored fabrics, and less so with dark colors.

JOINTS

Joints between square-edge panels with thin fabrics, tightly butted, tend to read as a monolithic, seamless installation. Wall panel joints are seen more clearly between panels with heavy or thick fabrics, or with beveled frame edges.

TACKABLE AND NAILABLE SURFACES

The heavier the yarn texture, the better for areas where pin-tacking or nailing is required. Linen works well in galleries because of its unobtrusive appearance behind artwork and because it is a hardy, natural fabric that maintains a good appearance through many exhibits. Satin and sateen weaves are not recommended for tacking.

FABRIC WEAVES

Taffetas and architectural silks, especially when treated with flame retardants, are subject to greater variance in expansion and contraction. They require limited fluctuation in temperature and humidity. Jacquards, damasks, and basket weaves—regardless of their yarn content—are more dimensionally stable and can be used in areas where greater variances in temperature and humidity may occur.

LIGHT-COLORED FABRICS

Light-colored (especially white) fabrics should be examined to verify that the wall construction will not read through the fabric and change its color. The fabric may need to be lined, and the lining may change the appearance of the upholstered wall. By placing the fabric under consideration over a light-colored surface and then over a dark-colored surface, the need for a lining can be determined,

Source: Stretchwall.

Annotated Specification Checklist
for Upholstered Wall Systems

Part 1 GENERAL

SUBMITTALS

Shop Drawings: Show seam locations, fabric dye lot locations, and details at adjacent building components. *It is easy to overlook the thickness of such a system and its effect on other aspects of the design. Requiring shop drawings will help to ensure that casework drawers, shelf brackets, doors, electrical outlets, and thermostats will be accessible and operational.*

Fabric Sample: 300 mm (12 in) square of upholstery material.

System Sample: Full size of upholstered fabric system 1 m (3 ft) square, showing upholstery material seam and wall panel joint.

QUALITY ASSURANCE

Qualifications: Installer certified by upholstered wall system manufacturer. *The installation of these systems requires skill and experience. Proper installation is imperative to the success of the system. If the system manufacturer trains and certifies installers, include the requirement here.*

Regulatory Requirements: Flame spread of 25 or less; smoke developed, 450 or less. *The flame spread rating required by the building code should be included here. A Class A or I rating (a flame spread of 25 or less) is the most commonly required.*

Mock-Ups: Install mock-up of upholstered wall system to demonstrate final effect and workmanship. *Consider the expense of a mock-up before specifying. Mock-ups can be used to verify the installer's skill and the aesthetic effect.*

PROJECT CONDITIONS

Environmental Requirements: Comply with manufacturer's written requirements. *Upholstered wall systems should not be installed until after the relative humidity and temperature in a space are at the levels at which they will be maintained during installation and occupancy.*

Field Measurements: Verify dimensions of surfaces on which upholstered wall systems will be installed. Record field measurements on the shop drawings. *Walls are rarely square. Field conditions (for example, the angle at which the ceiling meets the top of the wall) may have an effect on installation.*

MAINTENANCE

Extra Materials: Packaged and labeled, full-width upholstery material. *Extra lengths of extrusions and upholstery material should be required, especially if the material is custom-made or special ordered. Be specific about how much extra material will be required and where it will be stored.*

PART 2 PRODUCTS

MATERIALS

Upholstered Wall System: _____. *Include the manufacturer's description, frame thickness, and profile.*

Infill Material: _____. *Polyester batting, plywood, fiberglass board, and mineral fiberboard are commonly used as infill materials.*

PART 3 EXECUTION

INSTALLATION

Upholstery Material Seams: Vertical and plumb. *Horizontal seams are usually undesirable.*

Infill Material: Even with the face of the upholstered wall system frame.

A ceiling contains the volume of a space and breathes life into it by shaping the diffusion of sound and light. It is a prominent design element, making a substantial contribution to the ambience of a room. Ceilings serve as an important functional part of the design as well. Most commercial ceilings conceal the distribution of conditioned air, artificial light, and the fire suppression system. The space between a finished ceiling and the structure above, referred to as the **plenum**, is the main thoroughfare for the heating, air conditioning, fire suppression, and lighting systems in contemporary commercial interiors. This maze of ducts, conduits, wires, and pipes, as well as the underside of the concrete or steel deck above, can be left exposed or concealed behind a suspended ceiling system.

Suspended ceiling systems are hung from the structure above and incorporate such elements as sprinklers, lighting fixtures, and speakers. For the appearance of a traditional flat, smooth ceiling, gypsum board (or metal lath with plaster) can be attached to suspended furring channels. The gypsum board is taped and finished with the same procedures used for walls, but because this must be done overhead, labor costs are significantly higher. A major drawback to a suspended gypsum board ceiling is that there is no easy way to access the services behind the ceiling without destroying part of it.

Because of the importance of the structural integrity of a ceiling, building codes usually specify how suspended ceiling systems are to be installed.

CEILING FINISHES

Glass reinforced gypsum (GRG) is a high-strength, high-density gypsum, reinforced with continuous filament glass fibers or chopped glass fiber strands. It is molded in a manufacturing plant and shipped to a project site. GRG is also referred to as fiberglass reinforced gypsum (FRG) or glass fiber reinforced gypsum (GFRG).

Since its conception in 1978, GRG has continued to grow in popularity in applications such as column covers, decorative domes, and other shapes previously available only in plaster. GRG manufacturing techniques can produce thin, high-strength shapes that are inherently flame resistant. GRG is suitably lightweight for ceilings or other applications in which weight is a concern. Standard gypsum wallboard finishing techniques are required for the installation of GRG. GRG products can be field cut for plumbing, electrical, mechanical, or other penetrations with the use of conventional gypsum wallboard tools.

GRG products are made in molds, which are often customized for a particular project. There are two methods employed to produce GRG products: the hand lay-up method and the spray method. In the hand lay-up method, layers of glass fiber matt and gypsum are hand placed in a prepared mold. The spray method utilizes a nozzle that mixes chopped glass fiber strands into a plaster mix as it is sprayed into a mold. The GRG product is allowed to set and is then carefully removed from its mold. The product is carefully crated and stored to prevent warping or bowing.

Glass Reinforced Gypsum (GRG)

In specifying GRG products, particular attention should be paid to joint finishing. Because most GRG installations are designed to simulate monolithic plaster systems, a smooth, level finish is of particular concern. The Ceilings and Interior Systems Construction Association (CISCA) has prepared guidelines for joint and erection tolerances (Table 4.7).

TABLE 4.7 CEILINGS AND INTERIOR SYSTEMS CONSTRUCTION ASSOCIATION (CISCA) GUIDELINES FOR GRG JOINT AND ERECTION TOLERANCES

Joint Tolerances	
Designed and installed joint alignment tolerance	Not to exceed 3 mm (⅛ in)
Joint width	9 mm (⅜ in)
Joint finishing	In accordance with ASTM C 840 *Specification for Application and Finishing of Gypsum Board*
Erection Tolerances	
Plane alignment (panel to panel)	2 mm (1/16 in)
Variation from plumb	Plus or minus 3 mm per 3 m (⅛ in per 10 ft)
Variation from straightness	Plus or minus 6 mm per 7.6 m (¼ in per 25 ft)

Source: Ceilings and Interior Systems Construction Association (CISCA), Elmhurst, IL.

Annotated Specification Checklist
for GRG

PART 1 GENERAL

SUBMITTALS

Shop Drawings: Show design detail, erection tolerances, and anchorage details. Show location of cutouts for fire suppression systems, light fixtures, and so forth. *A licensed engineer may be required to design the GRG units and the suspension system. Seismic requirements should be verified.*

Samples: _____. *Depending on the size of the project and the number of GRG units specified, samples may be required.*

QUALITY ASSURANCE

Regulatory Requirements: Flame spread of 25 or less; smoke developed, 450 or less. *The flame spread rating required by the building code should be included here. A Class A or I rating (a flame spread of 25 or less) is the most commonly required.*

Mock-Ups: Install mock-up of GRG to demonstrate final effect and workmanship. *Describe which portion of the final project is to be mocked up. Mock-ups can be used to verify the installer's skill and the aesthetic effect. Consider the expense of a mock-up before specifying. Mock-ups can remain on the project site as a standard against which the finished installation will be judged.*

DELIVERY, HANDLING, AND STORAGE

Packing and Shipping: Pack GRG units to prevent exposure to moisture. *GRG units are particularly susceptible to warping and bowing caused by moisture.*

Storage and Protection: Comply with GRG manufacturer's written requirements.

PROJECT CONDITIONS

Environmental Requirements: Comply with manufacturer's written requirements. Do not install GRG units until relative humidity and temperature are at levels at which they will be continuously maintained during installation and after occupancy.

PART 2 PRODUCTS

MATERIALS

GRG Units: Comply with CISCA testing criteria.

PART 3 EXECUTION

PREPARATION

Acclimatize: Remove GRG units from packaging and store in the space in which they will be installed for not less than 24 hours prior to installation.

INSTALLATION

Tolerances: Comply with CISCA guidelines.

Joint Finishes: ASTM C 840.

Acoustic Ceilings

Acoustic ceilings allow easy access to the variety of systems they conceal. In general, a *panel* refers to the material laid in an exposed grid system, and a *tile* refers to the inserts in a concealed grid system. ASTM E 1264 *Classification for Acoustical Ceiling Products* provides a classification system for ceiling panels or tiles (Table 4.8). An acoustic ceiling panel is 610 mm × 610 mm (24 in × 24 in) or 610 mm × 1220 mm (24 in × 48 in). Acoustic ceiling tiles are 305 mm × 305 mm (12 in × 12 in) or 306 mm × 610 mm (24 in × 24 in). Most manufacturers are now making acoustic ceilings panels in true metric sizes of 600 × 600 mm and 600 × 1200 mm.

Exposed grid systems suspend square or rectilinear frames that hold attached or loose laid panels (Figure 4.20). Channel- or angle-shaped sections are attached to the wall to support perimeter panel edges. Various decorative profiles are available for both the exposed grid and the panel edge. These panels can be pushed up and temporarily moved out of place to gain access to the ceiling plenum.

TABLE 4.8   ASTM E 1264 CLASSIFICATION FOR ACOUSTICAL CEILING PRODUCTS

CEILING TYPES

(Types I and II cellulose composition ceilings are primarily for residential use.)

Type I—Cellulose base with painted finish

Type II—Cellulose base with membrane-faced overlay

(Types III and IV mineral base are the most commonly used types.)

Type III—Mineral base with painted finish
    Form 1—Nodular, cast, or molded
    Form 2—Water felted
    Form 3—Dry felted

Type IV—Mineral base with membrane-faced overlay
    Form 1—Nodular, cast, or molded
    Form 2—Water felted
    Form 3—Dry felted

(Types V through VII are for perforated metal faces with acoustic backings.)

Type V—Perforated steel facing (pan) with mineral or glass fiber base backing

Type VI—Perforated stainless steel facing (pan) with mineral or glass fiber base backing

Type VII—Perforated aluminum facing (pan) with mineral or glass fiber base backing

(Types VIII through XX are for specialty applications.)

Type VIII—Cellulose base with scrubbable pigmented or clear finish

Type IX—Mineral base with scrubbable pigmented or clear finish
    Form 1—Nodular, cast, or molded
    Form 2—Water felted
    Form 3—Dry felted

Type X—Mineral base with plastic or aluminum membrane-faced overlay, or both

Type XI—Mineral base with fabric-faced overlay
    Form 1—Nodular, cast, or molded
    Form 2—Water felted
    Form 3—Dry felted

Type XII—Glass fiber base with membrane-faced overlay
    Form 1—Plastic
    Form 2—Cloth
    Form 3—Other

Type XIII—Aluminum or steel strip with mineral or glass fiber base backing
    Form 1—Perforated
    Form 2—Nonperforated

Type XX—Other types (describe)

PATTERN DESIGNATION	PATTERN DESCRIPTION
A	Perforated, regularly spaced large holes
B	Perforated, randomly spaced large holes
C	Perforated, small holes
D	Fissured
E	Lightly textured
F	Heavily textured
G	Smooth
H	Printed
I	Embossed
J	Embossed-in-register
K	Surface scored
Z	Other patterns (describe)

Figure 4.20 Exposed grid suspended ceiling. Photo courtesy of Armstrong. Copyright © 1994 Armstrong.

Figure 4.21 Concealed grid suspended ceiling. Photo courtesy of Armstrong. Copyright © 1994 Armstrong.

Concealed grid systems, sometimes called concealed spline systems, provide the traditional look of a uniform ceiling, along with increased acoustic performance (Figure 4.21). Ceiling tiles have a kerfed (grooved or notched) edge that slides into a "T"- or "Z"-shaped bar (Figure 4.22). The methods by which concealed grid systems allow access to the ceiling plenum vary among manufacturers.

Figure 4.22 Kerfed edge acoustic ceiling panel, which slides into a T- or Z- shaped bar.

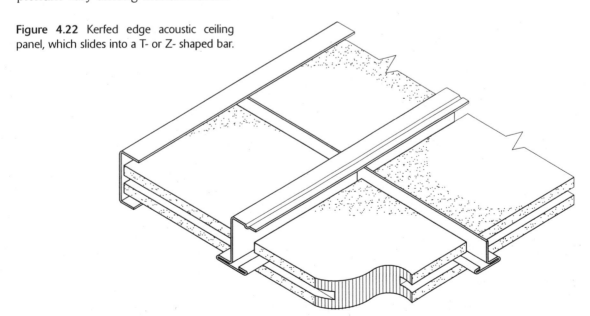

Acoustic Concerns

Acoustics are an important part of any interior design, especially when partial-height partitions, such as those common with systems furniture, are used. Without the proper acoustic treatment in an office space, it can be difficult for staff to have a private conversation (Figure 4.23).

There are two considerations in evaluating the acoustic properties of a ceiling tile: sound absorption and noise isolation. Sound absorbing materials have porous surfaces, are made essentially of trapped air spaces, and are consequently quite lightweight. Sound-isolating materials are typically dense and reflective. For purposes of comparison, these acoustic properties can be quantified by testing the materials or construction assembly.

SOUND ABSORPTION

The **Noise Reduction Coefficient (NRC)**, a rating of the sound-absorbing efficiency of a material, can be used to compare different ceiling panels. The NRC value is determined according to tests described in ASTM C 423 *Standard Method of Test for Sound Absorption of Acoustical Materials in Reverberation Rooms* and is expressed in increments of 0.05. The higher the NRC, the more sound a surface can absorb. Differences in NRC of less than .10 are seldom detectable in finished applications. Because it measures a surface area, the NRC does not address the acoustics of sound transmitted from space to space.

NOISE ISOLATION

ASTM E 1414 *Test Method for Airborne Sound Attenuation Between Rooms Sharing a Common Ceiling Plenum* is used to measure the attenuation (reduction) of sound provided by a suspended ceiling in the presence of a continuous plenum space. A barrier wall separating two rooms from floor to ceiling is constructed in a laboratory setting. The wall is designed so that virtually no sound can get through or around it. The only sound path is through the plenum. A speaker is placed in one room and a microphone in the other. The change in sound from the sending to receiving side is measured. The result of this test is a **Ceiling Sound Transmission Class (CSTC)** value. CSTC values are expressed in increments of 5. The CSTC value correlates with the reduction in sound; a CSTC of 35 means a reduction of 35 decibels (dB) from one side to the other. The higher the CSTC, the better the sound reduction capability of the ceiling system.

ASTM E 1111 *Test Method for Measuring the Interzone Attenuation of Ceiling Systems* is used to measure the sound-reflective characteristics of ceiling systems in spaces with partial-height partitions. The **Interzone Attenuation and Articulation Class (AC)** is a single-figure rating resulting from this test. This test is similar to the CSTC test, but the barrier wall is replaced with a partition that is 1.5 m (5 ft) high in a room with a 2.7 m (9 ft) ceiling height. In this situation, almost all of the sound bounces off the ceiling (Figure 4.24).

To further reduce sound transmission, acoustical sealants can be used. These sealants reduce airborne sound transmission through openings for

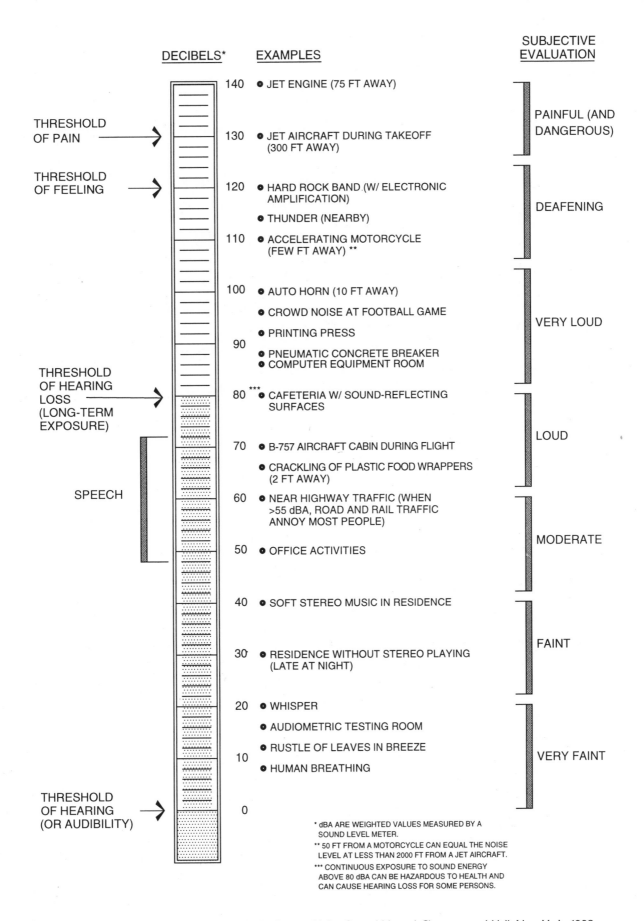

Figure 4.23 Common sounds in decibels. *Source: Noise Control Manual,* Chapman and Hall, New York, 1992.

Figure 4.24 The Interzone Attenuation and Articulation Class (AC) is a measure of the sound-reflective characteristics of ceiling systems in spaces with partial-height partitions. Steelcase.

outlets, crevices, and cutouts and at the perimeters of partitions. There are basically two types of acoustical sealants, those that are meant to be exposed and those that are not. Acoustical sealants that are not meant to be used in exposed locations are nonhardening, which means they remain as sticky as the day they were applied, and are available only in dark colors. They are usually applied between the framing channel at the top of the wall and the underside of the structure above. Acoustical sealants suitable for use in exposed areas cure to a firm, smooth consistency and are paintable and nonstaining. They are commonly applied between the edge of the suspended ceiling system and the wall.

Annotated Specification Checklist for Acoustic Ceilings

PART 1 GENERAL

SUBMITTALS

Samples: Full-size ceiling unit and grid member.

QUALITY ASSURANCE

Regulatory Requirements: Flame spread of 25 or less; smoke developed, 450 or less. *The flame spread rating required by the building code should be included here. A Class A or I rating (a flame spread of 25 or less) is most commonly required; A Class B or II rating is a flame spread of not more than 75.*

MAINTENANCE

Extra Materials: Packaged and labeled full-size units. *Extra ceiling tiles or panels are usually required, to have on hand to replace damaged or soiled tiles. Be specific about how much extra material will be required and where it will be stored.*

PART 2 PRODUCTS

MATERIALS

Ceiling Panels

    Manufacturer:_____.

    Surface Pattern:_____.

    Color:_____.

    Edge Profile:_____.

    Size:_____.

       Width:_____.

       Length:_____.

       Thickness:_____.

    NRC:_____.

    CSTC:_____.

    AC:_____.

Ceiling Suspension System: C 635.

    Light-duty.

    Intermediate-duty.

    Heavy-duty.

    Manufacturer: _____.

    Profile: _____.

    Color: _____.

    Acoustic Sealant: Nonstaining, continuous bead around all openings.

PART 3 EXECUTION

INSTALLATION

Suspension System: ASTM C 636.

Suspension System Requiring Seismic Restraint: ASTM E 580.

SCHEDULES

The schedule of ceiling finishes is usually provided on a finish schedule included either in the specifications or, more commonly, on the drawings.

FLOOR FINISHES

Flooring often dominates the visual field and can have a tremendous impact on the acoustics of a space. No other finish is subjected to as much wear as flooring. It is usually the most expensive finish selected — in maintenance cost alone — and often is the only material that the inhabitants of a space actually touch.

Hard Flooring There is a welcome familiarity in hard flooring choices. They more closely resemble elements found in nature — wood, stone, clay — than resilient or soft coverings. Durable and practical, hard floorings establish a sense of permanence and, if properly selected, can last the life of the building, not just the term of the lease.

Some hard floorings are substantially heavier than other flooring materials. Normal movement resulting from deflection, thermal stresses, and shrinkage can present problems with the inherent rigidity of hard flooring types. Existing structural conditions should be verified to ensure their stability and adequacy in supporting the additional flooring load.

Resilient flooring Resilient flooring combines the comfort underfoot and quietness associated with textile floor coverings, with the imperviousness of hard floorings. The resilient surface resists indentation while providing a dense, relatively easy-to-clean surface.

Today, vinyl composition tile is the most often specified type of resilient flooring because of its ease of installation and affordability. Vinyl sheet flooring is popular for applications in which a monolithic surface is required to prevent the penetration of dirt or moisture. There is also renewed interest in linoleum and cork flooring because they are biodegradable and produced from sustainable resources.

Soft Floor Covering Carpet is unmatched among floor coverings for a luxurious feel underfoot. Commercial carpet sales continue to increase at a phenomenal rate, in part because carpet's acoustic properties make the contemporary open office practical. It has become an essential element in the modern design palette. When properly selected, carpet is durable enough to last the life of most leases and is relatively easy to maintain.

Carpet tiles, available in 46-cm (18-in) or 61-cm (24-in) squares, are the latest advance in commercial carpeting. No other flooring permits the quick, inexpensive replacement of isolated worn areas or the easy access to under-floor utilities or flat wire without cutting or patching.

The foundation of a successful flooring installation is the proper preparation of the subfloor.

Subfloor Preparation

In general, a **subfloor**, the floor to which the finish floor is attached, must be free from oil, grease, wax, old floor finishes, paint, dust, dirt, old adhesives, and other coatings that adversely affect the flooring or the adhesive. In commercial projects, the subfloor is usually concrete.

Depending on the condition of the subfloor, an underlayment or leveling compound may be required before the finish flooring can be installed. An **underlayment** is used to level the floor and cover cracks. The most common material used for an underlayment is exterior grade plywood. Particleboard and ceramic tile backerboard are also used, depending on the application, but are not recommended for use under resilient flooring. **Leveling compounds** smooth over subfloor irregularities. These are typically cementitious mixtures and can be trowel applied or poured on. The poured compounds are referred to as *self-leveling*.

Flooring manufacturers must be relied on to provide the requirements for subfloors to ensure the performance of their finish flooring. Typically, the moisture emission rate and the alkalinity level of the slab are of concern.

MOISTURE TESTS

Moisture is the single greatest cause of adhesive bonding failures. It is a particular problem in new concrete slabs because of the naturally higher moisture content resulting from the curing process. A slab that is laid on grade or below can present a problem because of the natural moisture migration from the earth up through the slab into the building. Flooring manufacturers may require that new slabs cure for a minimum amount of time to reach an acceptable dryness. But even existing above-grade concrete floors can demonstrate unacceptable moisture conditions.

Flooring manufacturers must be relied on to specify the conditions under which moisture tests are conducted; the temperature can have a significant impact on the validity of the test results. Low temperatures can present inaccurate test data, because moisture migration is retarded by the cold. Tests should not be performed on slabs where the temperature is below 10°C (50°F).

A **calcium chloride moisture test** can be used to determine the moisture emission rate of a concrete slab. A clear plastic dish containing calcium chloride, a white powder, is placed under a sealed, clear plastic dome for 60 hours (Figure 4.25). A small amount of moisture will cause the calcium chloride powder to darken or cake. Larger amounts of moisture will cause drops to form on the powder, and if moisture conditions are severe, the calcium chloride will dissolve. A precise determination of the moisture content can be determined by weighing the calcium chloride sample and comparing it to the pretest dry weight. A precise measurement is required and is best done in a laboratory by the manufacturers of the test kit or by using a pharmacist's scale.

Another, less precise, method involves the use of a **hygrometer**, a device that measures relative humidity (Figure 4.26). The hygrometer is laid on the floor and covered with a 600-mm (2-ft)-square sheet of clear plastic film. The plastic film is sealed around the edges with a plastic moisture-resistant tape, such as duct tape. The hygrometer measures the moisture being emitted from the slab. A rough estimate of the moisture emission level can be obtained in 15 to 30 minutes. For a more accurate reading, 24 hours is required.

Figure 4.25 Calcium chloride moisture test. Photo courtesy Taylor Tools.

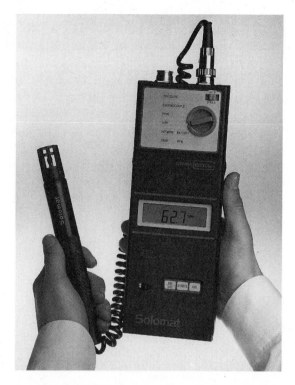

Figure 4.26 A hygrometer measures relative humidity. Photo courtesy of Solomat/Neotronics, Norwalk, CT.

Perhaps the easiest and most practical, but least precise, way to determine whether moisture is a problem is the **polyethylene film test**, described by ASTM D 4263 *Test Method for Indicating Moisture in Concrete by the Plastic Sheet Method.* A 450-mm (18-in)-square sheet of clear plastic film is sealed to the slab with tape and left for 16 hours. If there is no "sweating" or clouding on the underside of the plastic, then the slab may be considered dry enough by some flooring manufacturers for installation of their finish floor.

ALKALINITY TEST

Diluted alkaline salts can migrate from a concrete slab to the floor surface. These salts can cause adhesive failures and can be absorbed into the flooring materials. The test for pH levels is relatively quick and inexpensive. **pH** levels are expressed by a simple numeric scale with values from 0 to 14, indicating how acidic or basic (alkaline) a solution is: 0 represents a very acidic condition, 7 indicates neutrality, and a pH level of more than 7 shows alkalinity. Alkalinity can be determined by slightly wetting the floor and applying pH test paper or litmus paper. The color of the paper will change, indicating the nature of the solution—increasingly blue for increasing levels of alkalinity and increasingly pink for increasing levels of acidity. A pH range of 6 to 10 is satisfactory. A reading above 10 usually requires corrective measures if adhesives are involved in the flooring installation.

TABLE 4.9   WATER ABSORPTION OF TILE AS DEFINED BY ANSI A137.1

Type	Water Absorption	Ceramic Material
Nonvitreous	More than 7.0%	Natural clay
Semivitreous	More than 3.0%, but not more than 7.0%	Natural clay
Vitreous	0.5% to 3.0%	Natural clay
Impervious	0.5% or less	Porcelain

Specifications for Ceramic Tile and Tested by ASTM C 373 *Test Method for Water Absorption, Bulk Density, Apparent Porosity, and Apparent Specific Gravity of Fired Whiteware Products*

Ceramic Tile

Ceramic tile is made from clay or a mixture of clay and ceramic materials. Natural clay is most commonly used, but porcelain is also available. Porcelain tile is fine grained and smooth. It can be formed into sharply detailed designs. Polished porcelain pavers made to resemble granite and providing a highly durable flooring were introduced in the 1980s. They are often specified for applications requiring a high-end design statement and superior wear resistance, such as in a fine shopping mall.

The density and porosity of the ceramic tile determines its ability to absorb moisture. ANSI A137.1 *Specification for Ceramic Tile* quantifies four levels of water absorption: nonvitreous, semivitreous, vitreous, and impervious (Table 4.9). In general, the lower the water-absorption level of a tile material, the better able it is to resist staining. *Impervious* tile has the lowest absorption level, 0.5% or less. *Vitreous*, meaning glasslike, describes a tile that is slightly more absorptive than impervious tile, but still at a very low rate, ranging between 0.5% to 3.0%. Impervious and vitreous tiles are appropriate for use in exterior applications exposed to rain and freezing temperatures or in interior applications that require constant exposure to water, such as swimming pools. *Semivitreous* tile has an absorption level of more than 3.0%, but not more than 7.0%, and *nonvitreous* tile is the most absorptive, at a rate of more than 7.0%. Semivitreous and nonvitreous tiles should not be used in continually wet locations.

TILE TYPES

ANSI A 137 *Ceramic Tile* categorizes tile into five basic types: wall, ceramic mosaic, quarry, paver, and special purpose. Wall tiles are glazed, typically nonvitreous and cannot withstand high impact.

Ceramic mosaic tiles are usually 6 mm to 10 mm (¼ in to ⅜ in) thick. The term *mosaic* refers to the small size of the tile, which has a face area of less than 150 sq mm (6 sq in). The most common sizes are 25 mm × 25 mm (1 in × 1 in) or 50 mm × 50 mm (2 in × 2 in). Ceramic mosaic tiles can be made of either porcelain or natural clay and can be glazed or unglazed (Figure 4.27).

Paver tiles are essentially large ceramic mosaic tiles. They are 1150 sq mm (6 sq in) or more in size and are made of unglazed porcelain or natural clay. The slip resistance of pavers can be increased with textured surfaces or raised surface patterns such as a diamond design (Figure 4.28).

Figure 4.27 Ceramic mosaic tile. Photos compliments of Dal-Tile North, America's largest manufacturer of ceramic tile.

Figure 4.28 Paver tile. Photos compliments of Dal-Tile North, America's largest manufacturer of ceramic tile.

Figure 4.29 Quarry tile textured for slip resistance. Photos compliments of Dal-Tile North, America's largest manufacturer of ceramic tile.

Glazed tiles have an impervious finish composed of ceramic materials fused to the face of the tile. The body of a glazed tile may be nonvitreous, semivitreous, vitreous, or impervious. Glazes perform beautifully under exposure to dirt and stains. Spills wipe off with a damp cloth.

Quarry tiles are extruded and made from either natural clay or shale. They are similar to bricks in material, performance, range of colors, and methods of installation. Grout joints tend to be thicker, up to 6 mm (¼ in) (Figure 4.29).

INSTALLATION METHODS

The choices of tile, mortar, and grout are interdependent. The success of a tile installation depends on the appropriate selection of all three and the demands of the application. The Tile Council of America (TCA) is an association of tile, grout, and mortar manufacturers that promote standards for the manufacture and installation of ceramic tile. There are more than 20 ANSI (American National Standards Institute) standards addressing materials and installation that have been sponsored by the TCA. The TCA also publishes the *Handbook for Ceramic Tile Installation* annually.

There are two basic steps in tile installation: setting and grouting. Setting tile fixes it to the substrate. Tile is set in place with mortar or adhesive. Grouting fills in the spaces between the tiles, binding them into a continuous flooring surface.

Thick-set installations use portland cement mortar. A hefty mortar bed, 30 mm to 50 mm (1 ¼ in to 2 in) thick, is laid. Because of the thickness of the mortar bed, accurate floor slopes to drains can easily be accomplished by the tile installer, thus eliminating the need to rely on the precision of the substrate installation. This thickness also enables reinforcement with metal mesh or backing with membranes (Figure 4.30).

Thin-set installations are the most popular, accounting for nearly 90% of ceramic tile installations in the United States. All methods other than the conventional portland cement applications are considered thin set. Mortars for a thin set installation can be as thin as 2 mm ($\frac{3}{32}$ in) (Figure 4.31).

Cementitious backerboards are sometimes used as an underlayment for thin-set installations. These smooth, lightweight boards are designed to provide a water-resistant base for ceramic tile installations regularly exposed to water (for example, in a shower surround). **Cementitious backerboards** are made of portland cement or treated gypsum and lightweight aggregate and are reinforced with glass fiber.

Expansion joints depend entirely on the specific conditions and structural systems of each project. However, when the expanse of ceramic floor tile approaches 7 m to 10 m (24 ft to 36 ft) in each direction, expansion joints are usually required. If the tile is exposed to continuous moisture or thermal extremes (for example, direct sunlight) a joint may be required every 3.5 m to 5 m (12 ft to 16 ft).

The joint width for each application varies, but in general, for quarry or paver tiles, a joint should be the same width as the the grout joints but not less than 6 mm ($\frac{1}{4}$ in). For ceramic mosaic tile, joints should not be less than 6 mm ($\frac{1}{4}$ in) (Figure 4.32).

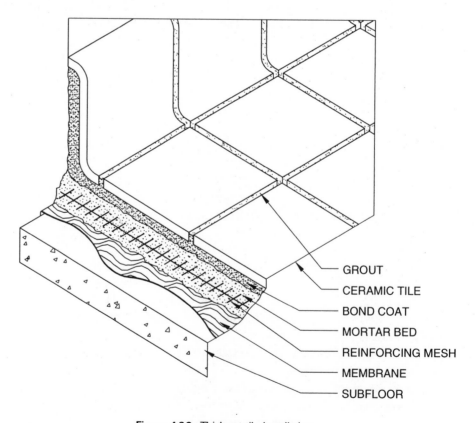

GROUT
CERAMIC TILE
BOND COAT
MORTAR BED
REINFORCING MESH
MEMBRANE
SUBFLOOR

Figure 4.30 Thick-set tile installation.

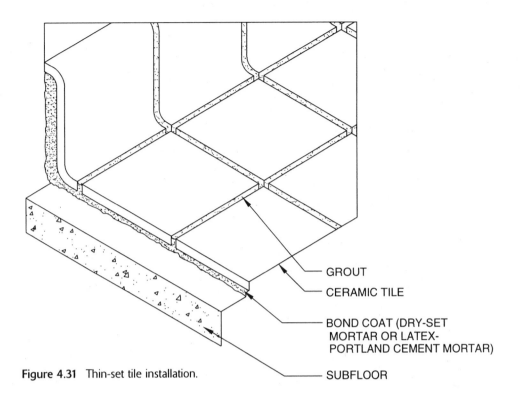

GROUT

CERAMIC TILE

BOND COAT (DRY-SET
MORTAR OR LATEX-
PORTLAND CEMENT MORTAR)

Figure 4.31 Thin-set tile installation.

SUBFLOOR

Figure 4.32 An expansion joint in a tile installation.

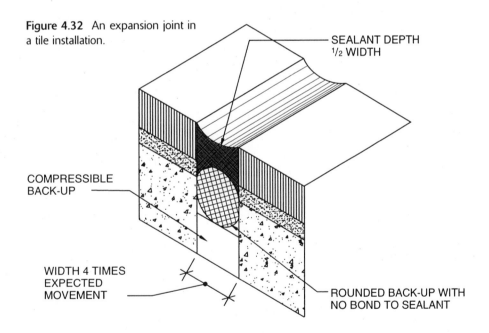

SEALANT DEPTH
$1/2$ WIDTH

COMPRESSIBLE
BACK-UP

WIDTH 4 TIMES
EXPECTED
MOVEMENT

ROUNDED BACK-UP WITH
NO BOND TO SEALANT

Waterproof membranes are often specified in applications that will be exposed regularly or continually to water (for example, a shower floor or the floor of an industrial laboratory that will be routinely cleaned with a hose). Waterproof membranes are flexible sheets or liquids that cure to a seamless membrane. Some flexible sheets include integral reinforcing fabrics for increased tensile strength. Both thick set and thin set installations can incorporate waterproof membranes.

INSTALLATION MATERIALS

Tile-setting materials should be matched with the backing materials and the conditions of installation and use. The selection of a setting material and grout is as important as the selection of the tile.

Setting materials include the traditional mortars and the relatively new adhesives (see Table 4.10). Cement-based mortars, the traditional setting materials, include portland cement, dry-set, and latex-portland-cement mortars. These can be used, to varying extents, to level an uneven subfloor. Noncement setting materials such as epoxies and furans are more expensive than cement-based mortars and require special skill on the part of the installer.

CEMENT-BASED MORTARS

Portland Cement Mortar

This is the traditional tile-setting material and is the only mortar used in a thick set application. Portland cement mortar is a mixture of portland

TABLE 4.10   SETTING MATERIALS FOR CERAMIC TILE FLOORS

Type	Description	ANSI Standards For Setting Material	For Installation	Features
CEMENTITIOUS MORTARS				
Portland Cement Mortar	1:5 portland cement and sand mixture	None	A108.1A, A108.1B, and A108.1C	
Dry-Set Mortar	Portland cement, sand, and additives	A118.1	A108.5	
Latex-Portland Cement Mortar	Portland cement, sand, and special latex additive	A118.4	A108.5	
NONCEMENTITIOUS MORTARS				
Epoxy Mortar	Epoxy resin and hardener	A118.3	A108.6	Chemical resistance
Modified Epoxy Emulsion Mortars	Emulsified epoxy resin and hardener	A118.8	A108.9	High bond strength, little or no shrinkage, not chemical resistant
Furan Resin Mortar	Furan resin and hardener	A118.5	A108.8	Chemical resistance
Epoxy Adhesive	Epoxy resin and hardener	A118.3	A108.4	High bond strength, ease of application
Organic Adhesive	Ready to use (no addition of liquids required), cures by evaporation	A136.1	A108.4	Not suitable for continuously wet applications (e.g., swimming pools) or temperatures exceeding 60°C (140°F)

cement, sand, and water. Absorptive ceramic tiles must be soaked before they are installed over this type of mortar bed so that moisture from the mortar is not absorbed by the tile, thus adversely affecting the mortar curing process.

Portland cement mortar is a popular choice for finish floors that must slope to a drain or trough (for example, the floor of a commercial kitchen). Because of the thickness of a portland cement mortar bed, alignment of the heights of adjacent floors can be an issue.

Dry-Set Mortar

This is the most common mortar used. Dry-set mortar is a combination of portland cement, sand, and additives. The additives increase the water retention capability of the mortar so that absorptive tiles do not have to be soaked in water before installation. Dry-set mortars are highly resistant to moisture and impact. They are appropriate for installation over concrete, cured portland cement mortar beds, cementitious backer units, and other hard finish floor surfaces such as stone.

Latex-Portland-Cement Mortar

This mortar is similar to portland cement mortar, but includes special latex additives that lend increased flexibility. It is designed for use with porcelain tiles. Latex-portland-cement mortar must dry thoroughly before being exposed to water, and is thus a poor choice for continually wet applications (for example, swimming pools). Depending on the location and climate of the installation, drying time can take more than 60 days. Because the latex additives vary, compliance with the mortar manufacturer's installation instructions is imperative.

NON-CEMENT-BASED MORTARS

Epoxy Mortar

Known for their chemical resistance, high bond strength, and impact resistance, epoxy mortars are available in high-temperature-resistant formulas. When the epoxy resin and hardener are mixed, a chemical reaction is started and the mortar must be used within a limited time.

Modified Epoxy Emulsion Mortars

Known for their high bond strength and ease of application, mortars of this type exhibit little or no shrinkage. Unlike their epoxy counterparts, they have no special resistance to chemicals. A highly stable substrate, such as concrete, is required.

Furan Resin Mortar

This two part mixture of furan resin and furan hardener is the most chemically resistant mortar type, suitable for use in laboratories and industrial applications. It is typically used with furan grout.

ADHESIVES

Unlike mortars, most adhesives do not require mixing. Known for their ease of application, they harden by evaporation. Underlayments are often used under adhesive setting materials because the subfloor must be smooth and level.

Epoxy Adhesives

Similar to organic adhesives in application, epoxy adhesives have a higher bonding strength and chemical resistance than organic adhesives.

Organic Adhesives

These are the most common types of adhesive. They provide a flexible bond at a low cost.

GROUTS

Material specifications are contained in ANSI A118.6 *Ceramic Tile Grouts.* Installation specifications are given in ANSI A108.10 *Installation of Grout in Tilework.*

Cementitious Grouts

Portland Cement Grout. The primary component of this formulation is portland cement. This is a water-resistant, dense, uniformly colored grout.

Sand-Portland Cement Grout. This grout, a combination of portland cement and sand, is mixed on the job.

Dry-Set Grout. This is a mixture of portland cement and additives, exhibiting the same characteristics as dry-set mortar. Dry-set grout is used for floors not subject to extraordinary conditions.

Latex-Portland Cement Grout. Special latex additives mixed with either portland cement, sand-portland cement, or dry-set grouts produce a latex-portland cement grout. The latex additives help to cure the grout and make it less absorptive.

Noncementitious Grouts

Epoxy Grout. This material is formulated similarly (and in some cases identically) to epoxy mortar. It is used where chemical resistance is the primary consideration.

Furan Resin Grout. This is an expensive material and requires special skill to install. Various furan grouts are available for specific chemical and temperature conditions.

Silicone Rubber Grout. This rubberlike grout resists stains, moisture, mildew, cracking, and shrinking. It can withstand subfreezing temperatures as well as hot cooking oils. Silicone rubber grout is expensive and should not be used on food-preparation surfaces unless the manufacturer has been consulted.

Annotated Specification Checklist
for Ceramic Tile

Part 1 GENERAL

SUBMITTALS

Shop drawings: Show tile pattern and expansion joints.

Samples: Ceramic tile and grout to be used in the project. *For detailed patterns or designs, a sample mounted on plywood 600 mm (2 ft) square, showing a full pattern repeat, may be required.*

DELIVERY, STORAGE, AND HANDLING

Packing and Shipping: ANSI A 137.1.

PROJECT CONDITIONS

Environmental Requirements: Comply with written requirements of ceramic tile and installation materials manufacturer. *Temperatures lower than about 16°C (60°F) can affect the performance of ceramic tile installation materials. Ceramic tile should not be installed until after the relative humidity and temperature in a space are at the levels at which they will be maintained during installation and occupancy.*

Field Measurements: Verify tile layout and pattern dimensions.

MAINTENANCE

Extra Materials: Packaged and labeled, full-size ceramic tile and trim units. *Be specific about how much extra material will be required and where it will be stored.*

PART 2 PRODUCTS

MATERIALS

Ceramic Tile: ASTM C 242 and ANSI A 137.1, standard grade.

Setting Material: _____. *Include the specific mortar or adhesive that has been selected for the application and coordinated with the ceramic tile and grout. Mortars include portland cement mortar, dry-set mortar, latex-portland cement mortar, epoxy mortar, modified epoxy emulsion mortar, and furan resin mortar; adhesives include epoxy adhesive or organic adhesive. ANSI A 118 applies to all setting materials except organic adhesive, which is specified in ASTM A 136.*

Setting and Grout Materials: ANSI A 118. *Include the specific grout that has been selected for the application and coordinated with the ceramic tile and mortar or adhesive. Grouts include portland cement grout, sand-portland cement grout, dry-set portland cement grout, latex-portland cement grout, epoxy grout, furan resin grout, modified epoxy emulsion grout, and silicone rubber grout.*

PART 3 EXECUTION

PREPARATION

Surface Preparation: Prepare subfloor to comply with written requirements of tile and installation materials manufacturer.

INSTALLATION

Installation: ANSI A 108 and the TCA *Handbook for Ceramic Tile Installation.*

SCHEDULES

The schedule for ceramic tile is usually given on a finish schedule, included either in the specifications or on the drawings.

Terrazzo

The word *terrazzo* is derived from the Italian *terrassa,* meaning "terrace." Fifteenth-century Venetian stone cutters commonly used marble scraps as floor surfaces for their patio terraces. They imbedded the small stone pieces in concrete and polished the surface to a level finish. Terrazzo is a very low-maintenance, seamless floor finish with the luxurious look of stone mosaic and a durability comparable to that of concrete. Often selected for its decorative possibilities, terrazzo artistry can produce striking medallions or intricate inlaid patterns (Figures 4.33a and 4.33b).

Terrazzo is basically a mixture of a binder and crushed aggregate, typically marble. Divider strips of brass, white alloy of zinc, or plastic are used

Figure 4.33a Terrazzo flooring. The National Terrazzo & Mosaic Association, Inc.

Figure 4.33b Brass divider strips separate fields of color. The National Terrazzo & Mosaic Association, Inc.

functionally as control joints and aesthetically as design elements to separate fields of color. A terrazzo application begins by setting the binder and aggregate mixture in place. After the surface has cured, it is ground down to a smooth finish. The floor is then grouted, to fill any voids, and sealed. A terrazzo floor consists of at least 70% stone. Because porosity can vary among stone types, the pores of both the stone and the binder require the protection of a sealer. For renovation work, terrazzo can be installed over practically any type of existing hard flooring.

The binder is either the traditional cementitious type or the more contemporary resinous type. Cementitious binders, which contain portland cement, are the most commonly used. Resinous binders are used to install the thinnest possible finish of terrazzo, as thin as 6 mm ($\frac{1}{4}$ in). Epoxy and polyester binders are two-part formulations, consisting of a resin and a catalyst, to which a dry mix is added. Resinous binders offer increased chemical and abrasion resistance and good impact strength. Moreover, resin-based terrazzo requires significantly less maintenance than its cement-based counterpart.

The National Terrazzo and Mosaic Association (NTMA), an association of terrazzo contractors, material suppliers, and distributors, publishes the *NTMA Technical Manual* which contains complete specifications for all terrazzo systems (Table 4.11).

TABLE 4.11   TERRAZZO SYSTEMS

System	Description	Advantages	Total Thickness	Weight
Sand Cushion	12 mm ($\frac{1}{2}$ in) terrazzo topping over 63 mm (2$\frac{1}{2}$ in) underbed reinforced with wire mesh, over an isolation membrane, over 1 mm ($\frac{1}{16}$ in) of sand, on a concrete slab. For interior use only.	The best available cement terrazzo system, because it is the only system that completely separates the finish from the subfloor. This protects against minor substrate defects telegraphing through to the finish surface.	76 mm (3 in) including 12 mm ($\frac{1}{2}$ in) terrazzo topping	206 kPa (30 psf)
Bonded	12 mm ($\frac{1}{2}$ in) terrazzo topping over 32 mm (1$\frac{1}{4}$ in) underbed, on a concrete slab. Interior or exterior use.	Requires less thickness than sand cushion. Can be used for walls.	44 mm to 57 mm (1$\frac{3}{4}$ in to 2$\frac{1}{4}$ in) including 12 mm ($\frac{1}{2}$ inch) terrazzo topping	124 kPa (18 psf)
Monolithic	12 mm ($\frac{1}{2}$ in) terrazzo topping on concrete slab. Performance dependent on the quality of the substrate. A level concrete slab must be provided.	Most economical system. Ideal for large areas such as shopping malls, schools, and stores.	12 mm ($\frac{1}{2}$ in) terrazzo topping	48 kPa (7 psf)
Thin-Set	4 mm to 9 mm ($\frac{1}{4}$ in to $\frac{3}{8}$ in) terrazzo topping over concrete slab. Thinnest system. Typically, most expensive system. Considered to be a resinous flooring type. Epoxy or polyester matrix is used.	Good for renovation work. Both epoxy and polyester resist many types of chemicals, making them suitable for labs, hospitals, and manufacturing facilities.	4 mm to 9 mm ($\frac{1}{4}$ in to $\frac{3}{8}$ in)	27.5 kPa (4 psf)
Precast	Prefabricated custom units for steps, bases, planters, benches, and wall panels.	Variety of uses.	Custom	Varies

Source: Reprinted courtesy of NTMA.

Annotated Specification Checklist
for Terrazzo

PART 1 GENERAL

SUBMITTALS

Shop Drawings: Show pattern and type of terrazzo.

QUALITY ASSURANCE

Quality Standard: NTMA recommendations for materials and installations.

PROJECT CONDITIONS

Field Measurements: Verify existing conditions.

PART 2 PRODUCTS

MATERIALS

Binder: _____. *Binders are either the traditional cementitious type or the more contemporary resinous type. The exact type of binder should be determined and coordinated with the method of installation.*

Aggregate: NTMA requirements.

Divider Strips: _____. *Divider strips of brass, white alloy of zinc, or colored plastic.*

Sealer.

PART 3 EXECUTION

EXAMINATION

Verification of Conditions: Verify compliance with NTMA requirements.

PREPARATION

Surface Preparation: NTMA requirements.

INSTALLATION

Installation: NTMA requirements.

More popular in residential applications, wood is occasionally used commercially as a design statement in reception areas, private offices, or high-end retail spaces. Hardwood is by far the most often specified type of wood flooring for commercial applications; oak is the popular choice. Maple is also a common choice for hardwood flooring. This is a dense, fine-fibered, nonsplintering wood, commonly used for gymnasium floors.

Because of wood's natural porosity, moisture is often the cause for failure in wood flooring installations. For this reason, wood is not recommended for use below grade. All subfloors, regardless of material, should be tested for moisture content before wood flooring installation begins.

Wood flooring comes in three basic forms: plank, strip, and parquet, all of which typically have a nominal thickness of 19 mm (¾ in) (the actual thickness is 19.84 mm [²⁵⁄₃₂ in]). **Planks** are the widest of these types, about 75 mm to 250 mm (3 in to 10 in) wide. A variety of widths are usually combined in wood plank floors and are effective when a rustic look is preferred. Wood **strip** flooring, the most popular choice, is between about 40 mm and 60 mm (1½ and 2½ inches) wide. **Parquet** flooring consists of small lengths of wood strips, either individual slats or preconfigured into tiles, that are arranged to form patterns.

Of the three types of wood flooring, strip is the only kind graded by industry associations. The National Oak Flooring Manufacturers Association (NOFMA) maintains a grading system for oak, beech, birch, pecan, and hard maple flooring (Table 4.12). However, some manufacturers of maple flooring belong to the Maple Flooring Manufacturers Association (MFMA) and abide by its grading system.

Wood Flooring

TABLE 4.12 NOFMA FLOORING GRADES

Flooring Type	Grade	Description
Unfinished Oak	Clear Plain or Clear Quartered	Best appearance. Best grade, most uniform color, limited small character marks.
	Select Plain or Select Quartered	Excellent appearance. Limited character marks, unlimited sound sap.
	Select and Better	A combination of Clear and Select Grades.
Unfinished Hard Maple (Beech and Birch)	First Grade	Best appearance. Natural color variation, limited character marks, unlimited sap.
	Second Grade	Varigated appearance. Varying sound wood characteristics of species.
	Second and Better Grade	A combination of First and Second Grades.
Unfinished Pecan	First Grade	Excellent appearance. Natural color variation, limited character marks, unlimited sap.
	Second Grade	Varigated appearance. Varying sound wood characteristics of species.
Prefinished Oak	Prime Grade	Excellent appearance. Natural color variation, limited character marks, unlimited sap.
	Standard Grade	Varigated appearance. Varying sound wood characteristics of species.

Source: National Oak Flooring Manufacturer's Association.

Wood flooring strips are plain sawed or quarter sawed (Figure 4.34). Plain sawed is the more popular, less expensive, and less wasteful cut. Quarter-sawed strips tend to have a greater dimensional stability, minimizing shrinkage and swelling in width. Oak is the only hardwood flooring that is readily available in quarter-sawed strips. Maple, beech, and birch are hard, dense woods that tend to be dimensionally stable either plain sawed or quarter sawed, and so the additional expense of quarter-sawed strips can be spared.

Most all strip flooring is milled in a tongue-and-groove shape. It is typically either installed over a plywood subfloor or wood sleepers and blind nailed (concealed nail head) above the "tongue" (Figure 4.35), or set in place with mastic.

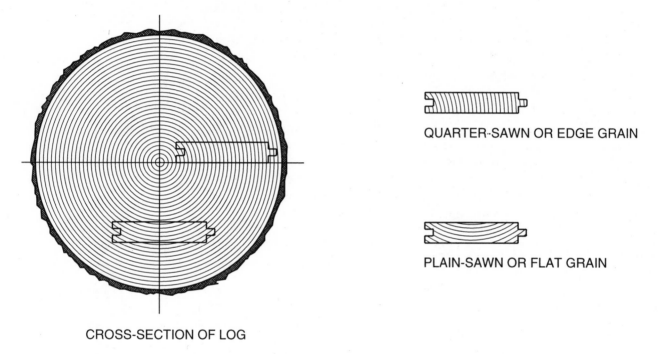

CROSS-SECTION OF LOG

QUARTER-SAWN OR EDGE GRAIN

PLAIN-SAWN OR FLAT GRAIN

Figure 4.34 Quarter-sawn and plain-sawn wood flooring.

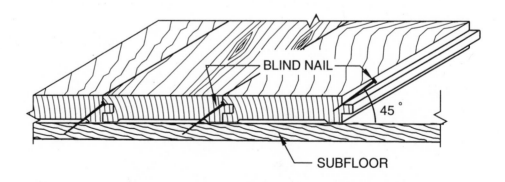

BLIND NAIL

45°

SUBFLOOR

Figure 4.35 Blind-nailed tongue-and-groove wood flooring.

WOOD FLOOR FINISHES

Particular care must be taken in specifying wood floors in areas subjected to direct sunlight. Although finishes protect the wood from abrasion and wear, they are not effective in shielding it from the effects of the sun. Depending on the finish selected, the finish may not change color from exposure to the sun, but the wood beneath it will. UV (ultraviolet ray) blockers are available in some floor finishes to diminish fading.

Field Finishes

Unfinished wood flooring can be stained to achieve an exact color match with other design elements or to mimic the appearance of a softer wood that might not have met the performance expectations of the installation.

Before the application of a field finish, wood floors are sanded so that they are level and smooth. Then one of several finishes is applied. All of these finishes are subject to wear and must be touched up or removed and reapplied during the life of the floor.

There are basically three types of commercial finishes for wood floors: acid curing, oil-modified polyurethanes, and water-based polyurethanes. **Acid-curing**, sometimes called *Swedish*, finishes are hard and durable. These are thicker and less viscous than other types of finishes, making for heavier coats. Acid-curing finishes are solvent-based, two-part formulations requiring on-site mixing. They have a naturally high VOC (volatile organic compound) content, and applicators typically wear masks because of their noxious odor. These finishes tend to be less expensive than water-based polyurethanes, but more expensive than oil-modified polyurethanes. **Oil-modified polyurethanes** also have a high VOC content. They are easy to apply and the least expensive of the three finishes. Oil-modified polyurethanes tend to amber (turn slightly orange) as they age. **Water-based polyurethanes** have a low VOC content and do not yellow or change color over time. Because they are thinner, more coats are required to achieve the same depth as produced by an acid-curing finish. Water-based polyurethanes tend to be the most expensive type of wood floor finish.

Factory Finishes

Acrylic-impregnated, sometimes called irradiated polymer, wood flooring is extremely durable. This most recent advance in finishes imparts many of the qualities of resilient flooring to the wood, such as an increased resistance to abrasion and bacterial growth. The process involves removing the air from the pores of dried wood and forcing liquid acrylic into the voids. The plastic-filled wood is then irradiated (exposed to radiation), causing the acrylic to polymerize.

Prefinished wood flooring is also available with multiple coats of polyurethane or other proprietary finishes.

Annotated Specification Checklist
for Wood Flooring

PART 1 GENERAL

SUBMITTALS

Shop Drawings: Show layout, patterns, location of reducer strips, and installation details.

Samples: 300 mm (12 in) long with required finish applied.

PROJECT CONDITIONS

Environmental Requirements: Comply with wood flooring manufacturer's written requirements. *Wood flooring with a high moisture content at the time of installation can adversely affect the performance of the flooring. Wood flooring should not be installed until after the relative humidity and temperature in the space are at the levels at which they will be maintained during the installation and occupancy.*

Field Measurements: Verify dimensions of flooring installation area. *Field verification of built dimensions is particularly important for floors with border detail or patterns.*

MAINTENANCE

Extra Materials: Packaged and labeled, full-length wood flooring. *Be specific about how much extra material will be required and where it will be stored.*

PART 2 PRODUCTS

MATERIALS

Species: _____.
NOFMA Grade: _____.
Cut: _____. *Plain sawn or quarter sawn.*
Adhesive: Comply with flooring manufacturer's written recommendation.

PART 3 EXECUTION

EXAMINATION

Verification of Conditions: Verify that subfloor conditions comply with flooring manufacturer's written requirements.

PREPARATION

Material Preparation: Acclimatize wood flooring in space in which it will be installed for 48 hours prior to installation.

INSTALLATION

Installation and Finishing: Comply with NOFMA *Hardwood Flooring Installation Manual* and flooring manufacturer's-written requirements.

PROTECTION

Protection: Do not cover wood flooring until finish has cured.

Unlike most other construction materials, stone does not lose its beauty with age. Stone, like no other flooring, conveys an enduring sense of timelessness. Often selected for public spaces and entry lobbies, stone projects an image of permanence (Table 4.13).

Stone

DIMENSION STONE

Dimension stone is defined as quarried stone with usually one or more mechanically dressed surfaces. These are thick slabs of stone that are marked as they are cut for matched pattern installations, such as book-match or end-match configurations. **Dimension stone tiles** are less than 19 mm (¾ in) thick. They provide the natural beauty of a stone floor without the weight, depth, and expense of dimension stone. However, their thinness makes stone tiles more prone to cracking from impact or normal floor deflection. Stone tiles are installed by either the thick-bed or the thin-set installation methods described in "Ceramic Tile" earlier in this chapter.

TABLE 4.13 TYPES OF ARCHITECTURAL STONE

Geology	Sedimentary	Metamorphic			Igneous
Definition	Rock formed in layers by water or air	Sedimentary or igneous rock altered by heat and pressure			Solidified molten rock
Stone	Limestone	Slate	Marble	Travertine (sedimentary form of marble)	Granite
Quarry Locations	NY to AL, IN to MS, IA, NE, KA, MO, OK, AR, TX, WI, CO, SD, WY, CA, MN	MA to GA, CA, AR	NY to AL, IN to MS, NE, KA, MO, OK, AR, TX, CO, SD WY, CA, MN, WI		MA, NH, VT, RI, CT, NY, NJ, MD, VA, NC, SC, GA, WI, MN, MO, OK, TX, CA, SD, ME, PA
Finishes	Polished, smooth, honed, natural cleft, sand-rubbed	Polished, fine abrasive, textured			Polished, honed, fine-rubbed, thermal
Colors	White, cream, gray, rust, pink, black, buff, tan, ivory, blue, rose	Blue, green, black, purple gray	White, gray, red, pink, buff, rose, gold, green, yellow, black, brown, tan		Pink, brown, gray, white, blue, black, green, red

Source: Marble Institute of America, Inc.

GRANITE

Granite is a hard, durable, low-maintenance stone. It is a grainy igneous rock (formed by volcanic action) that imparts a visual strength. Granite is relatively uniform in color and texture. Patterns that can be formed by panel placement with highly veined stones such as marble cannot be acheived with granite.

MARBLE

Identified by its varigated, veined surface, marble is valued for its range of colors and luxurious appearance. Marbles are comparatively soft, easily scratched stones and require dedicated maintenance, especially if a polished finish is selected. The Marble Institute of America (MIA) classifies marble according to the level of effort required for fabrication, not on quality (Table 4.14). The marbles in Groups C and D are more fragile than those in Groups A and B.

LIMESTONE

The color range of limestone is limited to a neutral pallette of buff and gray. More commonly used as exterior cladding for buildings, limestone is susceptible to staining and should not be exposed to excessive soil. Limestone is classified by ASTM C 568 *Specification for Limestone Dimension Stone* into three densities: Type I—Low Density, Type II—Medium Density, and Type III—High Density.

TABLE 4.14   MARBLE INSTITUTE OF AMERICA, SOUNDNESS CLASSIFICATIONS

GROUP A

Marbles and stones unimpaired by weakened planes with very little variation in fabrication quality.

GROUP B

Marbles and stones with a nature similar to the preceding group. Working qualities are somewhat less favorable. Stones in this group may have natural faults requiring some waxing and sticking.

GROUP C

Marbles and stones with even greater variations in working qualities; natural flaws, voids, stains, and lines of separation are more common. These variations in the stone are usually repaired before installation by sticking, waxing, and filling the voids. When necessary, liners, strong backs, or other forms of reinforcement are used.

GROUP D

Marbles and stones similar to the preceding group, but containing a larger proportion of natural faults and a maximum variation in working qualities, requiring more of the same methods of finishing. Many of the more varigated marbles fit into this group.

Source: Marble Institute of America, Inc.

Figure 4.36 Slate flooring. Photo compliment of Dal-Tile North, America's largest manufacturer of ceramic tile.

SLATE

Historically used for roofing, slate is commonly used as a contemporary interior floor or wall finish (Figure 4.36). It is available in a pallette of dark, rich colors. Slate splits easily into thin sheets. The finish resulting from the natural face is referred to as a *cleft* finish. Slate can also be sand rubbed to a smooth finish or honed.

TRAVERTINE

Travertine is distinguished by its natural cavities, formed by plants embedded during the rock's formation, which must be filled to achieve a smooth surface. Filling materials are typically portland cement, epoxy resins, or polyester resins. Travertine is actually a kind of limestone, but some types that take a polish are classified as marble. It is popular for use as a flooring because its visual texture conceals dirt much better than most other stones. Travertine has a soundness classification of Group D.

STONE FINISHES

The finish affects the perception of the color and the slip resistance of stone flooring. **Polished** finishes are the most reflective. These high-maintenance finishes should be selected with care. For high traffic public areas, such as lobbies, polished floor finishes are often eventually hidden under non-skid matts. **Honed** finishes have a dull sheen. These satin smooth surfaces are often good choices for commercial floors because of their slip resistance. **Thermal**, sometimes called flamed, finishes are achieved by the application of intense flaming heat to the surface of the stone. Thermal finishes are usually applied to granite.

Annotated Specification Checklist
for Stone Flooring

PART 1 GENERAL

SUBMITTALS

Shop Drawings: Show layout, patterns, and installation details.

Samples: Stone and grout to be used in the project.

PROJECT CONDITIONS

Environmental Requirements: Comply with stone supplier's written requirements. *Stone flooring should not be installed until after the relative humidity and temperature in a space are at the levels at which they will be maintained during installation and occupancy.*

Field Measurements: Verify existing conditions. *Field verification of built dimensions is particularly important for floors with border detail or patterns.*

PART 2 PRODUCTS

MATERIALS

Granite: ASTM C 615.
Marble: ASTM C 503.
Slate: ASTM C 629.
Limestone: ASTM C 568.
Stone Finish: _____. *Finish designations vary depending on the type of stone.*
Setting and Grouting Materials: ANSI A 118.

PART 3 EXECUTION

EXAMINATION

Verification of Conditions: Verify that subfloor conditions comply with flooring manufacturer's written requirements.

PREPARATION

Surface Preparation: Prepare subfloor to comply with written requirements of stone and installation materials manufacturer.

INSTALLATION

Installation: ANSI A 108 and the TCA *Handbook for Ceramic Tile Installation.*

There are five ingredients commonly found in vinyl flooring: polyvinyl chloride, fillers, pigments, plasticizers, and stabilizers. The way in which vinyl flooring is produced and the chemical composition of the ingredients varies considerably among manufacturers. This can make it difficult to evaluate the various vinyl flooring products. Fortunately, there are standards that facilitate comparisons based on performance.

Polyvinyl chloride (PVC) resin is the most important, and most expensive, ingredient in vinyl flooring. It gives the flooring its wear resistance and durability. PVC is the basis of the binder, which constitutes most of the wear surface. The binder consists of PVC that has been compounded with plasticizers and stabilizers. **Plasticizers** increase flexibility so that the flooring can be rolled without cracking or breaking. **Stabilizers** provide color permanence and stabilize the pigments against heat and light deterioration. **Fillers** are sometimes added to supplement the bulk and thickness of the flooring. Mineral fillers, the most common, also serve to improve the flooring's fire resistance. **Pigments** are required for color because most vinyl is clear.

SHEET VINYL

Unlike vinyl tile, sheet vinyl allows a continuous surface to be formed. Because such flooring has fewer joints, it is popular for applications where spills, dirt, or bacterial growth is of concern (for example, in hospitals) (Figure 4.37). Sheet goods can also form an integral or monolithic wall base, sometimes referred to as a **flash cove**, to simplify maintenance

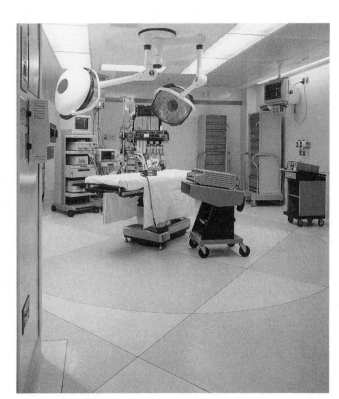

Figure 4.37 Sheet vinyl flooring has fewer joints, making it a popular choice in applications where spills or bacterial growth are a concern. Photo courtesy of Armstrong. Copyright © 1994 Armstrong.

Figure 4.38a Sheet vinyl flash cove, an integral, monolithic wall base.

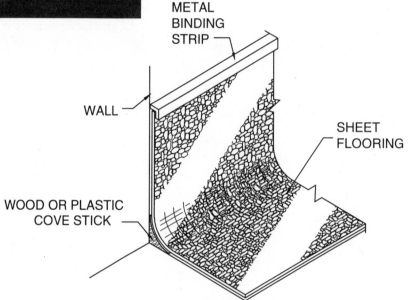

Figure 4.38b Cove detail.

(Figures 4.38a and 4.38b). There are essentially two kinds of sheet vinyl flooring: sheets that have a backing and those that do not.

Homogeneous, or solid, sheet vinyl floorings have no backing. The pattern continues all the way through the sheet (Figure 4.39a). This flooring is ideally suited for heavy wear applications; even if the surface is worn down, its appearance will remain consistent (Figure 4.40). Homogeneous vinyl sheet also has superior resistance to indentation, rolling loads, and chemicals. It contains much more vinyl than backed sheet vinyls, making it more resilient. Increased resiliency means that the wear surface is better able to bounce back from indentation. The increased amount of vinyl also makes it more expensive.

Backed sheet vinyls consist of a vinyl wear layer that is bonded to a backing, with or without an interlayer between the two. The wear layer is the thin upper layer of the floor covering that contains or protects the pattern. It does not include applied finishes or maintenance coatings. The wear layer consists mainly of a vinyl binder and may include pigments, fillers, and other ingredients (Figure 4.39b). The interlayer may include materials to impart a desired performance attribute. For example, a high-density foam interlayer reduces impact sound and noise transmission and has a cushioning effect, thus reducing foot fatigue. Another kind of backed sheet vinyl is formed with a transparent or translucent wear layer applied over a printed surface (Figures 4.39c).

SOLID VINYL PARTICLES EXTENDING ALL THE WAY THROUGH FOR UNIFORM APPEARANCE AS FLOORING WEARS

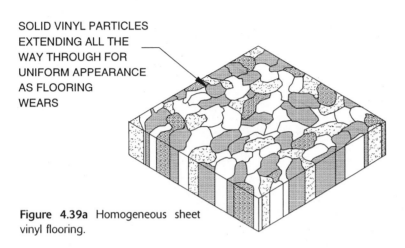

Figure 4.39a Homogeneous sheet vinyl flooring.

Figure 4.40 The appearance of homogeneous vinyl flooring remains consistent as the surface wears. Photo courtesy of Armstrong. Copyright © 1994 Armstrong.

VINYL CHIPS SUSPENDED IN PURE VINYL

BACKING

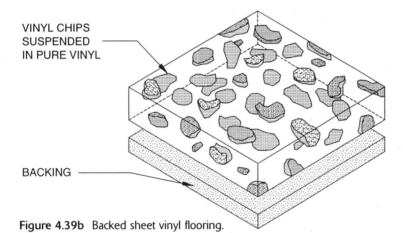

Figure 4.39b Backed sheet vinyl flooring.

CLEAR VINYL

DESIGN PRINTED ON BACKING OR ON UNDERSIDE OF WEAR LAYER

BACKING

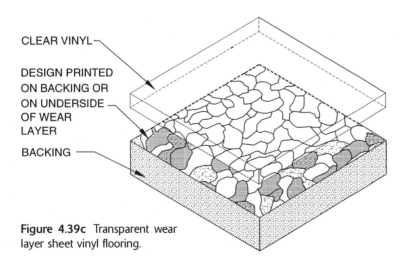

Figure 4.39c Transparent wear layer sheet vinyl flooring.

TABLE 4.15   GRADES OF SHEET VINYL FLOOR COVERING WITH BACKING
ACCORDING TO ASTM F 1303

Type	Grade	Wear Layer Thickness, Minimum	
		(in)	(mm)
I	1	0.020	0.51
	2	0.014	0.36
	3	0.010	0.25
II	1	0.050	1.27
	2	0.030	0.76
	3	0.020	0.51

Type I is defined by a wear layer binder content of not less than 90%. Type II is defined by a wear layer binder content of not less than 34%.

Each manufacturer has a different method of producing backed sheet vinyl. The result is an array of compositions that make comparisons difficult. To help specifiers select a sheet vinyl with the required performance characteristics, ASTM F 1303 *Standard Specification for Sheet Vinyl Floor Covering with Backing* provides a classification based on the wear layer's binder content and thickness (Table 4.15). Generally, the thicker the wear layer and the higher the binder content, the better the durability and the resistance to abrasion of the vinyl floor covering.

Installation

Sheets of vinyl flooring are seamed through either heat welding or chemical welding. **Heat-welded** seams are formed by melting a vinyl rod between the sheets (Figure 4.41). Solid color or patterned welding rods can either accent or camouflage seams. Heat welding, which provides a slightly wider joint, is an expensive operation, requiring special equipment and trained installers. It is commonly specified in hospital operating rooms and other areas where resistance to bacterial growth is the primary concern.

Chemical welding is accomplished with the application of a one- or two-part solvent that is mixed on-site. This softens the edges of the vinyl, essentially melting them together. Chemical welding is more economical than heat welding.

VINYL TILE

The advantages of tile over sheet vinyl are lower installation costs and easier replacement of damaged flooring. **Vinyl composition tile (VCT)** is the most popular and economical type of resilient flooring (Figure 4.42). The tiles are composed mostly of fillers with a comparatively small amounts of binder and pigments. VCT is more brittle than vinyl sheet flooring because it contains much less PVC.

There are three classes of VCT, based on the tile's construction. These are defined by ASTM F 1066 *Specification for Vinyl Composition Floor Tile*, as follows: Class 1 designates solid-color tiles; Class 2 designates through-pattern tiles; and Class 3 refers to surface pattern tiles.

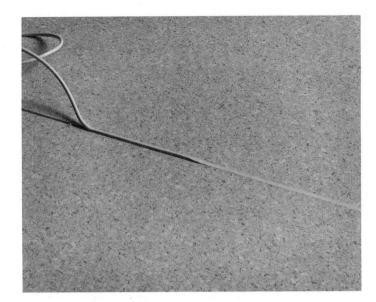

Figure 4.41 Heat-welded seam. Photo courtesy of Armstrong. Copyright © 1994 Armstrong.

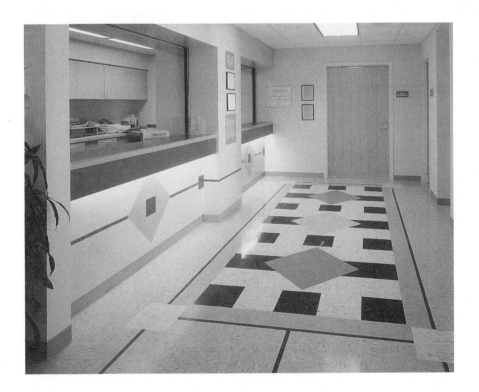

Figure 4.42 Vinyl composition tile (VCT). Sharp Chula Vista, Maternal Infants Pavilion, Jain Malkin Interiors. Photo courtesy of Tarkett.

Originally, the fillers used in vinyl tile contained asbestos. The product was called *vinyl asbestos tile*, or VAT. Because of the health risks associated with asbestos, it is no longer used in construction materials.

Homogeneous, or solid, vinyl tile contains much more PVC than VCT, making it more resilient and resistant to abrasion. Homogeneous vinyl tile has superior indentation and rolling load resistance. Because the pattern is continuous through the thickness of the flooring, its appearance will remain consistent even after heavy wear or abrasion.

Rubber Flooring

Figure 4.43 Laminated rubber tile. Tuflex Rubber Products Flooring Since 1957.

Rubber sheet or tile is composed of natural rubber, synthetic rubber (styrene butadiene), or both, in combination with mineral fillers and pigments. Rubber is highly resistant to a wide variety of harsh chemicals and solvents. Because of its high durability and natural resistance to cigarette burns, rubber is a good choice for high-traffic public areas such as airport terminals.

There are two types of rubber tile: homogeneous and laminated. The slip resistance of homogeneous rubber tile is often further enhanced by a raised surface pattern. This material is popular for use as stair treads and nosings. Laminated rubber tile (Figure 4.43) is puncture resistant and extremely resilient; when pressure is removed from the flooring surface, it springs back to its original shape. It is frequently selected for use in playground areas, health clubs, or off-ice areas at ice skating rinks.

Linoleum

Linoleum, the predecessor to contemporary synthetic resilient flooring, was developed in England in the 1860s. Its market remains deeply rooted in Europe; it is not manufactured in the United States. There is, however, a renewed interest in linoleum because it is produced mainly with natural materials from sustainable crops and its waste is biodegradable.

The term **linoleum** is derived from the Latin botanical terms for "flax," *linum*, and for "oil," *oleum*. Linoleum is composed of oxidized linseed oil or other resins, mixed with ground cork or wood flour, mineral filler, and pigments. This mixture is bonded to a fiber backing, typically burlap (Figure 4.44). The linseed oil is oxidized and a natural resin is added, producing a cementitious type of material. Powdered cork is also added to lend flexibility, and wood flour and powdered limestone are added to impart strength and hardness. Because of the air pockets found naturally in cork (it is 50% air), linoleum is a superior thermal and acoustic insulator.

When sheet or tile linoleum is first laid, it is relatively porous. However, the oxidization process continues over the life of the floor and it becomes progressively more nonporous. Linoleum is manufactured thicker than vinyl sheet, providing a deeper wear surface. It is popular for use where superior resilience is required, for example, in floors of dance rehearsal studios.

Cork

Another natural resilient flooring is cork. **Cork** is actually the outer layer of the cork oak tree, which is grown in Mediterranean regions. It is harvested, without harm to the tree, when the bark becomes loose. Cork is self-replenishing; the bark grows back and is ready to be removed again every nine years (Figure 4.45).

Cork tile is composed of granulated cork and synthetic resins. A protective finish coat is applied to the completed tile. Cork offers excellent acoustic and thermal insulation. However, because of its absorptive nature, moisture and stains are of concern. Cork can also be used as an underlayment to increase the resiliency of other types of finish floors (Figure 4.46).

Figure 4.44 Linoleum, finish surface (top) and burlap backing (bottom). Photo credit: Michael E. Dolan.

Figure 4.45 Cork being harvested from cork oak trees in Portugal. Cork is self-replenishing. Photo: Ipocork S.A. Copyright IPOCORK S.A.

Figure 4.46 Cork flooring, an excellent acoustic insulator, was selected for this library installation. Photo: Ipocork S.A. Copyright IPOCORK S.A.

Resilient Flooring Accessories

A variety of flooring accessories are available in both rubber and vinyl for use with hard, soft, or resilient finish floors. A **wall base** conceals the joint where a wall meets the floor. It helps to prevent dirt accumulation and protects the base of the wall finish from the impact of shoes and maintenance equipment. There are two common profiles of wall base: straight or standard cove. Less common and available from a limited number of manufacturers, is the butt cove wall base. A butt cove wall base must be installed before the flooring; then the finish floor is butted up against it. The fade resistance of rubber wall base is generally better than that of vinyl wall base. **Reducing, or transition, strips** create a smooth connection between floorings of different types. They act to conceal the seam and smooth the transition between slightly different heights (Figures 4.47a and 4.47b).

Figure 4.47a Transition strip between rubber and carpet flooring. The transition strip is aligned with the door frame so that it is concealed when the door is in a closed position. Photo courtesy of Mercer Products Company, Eustis, FL.

Figure 4.47b Transition strip between vinyl sheet and carpet flooring. The vinyl wall base is notched so that it fits tightly to the finish floor surface on either side. Photo courtesy of Mercer Products Company, Eustis, FL.

Annotated Specification Checklist
for Resilient Flooring

Part 1 GENERAL

SUBMITTALS

Product Data: Include composition of resilient floor product.

Shop Drawings: Show location of transition strips.

Shop Drawings: Show location of seams and patterns. *Seams in sheet vinyl, especially those heat welded, should be carefully considered, because they will be noticeable in the completed flooring installation.*

Samples: Full-size of each type of resilient flooring.

QUALITY ASSURANCE

Qualifications: Installers trained and certified by flooring manufacturer. *This requirement is important for heat welding seams, which requires expensive equipment and skilled workers. Not all manufacturers certify installers, so requirements included here must be coordinated with the qualification methods available.*

Regulatory Requirements: A Critical Radiant Flux of 0.45 watts per sq cm or more. *The Critical Radiant Flux (see "Flammability Standards" in Chapter 2) required by the building code should be included here.*

PROJECT CONDITIONS

Environmental Requirements: Acclimatize materials before installation.

MAINTENANCE

Extra Materials: Full-size units labeled and sealed in cartons. *Require full-size units to avoid receiving scraps left over after installation.*

PART 2 PRODUCTS

MATERIALS

Backed Vinyl Sheet: ASTM F 1303.

Vinyl Tile: ASTM F 1066.

Rubber Floor Tile: ASTM F 1344.

Welding Rods: _____. *Welding rods, either patterned or solid, are included for welded seam sheet vinyl or linoleum.*

Vinyl Wall Base: FS SS-W-40. *Specify whether the wall base corners are preformed or formed on the site. Not all wall base is available preformed.*

Rubber Wall Base: FS SS-W-40.

Adhesives: As recommended in writing by the flooring manufacturer and as compatible with the substrate.

PART 3 EXECUTION

EXAMINATION

Verification of Conditions: Verify that substrates are in compliance with flooring manufacturer's requirements before installation begins. *Proper substrate preparation is essential to the performance of the flooring adhesive. Subfloor or underlayment surface imperfections tend to telegraph through to the surface of vinyl flooring.*

PREPARATION

Surface Preparation: ASTM F 710. *ASTM F 710 is entitled* Standard Practice for Preparing Concrete Floors and Other Monolithic Floors to Receive Resilient Flooring. *It states that the floor surface must be "firm, dry, and free of surface contamination like dust, solvent, scaly paint, wax, oil, grease, asphalt, sealing compounds, and other extraneous foreign materials." It does not address two important issues: priming concrete slabs and checking for the moisture content of the slab (see page 155). Some flooring manufacturers recommend priming a concrete slab before the finish floor is installed to prepare the floor for a good bond with an adhesive. If existing resilient floor covering is to be removed before new flooring is installed, comply with the* Recommended Work Practices for the Removal of Resilient Floor Coverings *issued by the Resilient Floor Covering Institute.*

INSTALLATION

Integral cove: Installed as recommended in writing by the flooring manufacturer. *Some floorings, for example, linoleum, require prefabricated flash coving because the material is too stiff and brittle to be flash coved on-site.*

Seaming Method: _____. *Heat welding or chemical welding must be selected for sheet vinyls and linoleum. Heat welding is more expensive.*

Most vinyl tiles have a directional pattern, sometimes referred to as a grain. Either specify the direction of the pattern here or show it on the drawings.

SCHEDULES

The schedule of floor finishes is usually shown on a finish schedule included in the specifications or, more commonly, on the drawings.

Carpet and Carpet Tile

Carpet construction refers to the carpet manufacturing method. The three basic construction methods for carpet are tufting, weaving, and fusion bonding (figure 4.16). Broadloom carpet [carpet that is manufactured 1370 mm (54 in) wide or wider] is tufted or woven. Carpet tiles, sometimes referred to as modules, are tufted, needlepunched, or fusion bonded. Because of the fundamental differences in the manufacturing processes, different terms are used to describe carpet density for each type of carpet construction.

TUFTED CARPET

Tufting has transformed the carpet industry since its introduction in the early 1950s. It is far less expensive and faster to produce than woven carpet. This process has enabled the mass production of an affordably priced textile floor covering. More than 90% of the carpet produced in the United States is tufted.

Tufted carpet is constructed by punching tufts of yarn into a backing. Yarns are threaded through hundreds of individual needles on a device that extends the entire width of the finished carpet. Much as in a sewing process, the needles are forced through a loosely woven or nonwoven primary backing material, forming loops, or tufts.

To hold the tufted loops in place, the underside of the primary backing is coated with latex adhesive, a rubbery substance that dries hard but remains bendable. A secondary backing is added for strength and stability. Secondary backing materials are usually woven jute or polypropylene. Jute is dimensionally stable and heat resistant; however, when wet, it tends to shrink and can stain the carpet face fibers. Polypropylene is more popular as a backing material because it is moisture resistant. Alternatives to secondary backings are attached carpet cushions, solid vinyl composites, and coatings referred to as unitary backings.

Density Measurements for Tufted Carpet

Widthwise Density Measurement. **Gauge** is the measure of the spacing of the tufting needles, center to center, across the width of the carpet. Gauge is measured in fractions of an inch. For example, ⅛ gauge means that the tufting needles are spaced ⅛ inch (3 mm) apart, producing 8 yarn ends per inch.

Lengthwise Density Measurement. **Stitches** define the number of ends sewn by the needles down the length of the carpet. Generally, the number of stitches per inch and the number of needles per inch are approximately the same.

Pile height is the length of a tuft from the backing surface to the tip of the tuft. It is measured in fractions of an inch. Although a deep pile may provide a more luxurious feel underfoot, it also has a greater tendency to crush and show wear.

WOVEN CARPET

Weaving, the traditional carpet construction method, produces carpet on a loom. The process is different from that used in constructing tufted carpet. In woven carpets the pile and backing yarns are integrated into the carpet fabric in the same operation. Most woven carpet is heavy, dimensionally stable, and strong as a result of the weaving process and does not require a secondary backing as tufted carpet does.

Weaving is a slower, more labor-intensive process than tufting and consequently is more expensive. Installation costs for woven carpet are also typically higher. There is usually an intricate pattern that must be matched, and proper installation generally requires power stretching and hand-sewn seams.

TABLE 4.16   THE THREE MAJOR TYPES OF CARPET CONSTRUCTION

	Tufted	Fusion Bonded
Manufacturing Process	*(diagram: NEEDLES, PRIMARY BACKING, STITCHES (PER INCH), GAUGE, PILE, LOOPER)*	*(diagram: "I" Method — SUBSTRATE, ADHESIVE, USE SURFACE / PILE, CUTTER, ADHESIVE, SUBSTRATE)* *("U" Method — SUBSTRATE, ARM, ADHESIVE, USE SURFACE / PILE, CUTTER, ARM, USE SURFACE / PILE, ADHESIVE, SUBSTRATE)*
Cross Section	*(diagram: PRIMARY BACKING, LATEX, SECONDARY BACKING)*	*(diagram: ADHESIVE LAYER, FIBERGLAS PRIMARY BACKING LAYER, SECONDARY BACKING LAYER)*
Backing	Pile yarn is tufted or sewn through backing	Pile yarn is embedded into adhesive and adhered to backing
Wear Surface as % of Total Weight	70 to 85%	70 to 85%

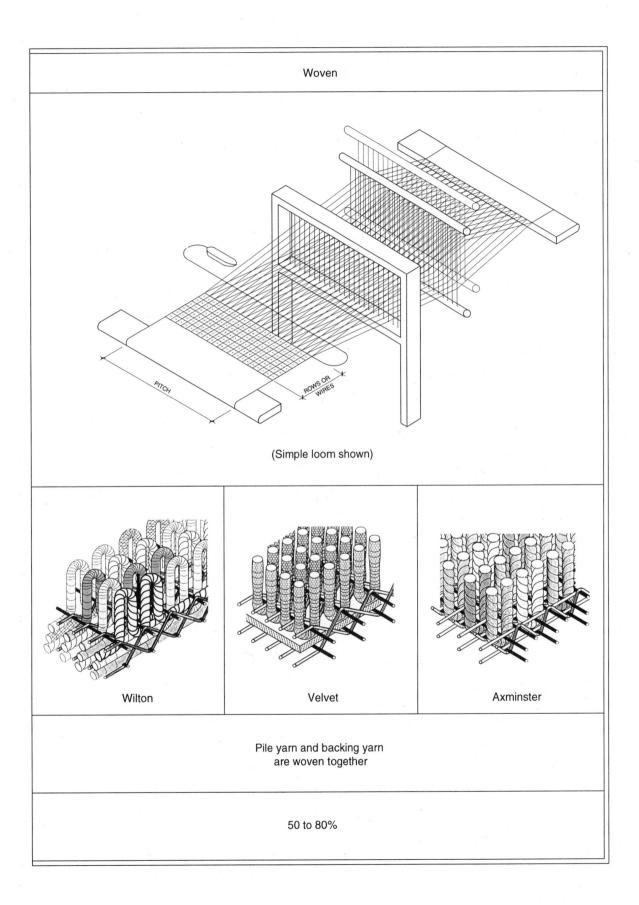

Woven

(Simple loom shown)

PITCH

ROWS OR WIRES

Wilton

Velvet

Axminster

Pile yarn and backing yarn
are woven together

50 to 80%

Weaving accounts for less than 2% of the carpet market in the United States. Its primary use is in the hospitality industry, where long-term durability and intricate pattern detail are primary considerations. There are three basic types of weaving processes: velvet, Wilton, and Axminster.

Velvet. Velvet is the least complex weaving method. It is used primarily to produce solid color carpets, but variations in color and pattern are possible. Velvet carpets are made on looms similar to Wilton looms, but without the Jacquard mechanism.

Wilton. Wilton carpets are constructed on a modified Jacquard loom. Perforated cards control the creation of the pattern. The Wilton weaving method is usually used to produce carpet of more than one color, with as many as five colors possible. Floral-patterned hotel lobby carpet is a common example of a Wilton. A Wilton carpet is thick and heavy because yarn of every color used is carried beneath the pile surface.

Axminster. The Axminster loom, named after Axminster, England, was developed in the United States in the eighteenth century. Patterns and colors are virtually limitless, because the colored yarns are inserted individually as they are required by the design (Figure 4.48). Because each tuft is inserted separately, the Axminster loom emulates the hand-weaving process. The distinguishing characteristics of this weave type are intricate, multi-colored patterns and a backing so heavily ribbed that the carpet can be rolled only lengthwise. Axminsters tend to stretch quite a bit in length and very little in width. Axminsters are cut pile face construction.

Figure 4.48 Axminster carpet. Copyright © U.S. Axminster, Inc.

Density Measurements for Woven Carpet

Widthwise Density Measurement. **Pitch** is the number of ends in a 27-in (685-mm) width of carpet. A yarn loop in the surface of a carpet is referred to as an **end**. The pitch can be divided by 27 to compare widthwise density with that of a tufted carpet. For example, if the pitch is 216, it is divided by 27, which equals 8 ends per inch, or ⅛ gauge in a tufted carpet.

Lengthwise Density Measurement. The terms **rows** in Axminster, and **wires** in Wilton and velvet carpets, refer to the number of ends per inch lengthwise.

In woven carpet, the pile height is referred to as the **wire height**, referring to the height of the steel blades in the loom on which the tufts are formed. Wire height is stated in decimals of an inch.

FUSION-BONDED CARPET

Fusion bonding is a thermoplastic process, developed by Milliken, whereby yarns are attached to a backing material by means of adhesion rather than stitching (as in tufted carpet) or weaving. The adhesive is applied to the backing material and the yarns are implanted in it. Because the yarn is typically imbedded between two parallel backings that must be sliced apart, fusion-bonded carpet is necessarily cut pile. Fusion-bonded carpet has the greatest percentage of yarn available for wear, but is more expensive than tufted carpet. Fusion bonding initially dominated the carpet tile market; however, tufted loop constructions are now more popular. The cut pile construction of fusion bonding offers greater pile densities at comparable yarn weights than tufted constructions. However, the graphic styling capabilities of modern tufting machines have prompted the shift from fusion bonding to tufting.

KNITTED CARPET

As in the construction of woven carpet, the knitting process integrates pile and backing yarns in one operation. Needles are used to interlace yarns in a series of connecting loops, similar to the hand-knitting process (Figure 4.49). Knitted carpets are known for their plush piles, because there is

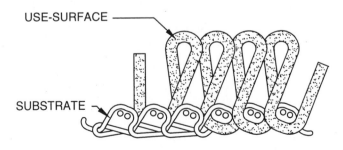

USE-SURFACE

SUBSTRATE

Figure 4.49 Knitted carpet.

more yarn in the wear surface than tufted carpets. Knitted carpet has a tendency to stretch, especially on the diagonal, and is difficult to seam during installation. Knitted carpet represents a very small percentage of the carpet produced in the United States.

NEEDLEPUNCHED CARPET

Needlepunching is achieved by layering thick fiber batts, typically polypropylene, over a support fabric. Hundreds of barbed needles punch through the support fabric, compressing and entangling the fibers (Figure 4.50). Needlepunched carpets are permeable, which presents a problem when liquids are spilled on a wall-to-wall interior installation. The most common application of needlepunched carpet is outdoor carpet.

PILE TYPES

Pile consists of yarns or fibers projecting from a substrate, acting as a wear surface (Figures 4.51 to 4.57). The selection of a pile type depends on the desired visual effect and performance expectations.

There is a phenomenon in the carpet industry, associated primarily with cut pile carpet, called *watermarking* or *pooling* because a pool of water appears to be sitting on the carpet (Figure 4.58). It tends to be most noticeable with solid color carpets installed in large open areas. Watermarking is not a manufacturer's defect. There is no known cause or remedy for watermarking. One of the theories of watermarking is that of subfloor irregularities, but various other theories exist. Where a cut pile carpet is preferred, the client should be notified in writing that watermarking may occur.

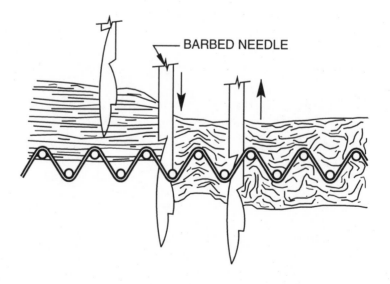

Figure 4.50 Needlepunched carpet.

Figure 4.51 Level loop. Level loop pile is made of uncut pile yarns of the same height. It has a pebbled surface texture that hides footprints and other indentations such as chair caster and furniture marks.

Figure 4.52 Multilevel loop. Multilevel loop pile creates a sculptured effect.

Figure 4.53 Random tip sheared. Random tip sheared pile produces tonal contrast between the cut and uncut loops of varying heights.

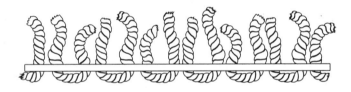

Figure 4.54 Frieze. Frieze (pronounced *free-zay*) pile is made of tightly twisted, heat-set yarns imparting a grainy appearance. This pile type hides dirt well.

Figure 4.55 Cut and loop. Cut and loop pile creates a carved or sculptured effect.

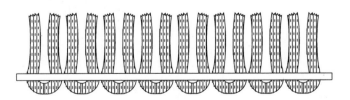

Figure 4.56 Velvet or plush. Velvet or plush pile is a smooth cut pile. The yarn ends blend together for a consistent surface appearance. Plush piles may show footprints and shading.

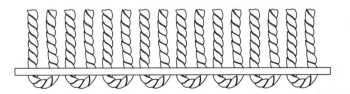

Figure 4.57 Saxony. Saxony pile is similar to plush pile but has twisted yarn, which gives definition to each tuft. The loops are cut during the construction process. Saxonies are made with heat-set yarn, usually in a dense, low-pile construction. This pile type shows footprints and shading marks.

Figure 4.58 Watermarking is most noticeable with solid color carpets.

Carpet Performance

In evaluating a carpet, several factors must be considered, including delamination strength, colorfastness, and tuft bind, to name a few (Table 4.17). Face weight and pile density are two of the most important factors in determining a carpet's performance. Other important factors include appearance retention, fiber type, and static dissipation.

Face weight, also referred to as pile weight or yarn weight, is the weight of the pile yarn in ounces per square yard of carpet. It does not include the weight of the backings or coating. The face weight describes the amount of yarn in the wear surface of the carpet.

The **total weight**, or finished weight, includes the face weight and the weight of backing materials, finishes, and coatings. It is expressed in ounces per square yard of carpet. Total weight is less of an indication of quality than face weight.

Pile density is the weight of pile yarn in a given volume of carpet face. It is determined by the number and size of the tufts. Pile density is the most important selection factor in high traffic installations. For example, nylon is a very durable fiber. However, if the pile density of a nylon carpet is too low, crushing can occur, and although the nylon may succeed in performance, it can fail in appearance.

Average pile density is determined by the following formula:

$$D \text{ (oz/cu yd)} = \frac{36 \times W \text{ (oz/sq yd)}}{T \text{ (in)}}$$

[D (oz/cu yd) ÷ 26,944.67 = g/cu cm], in which D is the density, W is the pile yarn weight, and T is the pile height or thickness.

Pile yarn is the most expensive component in carpet manufacturing. For a given weight, a lower pile height and a higher pile density provide the greatest performance value. The industry standard for measuring aver-

TABLE 4.17   SUGGESTED PHYSICAL REQUIREMENTS OF FINISHED
COMMERCIAL CARPET

Characteristic	Requirement (based on finished carpet)	Test Method
Average pile yarn weight(ounces/square yard)	No less than −6% as specified	ASTM D 418
Tufts/square inch	As specified	ASTM D 418
Pile height and/or pile height differential	As specified	ASTM D 418
Tuft bind	10.0 pounds-force (44.5 N) for loop pile only (minimum average value)	ASTM D 1335
Dry breaking strength	100 pounds-force (445 N) (minimum average value)	ASTM D 2646
Delamination strength of secondary backing	2.5 pounds-force per inch (11.1 N per 25.4 mm) (minimum average value)	ASTM D 3936
Resistance to insects (wool only)	"Resistant"	AATCC—24
Colorfastness to crocking	4 minimum, wet and dry, using AATCC color transference scale	AATCC—165
Colorfastness to light	4 minimum after 40 AFU (AATCC fading units) using AATCC gray scale for color change	AATCC—16E
Electrostatic propensity	3.5 kv (maximum value) for general commercial areas, 2.0 kv (maximum value) for critical environments	AATCC—134
Dimensional tolerance—width	Within 1% of specifications—Physical measurement	

Source: Reprinted with permission from the Carpet and Rug Institute, *Specifier's Handbook.*

age pile yarn weight, tufts per square inch, and average pile density is ASTM D 418 *Standard Methods for Testing Pile Yarn Floor Covering Construction.*

Delamination is the separation of the secondary backing or attached cushion from the primary backing of a carpet. ASTM D 3936 *Standard Test Method for Delamination Strength of Secondary Backing of Pile Floor Coverings* is the standard test used to measure the force required to remove a secondary backing (Figure 4.59). The secondary backing material gives the carpet strength, added body, and the dimensional stability required for stretch-in installations. Problems with adhesion of the secondary backing include stretching, separating at seams, and face fiber loss.

Colorfastness is tested by two methods: resistance to fading by exposure to light and resistance to **crocking**, or rubbing off. AATCC—16 *Colorfastness to Light* and AATCC—165 *Colorfastness to Crocking: Carpets— AATCC Crockmeter Method* are the test methods used to judge carpet colorfastness.

Static generation, or the tendency of a carpet to generate static electricity, is measured by AATCC—134 *Electrostatic Propensity of Carpets.* The

Figure 4.59 ASTM D 3936 is the standard test method used to measure the force required to remove a carpet's secondary backing. Carpet & Rug Institute.

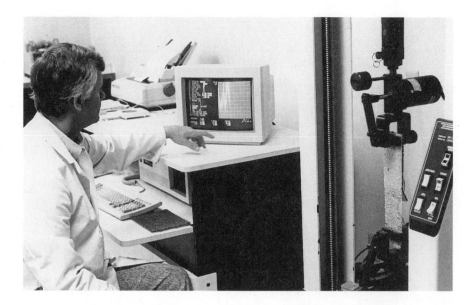

Figure 4.60 ASTM D 1335 describes the test method used to measure the force required to pull out a carpet tuft. Carpet & Rug Institute.

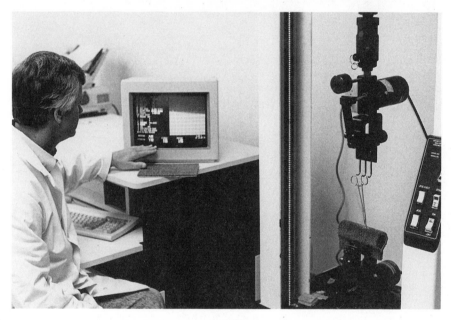

test simulates the actual conditions under which static electricity is commonly generated. A person walks across a carpet while linked to a electrometer, a device that measures voltage build-up. It is important to verify that antistatic carpet is manufactured to be inherently resistant to static. Some carpets are processed with an antistatic treatment that may wash out. However, most incorporate fibers or filaments that have the ability to conduct electrical current, allowing static charges to dissipate.

Tuft bind is the force required to pull a tuft out of a finished carpet. The industry standard for measuring tuft bind is *ASTM D 1335 Standard Test Method for Tuft Bind of Pile Floor Coverings* (Figure 4.60). The result of a low tuft bind in loop pile carpets is that loops formed by a single tufting needle can be pulled out for the length of the yarn. In a cut pile carpet, a low tuft bind can result in the loss of tufts in areas exposed to heavy wear.

Figure 4.61 A Taber Abraser. Taber Industries.

Wear resistance of a carpet, like that of other textiles, is affected by many factors, such as the type and length of the fiber, the structure of the yarn, and the construction of the carpet. Abrasion resistance is sometimes used as a relative measure of a carpet's durability. ASTM D 3884 *Standard Test Method for Abrasion Resistance of Textile Fabrics (Rotary Platform, Double-Head Method)* describes the procedures for the Taber Abraser test, named after the company that manufactures the test equipment (Figure 4.61). In this test, a sample is abraded using a rotary rubbing action. As the sample rotates on a turntable-like platform, two emery wheels rub against the carpet, one rubbing outward and the other, inward toward the center of the sample. The results of the test are typically reported in terms of number of cycles (revolutions of the turntable) required to expose the backing material. Because modern synthetic fibers are highly resistant to abrasive wear, wear resistance is not tested for as often as appearance retention.

Appearance retention tests aim to simulate floor traffic with mechanical devices. Pile appearance changes due to wear are commonly tested by either of two methods: the hexapod tumbler test or the Vettermann Drum Test. The Vettermann Drum Test is defined by ASTM D 5417 *Standard Practice for Operation of the Vettermann Drum Tester*. A steel ball with 14 rubber studs rolls randomly over a carpet sample mounted inside a rotating drum (Figure 4.62). ASTM D 5252 *Standard Practice for the Operation of the Hexapod Drum Tester* describes the requirements for the hexapod (meaning six-legged) test. It is similar to the Vettermann Drum Test, except that a 50-mm (1.97-in) metal cube, with a polyurethane stud screwed into each of its six faces, rolls over the carpet surface.

ACOUSTICAL CONSIDERATIONS

One of the most important contributions of carpet to the appeal of a space is its acoustical properties. These properties are measured in three ways:

Noise Reduction Coefficient (NRC)

Impact Noise Rating (INR)

Impact Insulation Class (IIC)

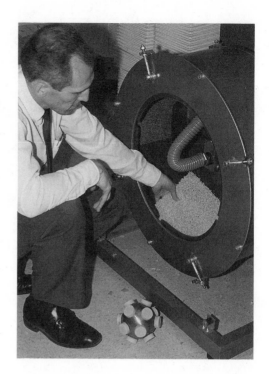

Figure 4.62 The Vetterman Drum Test. Carpet & Rug Institute.

Sound Absorption

The **Noise Reduction Coefficient (NRC)** is the average of four absorption coefficients measured at frequencies from low- to high-pitched sounds and rounded off to the closest 5%. The NRC is determined by ASTM C 423 *Standard Method of Sound Absorption and Sound Absorption Coefficients by the Reverberation Room Method*. The NRC is used in calculating the required amount of sound absorbing material and can be used to compare the sound absorption qualities of one material with another. The higher the NRC, the greater the sound absorption.

Cut pile carpets are somewhat more effective in absorbing sound than loop piles. The fiber content of the carpet has little effect on its ability to absorb sound.

Noise Transmission

The **Impact Noise Rating (INR)** or **Impact Insulation Class (IIC)** measures the sound insulation of a floor and ceiling assembly. Impact noises created on the floor surface of the assembly are recorded by a microphone in an isolated room below. The higher the value, the less noise is transmitted. An IIC value can be estimated by adding 51 to the INR value.

CARPET FIBER CHARACTERISTICS

The pile fiber type plays an important part in the carpet selection process. A successful carpet installation is heavily dependent on matching the application to the appropriate fiber. Fibers are discussed in greater detail in "Textiles and Leather" in Chapter 3.

Acrylic

One of the first synthetic fibers to be used successfully in the production of carpet, acrylic was once very popular for such use. Acrylic is always used as a staple fiber and has many of the characteristics of wool, including resistance to chemicals and to fading caused by sunlight.

Nylon

Nylon is the most popular carpet fiber used today. Since its introduction in 1947, nylon has evolved through five generations of carpet fibers, improving resistancy to soil and static generation. Many types of nylon are available, each with its own performance attributes. Because of nylon's excellent durability, appearance retention is a concern. Long before a nylon carpet wears out, its appearance can be permanently ruined.

Polypropylene

Polypropylene is the lightest commercial carpet fiber. Polypropylenes are known for their excellent stain and mildew resistance, low moisture absorbency, excellent colorfastness in sunlight, and high strength. Olefin is a polypropylene. Polypropylene is commonly used in outdoor carpeting.

Polyester

Polyester fibers are known for their color clarity and their ability to retain color. More popular for residential carpet applications than for commercial uses, polyester has a luxurious feel.

Wool

Used for centuries in the manufacturing of carpet, wool is still the standard against which other carpet fibers are judged. It is generally the most expensive carpet fiber and is commonly used in woven carpets. The outer layer of wool fiber is scaly, which diffuses light, thus hiding soil. The inner core is composed of long, rounded cells that provide the elasticity essential for excellent appearance retention.

When exposed to flame, wool chars, rather than melting like most synthetic fibers, making it naturally flame resistant.

Sisal

Sisal is a strong, woody fiber produced from the leaves of the agave plant, which is found in Central America, the West Indies, and Africa. Used mostly in twine and rope, it has become a popular contemporary flooring fiber.

COLORING

Carpet coloring is accomplished by predyeing the carpet fibers before the carpet is manufactured, or postdyeing the finished piece of carpet. Most carpet is postdyed, because this process allows manufacturers to respond quickly to the needs of the market.

Predyeing Methods

In the manufacturing of synthetic fibers, when dye is combined with the fiber chemicals before the extrusion process, it is called **solution dyeing**. The color of solution-dyed yarn is consistent throughout the fiber. Solution-dyed yarns have excellent colorfastness qualities, against both sunlight and crocking, and can withstand cleaning with harsh chemicals. Polyester and nylon are sometimes solution dyed, but polypropylene is the fiber most commonly dyed in this manner. Solution-dyed yarn holds a large share of the commercial market but only a small portion of the residential market.

Stock dyeing, the oldest method of fiber coloring, is still popular for wool. Staple fibers are placed in large kettles, and the dye is circulated through the fiber. Stock dyeing applies the color to the staple fibers before they are spun into yarn. The color of stock-dyed yarns varies slightly from batch to batch. During the spinning operation, fibers from different dye lots are combined, providing a depth of color not achievable with solution dyed fibers.

Skein dyeing is a coloring process that applies color after the fibers have been spun into yarn. Skein dyeing is labor-intensive and has limited dye lot capacities. These factors can result in higher dyeing costs than other methods. Skein dyeing is commonly used in dyeing yarn for woven carpets.

Postdyeing Methods

The application of color to **greige** (pronounced gray) goods, or undyed carpet, immersed in a dye bath is called **piece dyeing**. After the carpet has been tufted onto its primary backing, and before a secondary backing has been attached, the carpet is dyed. Piece dyeing is generally used for solid-color carpets, but a limited range of patterns are possible by the use of fibers varying in their propensity to accept different dyes. There are three types of piece dyeing: open beck, jet beck, and continuous.

Open beck dyeing produces about 1,000 yards of dyed carpet. The carpet ends are attached to form a large loop, which is submerged in a dye vat.

Jet beck dyeing achieves a very consistent level of color. Carpet is sewn together end to end, forming a continuous loop placed in large circular tubes called jet becks. The carpet loop is circulated under a jet of dye liquor.

Continuous piece dyeing is faster than beck dyeing. The greige goods travel through a long production line. First, an applicator spreads dye on the greige goods, then the dye is fixed in a steamer, and the piece is washed and dried.

Printing

In some cases, patterns are applied to carpet (printed) after the finishing process. Printed carpet simulates the intricate patterns of woven carpet at a much lower cost. Printing methods include screen printing, similar to that used for textiles, and jet printing. Jet printing utilizes rows of very closely spaced jets which spray the carpet with color as it passes by. The texture of jet printed carpet is often preferred because, unlike screen printing, this process does not crush the carpet pile.

There are two types of carpet installation: stretch-in and adhesive. For broadloom carpet there are three types of adhesive installation: direct glue-down, double glue-down, and the newest installation type, self-stick. Releasable adhesives can facilitate carpet repair or replacement.

STRETCH-IN INSTALLATION

Stretch-in installation is the traditional method of carpet installation whereby the carpet is stretched over a cushion and attached at the perimeter with a tack strip (Table 4.18). This is the most common installation method for residential applications and is used commercially for woven wool carpets and in areas where underfoot comfort and luxury are required (for example, in hotel lobbies and board rooms). Stretch-in applications allow for easy removal and replacement of the carpet and cushion. Because stretch-in carpet is secured only around the perimeter, such installations can ripple, causing problems for disabled persons and may not be appropriate for large areas and heavy commercial or rolling traffic.

Power stretchers are used to put the carpet in tension and stretch it drum tight. The carpet should be stretched to its fullest to withstand changes in temperature and humidity and other stresses. Cushion selection should be coordinated with the carpet manufacturer to ensure that the carpet warranty is not voided.

ADHESIVE INSTALLATION

Direct Glue-down. The most common method of commercial installation, direct glue-down is economical and practical. The carpet is glued directly to the floor without a cushion (Table 4.19). This is the most dimensionally stable installation method and is often required for stair or ramp applications even if different installation methods are specified for other areas of the project. Proper substrate conditions are imperative for a successful glue-down installation. Uneven substrates can cause irregular wear patterns.

TABLE 4.18   REASONS TO SPECIFY A STRETCH-IN CARPET INSTALLATION

- Patterned carpet more easily matched
- More resilient than direct glue-down
- Extends carpet life
- Less crushing and packing of pile
- Adds insulation value (R value)
- Gives higher sound absorbency (NRC) values
- Responds better to vacuuming
- Can be used over floors that may be unacceptable for direct glue-down
- Removal usually costs less than removal of a direct glue-down installation
- Corrective measures, such as seam repair, easier to perform

---

TABLE 4.19   REASONS TO SPECIFY A DIRECT GLUE-DOWN CARPET INSTALLATION

- Cushion cost eliminated
- Labor for direct glue-down usually less expensive
- Suitable for rolling traffic and ramp areas
- Seams more durable because there is no vertical flex
- Buckling minimized in buildings that have heat and air conditioning turned off for extended periods, such as schools, churches, and theaters
- No restretch situations
- Facilitates access to electrical and telephone lines under the floor
- Seam peaking practically eliminated
- Unrestricted as to size of area
- Intricate border and inlay capabilities

If carpet with an attached cushion is installed with the direct glue-down method, the following additional considerations apply:

- Improved appearance retention and foot comfort compared to direct glue-down (with no attached cushion) installations
- Increased delamination strength, improved edge ravel resistance
- Functions as an effective moisture barrier
- Improved thermal and acoustical contribution
- Eliminates second adhesive required for double glue-down installation

Double Glue-down

This installation method combines the underfoot comfort of stretch-in installation with the stability of the direct glue-down method. The carpet cushion is adhered to the floor and the carpet is then glued to the cushion (Table 4.20).

With either the direct or the double glue-down method, traffic before the adhesive has had time to cure can cause the installation to fail. Hardboard or plywood is typically recommended as protection for an adhesive installation. Covering a new adhesive installation with plastic sheeting may prevent proper curing and cause mold or mildew to develop.

Self-stick

This is the latest development in carpet installation techniques. A flexible adhesive layer is applied to the carpet backing and covered with a protective plastic film. The labor involved in adhesive application and the time required to ensure the proper tackiness are eliminated. This type of carpet type typically comes in smaller widths, about 1.8 m (6 ft), for ease of manipulation during layout and installation.

TABLE 4.20   REASONS TO SPECIFY A DOUBLE GLUE-DOWN CARPET INSTALLATION

- Combines the stability of direct glue-down carpet with the cushioning benefits of a separate cushion, stretch-in installation
- Improves carpet appearance retention, foot comfort, and overall performance as compared with direct glue-down
- Simplifies carpet bordering and inlaying
- Suitable for wheeled traffic areas
- Unrestricted as to size of area

CARPET TILE INSTALLATION

There are three methods of carpet tile installation: free lay, full glue, and with a tile that has a preapplied pressure-sensitive adhesive coating (Figure 4.63). In free lay installations, a strip of adhesive is applied about every 4.5m (15 ft) and around the room perimeter. Tiles in those areas are anchored in place and surrounding tiles are butted snugly against each other. Full glue installations should be specified where heavy or wheeled traffic is anticipated. In this case, tiles are typically installed with a "stair-step" technique. The installation grows from the center of the room (Figure 4.64).

CARPET CUSHION

Carpet cushion can significantly increase the acoustic value of the flooring assembly and extend the life of a carpet. Environmental conditions, anticipated traffic, and desired feel underfoot should be considered in the selection of a carpet cushion (Table 4.21). Carpet cushion can be installed under a carpet in the traditional manner or may be factory attached as an integral part of the carpet. Carpet cushions can be categorized by three types: fiber, sponge rubber, and polyurethane foam.

Figure 4.63 Carpet tiles installed in a herringbone pattern emphasize their modularity. Lees modular carpets.

Figure 4.64 Carpet tile installed with a "stair-step" technique.

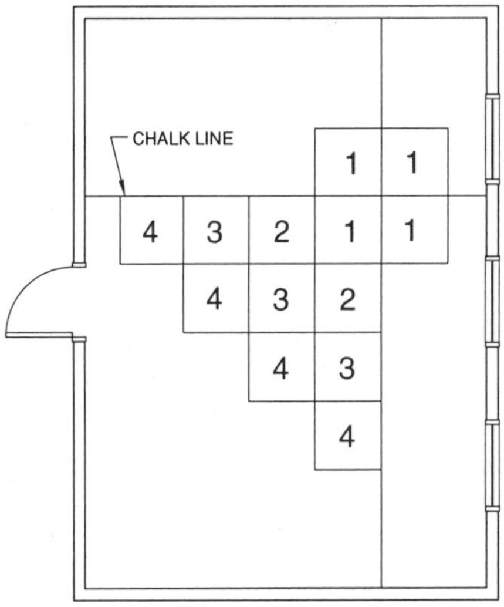

TABLE 4.21 THE CARPET CUSHION COUNCIL'S MINIMUM RECOMMENDED CRITERIA FOR SATISFACTORY CARPET CUSHION PERFORMANCE IN COMMERCIAL INSTALLATIONS

Types of Cushion	Class I—Moderate Traffic	Class II—Heavy Traffic	Class III—Extra Heavy Traffic
Commercial Application	**Office Buildings:** Executive or private offices, conference rooms **Healthcare:** Executive, administration **Schools:** Administration **Airports:** Administration **Retail:** Windows and display areas **Banks:** Executive areas **Hotels/Motels:** Sleeping rooms **Libraries/Museums:** Administration	**Office Buildings:** Clerical areas, corridors (moderate traffic) **Healthcare:** Patients' rooms, lounges **Schools:** Dormitories and classrooms **Retail:** Minor aisles, boutiques, specialty **Banks:** Lobbies, corridors (moderate traffic) **Hotels/Motels:** Corridors **Libraries/Museums:** Public areas (moderate traffic) **Convention Centers:** Auditoriums	**Office Buildings:** Corridors (heavy traffic), cafeterias **Healthcare:** Lobbies, corridors, nurses' stations **Schools:** Corridors, cafeterias **Airports:** Corridors, public areas, ticketing areas **Retail:** Major aisles, checkouts, supermarkets **Banks:** Corridors (heavy traffic), teller windows **Hotels/Motels:** Lobbies and public areas **Libraries/Museums:** Public areas **Country Clubs:** Locker rooms, pro shops, dining areas **Convention Centers:** Corridors and lobbies **Restaurants:** Dining areas and lobbies
FIBER, oz/sq yd			
Natural (hair, jute, etc.)	Wt: 32 oz Th: 1/4" + 5% max.	Wt: 40 oz Th: 5/16" + 5% max.	Wt: 50 oz Th: 3/8" + 5% max.
Synthetic, needled	Wt: 22 oz Th: 1/4" + 5% max.	Wt: 28 oz Th: 5/16" + 5% max.	Wt: 36 oz Th: 3/8" + 5% max.
SPONGE RUBBER, oz/sq yd			
Flat Sponge	Wt: 56 oz Th: .225" + 5% CLD @ 25%: .75 psi	Wt: 64 oz Th: .250" + 5% CLD @ 25%: 1.0 psi	Wt: 80 oz Th: .250" + 5% CLD @ 25%: 1.5 psi
Ripple Sponge	Wt: 64 oz Th: .350" + 5% CLD @ 25%: .75 psi	Wt: 80 oz Th: .400" + 5% CLD @ 25%: 1.0 psi	
Reinforced Foam Rubber	Wt: 56 oz Th: .225" + 5% CLD @ 25%: .75 psi	Wt: 64 oz Th: .235" + 5% CLD @ 25%: 1.0 psi	Wt: 80 oz Th: .250" + 5% CLD @ 25%: 1.5 psi
POLYURETHANE FOAM, lbs/cu ft (pcf)			
Bonded Urethane	Polyester foam content not to exceed 50% Particle size not to exceed 1/2" D: 5.0 pcf ± 5% Th: 3/8" ± 1/32" CLD @ 65%: 4.0 psi	Polyester foam content not to exceed 50% Particle size not to exceed 1/2" D: 6.5 pcf ± 5% Th: 5/16" ± 1/32" CLD @ 65% (3/8"): 5.0 psi	Polyester foam content not to exceed 50% Particle size not to exceed 1/2" D: 8.0 pcf ± 5% Th: 1/4" + 1/32" CLD @ 65% (1"): 7.0 psi
Modified Prime Urethane	D: *2.5 pcf ± 5% Th: 1/4" + 1/32" ILD @ 25%: 100 lb ± 10%	D: *2.7 pcf ± 5% Th: 1/4" + 1/32" ILD @ 25%: 100 lb ± 10%	D: *3.2 pcf ± 5% Th: 3/16" + 1/32" ILD @ 25%: 120 lb ± 10%
Densified Prime Urethane	D: *2.1 pcf Th: .350" ± 1/32" CLD @ 65%: .85 psi	D: *3.5 pcf Th: .265" –.015" + .031" CLD @ 65%: 1.8 psi	D: *4.5 pcf Th: .265" –.015" + .031" CLD @ 65%: 2.3 psi

*Weights are /cu ft polymer density only.

Source: Reprinted with permission of the Carpet Cushion Council, *Selecting the Correct Contract Carpet Cushion for Every Traffic Area,* 1990.

Fiber cushions are made by needlepunching natural fiber, synthetic fiber, or a combination of the two, into a feltlike pad. Antimicrobial treatments are recommended for natural fiber pads because they are susceptible to mold and mildew. Fiber cushions tend to have a firm feel underfoot. Over time, felted fiber cushions may be crushed under heavy wear.

Sponge rubber cushions are either flat sponge, ripple (waffle) sponge, or reinforced foam rubber. Flat sponge rubber cushions provide a firm feel; ripple sponge rubber, a softer feel. Unlike felted fiber cushions, rubber cushions are highly compressible. Reinforced foam rubber has a smaller cell structure than sponge rubber, thus providing more uniform support. Sponge rubber cushions are generally open cell foams.

Open cell foams are made from materials mechanically frothed with air to create a foam that is then cured. The cells are not complete bubbles when cured. Closed cell foams utilize a chemical agent to create a "blown foam" during the curing process. Closed cell foams have, as the term implies, sealed cells or pockets formed by expanding gas. Closed cell foams are typically more resilient than open cell foams.

Polyurethane foam cushion types include bonded, modified prime, and densified prime urethane foam. The chemical compositions of these three types are similar, but their different cellular structures affect their performance. Bonded polyurethane foam (or rebond, as it is sometimes called) is manufactured from scraps of foam bonded together through an adhesive and heat fusion process. Modified prime polyurethane foam is manufactured in a continuous sheet and, unlike densified foam, may contain fillers. Densified foam is denser than modified prime foam and is highly resistant to bottoming out.

Annotated Specification Checklist for Carpet and Carpet Tile

Part 1 GENERAL

SUBMITTALS

Shop Drawings: Show location of seams. Show carpet borders. Show location of transition strips.

Samples: 600-mm (24-in) square of each type of carpet, carpet tile, or carpet cushion.

QUALITY ASSURANCE

Regulatory Requirements: Flame spread of 25 or less; smoke developed, 450 or less. *The flame spread rating, if it is required by the building code, should be included here. A Class A or I rating (a flame spread of 25 or less) is the most commonly required.*

Regulatory Requirements: Critical Radiant Flux Class I, not less than 0.45 W/sq cm as tested by ASTM E 648; *or* Critical Radiant Flux Class II, not less than 0.22 W/sq cm as tested by ASTM E 648. *The Critical Radiant Flux Class, if required by the building code, should be included here.*

DELIVERY, STORAGE, AND HANDLING

Handling: CRI 104, Section 5.

PROJECT CONDITIONS

Environmental Requirements: Comply with manufacturer's written requirements. *Low temperatures can affect the performance of carpet adhesives. Carpet or carpet tile should not be installed until after the relative humidity and temperature in a space are at the levels at which they will be maintained during installation and occupancy.*

Existing Conditions: Test subfloor for moisture and alkalinity. Comply with manufacturer's written requirements. *Moisture is the single greatest cause of adhesive bonding failure. It is a particular problem in new concrete slabs because of the naturally higher moisture content of the curing slab. (Some standard tests for moisture are described on page 155.) Alkaline salts can migrate from a concrete slab to the floor surface. These salts can cause adhesive failure and can be absorbed into the flooring materials. The test for pH levels is relatively quick and inexpensive and is described on page 156.*

MAINTENANCE

Extra Materials: Packaged and labeled. *Extra carpet is frequently used to patch stained or worn areas and should be required, especially if the material is custom-designed or special ordered. Be specific about how much extra material will be required and where it will be stored.*

PART 2 PRODUCTS

MATERIALS

Carpet:

Manufacturer: _____.

Color: _____.

Pattern: _____.

Fiber Content: _____.

Gauge: _____.

Stitches: _____.

Total Weight: _____.

Pile Type: _____. *Specify pile type for tufted carpet.*

Pile Height: _____ per ASTM D 418.

Surface Pile Weight: _____.

Carpet Cushion:

Material: _____. *Refer to table 4.21 (page 204) to select a cushion appropriate to the application.*

Weight: _____. *Specify weight only for fiber carpet and sponge rubber carpet cushions.*

Density: _____ per ASTM D 3574. *Specify density only for urethane foam carpet cushion.*

Thickness: _____. *Specify thickness for all types of carpet cushion.*

Adhesives: Comply with manufacturer's written requirements.

PART 3 EXECUTION

EXAMINATION

Verification of Conditions: Verify that subfloor complies with carpet manufacturer's written requirements. *Proper subfloor preparation is crucial to the success of a carpet installation.*

PREPARATION

Surface Preparation: Level subfloor.

Acclimatize Carpet: Unroll carpet and carpet cushion in the space in which it is to be installed, not less than 12 hours prior to the beginning of installation.

INSTALLATION

Direct Glue-down: CRI 104, Section 8.
Double Glue-down: CRI 104, Section 9.
Stretch-in: CRI 104, Section 11.
Stair: CRI 104, Section 12.
Carpet Tile: CRI 104, Section 13.

PROTECTION

Protection: CRI 104, Section 15.

SCHEDULES

The schedule of floor coverings is usually given in a finish schedule included either in the specifications or on the drawings.

Furniture and Furnishings

CASEWORK

The term *casework* is not strictly defined but is generally used to mean cabinets, cases, fixtures, and other storage units that are built in or attached to a base building. Casework can be custom designed and built for a specific project or can be selected from prebuilt stock items manufactured in standard sizes. The Architectural Woodwork Institute (AWI) refers to custom-built casework as *architectural cabinets*; prebuilt casework is referred to as *modular casework*.

Custom Casework

The AWI and the Woodwork Institute of California (WIC) define three grades of custom casework: premium, custom, and economy (Figure 5.1). AWI defines the grading criteria and cabinet construction (Table 5.1) in Section 400, "Architectural Cabinets," of the *Architectural Woodwork Quality Standards*.

Premium grade casework is of the highest quality workmanship, materials, and installation. If wood veneers are used, they are matched across doors and drawer faces and balance or center matched across the face of an individual cabinet. If a cabinet is faced with plastic laminate, it must be 0.7-mm- (.028-in-) thick high pressure decorative laminate (HPDL). Dovetail or doweled drawer joints are used, and combination metal and roller bearing drawer slides are required for drawer hardware. Recessed standards or multiple holes are required for adjustable shelf supports.

Custom grade accounts for the vast majority of casework and represents a good quality of workmanship and materials. The wood veneer grain must be continuous across the doors of an individual cabinet or, in a plastic laminate-faced cabinet, must be either HPDL or thermoset decorative laminate. See "Plastics" in Chapter 3 for further discussion on thermoset decorative laminates. The drawer joint construction is a lock

TABLE 5.1   TYPES OF CABINET CONSTRUCTION

Cabinet Construction	Description	Example of Cabinet Face
Flush Overlay	Doors and drawer faces cover the cabinet body (the most common type of cabinet face).	
Reveal Overlay	Doors and drawer faces partially cover the cabinet body.	
Flush Inset	Doors and drawer faces are inset within cabinet members. (This is a custom-made cabinet construction and not available in prebuilt cabinets.)	

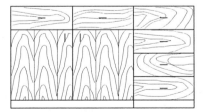

Custom Grade

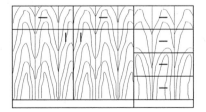

Premium Grade

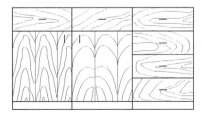

Economy Grade

Figure 5.1 Direction and matching of wood veneer grain for the three grades of architectural cabinets. AWI, Architectural Woodwork Institute, 1952 Isaac Newton Square, Reston, VA 22090.

shoulder joint, and the drawer hardware is the same as for the premium grade. Multiple holes are used if the casework has adjustable shelves.

Economy grade refers to casework of an acceptable quality and is usually selected when cost is the primary consideration. Veneer matching on a cabinet face is not required. If a plastic laminate face is desired, it need be only a thermoset decorative laminate finish. A square shoulder joint that is nailed or stapled is required for drawer joints, and plastic roller or friction glides are acceptable for drawer hardware. Surface-mounted standards are used if the cabinet design incorporates adjustable shelves.

Prebuilt Casework

There is an inherent affordability in mass produced items. Through standardization of parts, materials, and dimensions, good quality casework can be produced for far less than custom-made cabinets. In using prebuilt casework, standard-size cabinets are selected to fit a space as well as possible. Filler strips, which are finished to match the cabinet face, are used to compensate for the difference. Most manufacturers can accommodate requests for custom cabinets or special features, but only to a limited extent.

For prebuilt, modular cabinets, the Kitchen Cabinet Manufacturers Association has sponsored ANSI A161.1 *Recommended Performance and Construction Standards for Kitchen and Vanity Cabinets*. This is a minimum standard and does not classify cabinets by quality. The finest quality casework can pass the tests of this standard, as can the more affordable cabinets that can be purchased at a hardware store. ANSI A161.1 tests structural and impact loading of shelves and cabinet bottoms, door and drawer operation, and the heat and chemical resistance of the cabinet finish.

The AWI describes the construction, material, and finish criteria for prebuilt cabinets in Section 1600, "Modular Cabinets," of the *Architectural Woodwork Quality Standards*. Unlike the ANSI A161.1, this standard does not test the completed cabinet. It specifies minimum thicknesses for cabinet members, lumber and panel products, drawer materials and construction, and cabinet hardware, among other things.

Countertops

Although natural materials such as stone, ceramic tile, and wood are used as countertop surfaces, high pressure decorative laminate (HPDL), commonly referred to as plastic laminate, remains the most popular choice (see page 100). It is comparatively affordable, wears beautifully, and is available in an unlimited number of colors. ANSI A162.2 *Performance Standard for Fabricated High Pressure Decorative Laminate Countertops* is the performance standard for fabricated countertops.

HPDL countertops are fabricated by adhering plastic laminate to a substrate. Particleboard is often preferred as a substrate because it has a fine, smooth face without imperfections that could telegraph through the plastic laminate. Exterior grade plywood is preferred for countertops exposed to liquids or high humidity because of its increased resistance to moisture. A backer sheet is applied to the unexposed, underside of the substrate to prevent warping and dimensional instability in changing temperature or humidity. A number of different edge details can be achieved by varying the profile of the substrate.

The National Electrical Manufacturers Association (NEMA) publishes the standard for HPDLs — NEMA LD 3 *High Pressure Decorative Laminates*. The three types of HPDL sheets defined by NEMA LD 3 are as follows:

GP, General Purpose. Used for countertops

BK, Backer. Economical, nondecorative sheets used on the underside of a countertop to prevent the substrate from warping because of changes in temperature or humidity

PF, Postforming. Used for tightly radiused curves, e.g., at the edge of a formed countertop

These designations are typically followed by the sheet's thickness in hundredths of an inch. For example, *GP50* means General Purpose type HPDL that is 0.050 in thick.

The most recent development in plastic laminate technology is *colorthrough* laminates. These HPDLs are a solid color through the thickness of the sheet. This eliminates the problem of the HPDL's brown kraft paper core showing when the cut edge is exposed. Colorthrough HPDL is manufactured in thicknesses from 1.3 mm to 1.5 mm (0.050 in to 0.060 in) and must be carefully adhered to the substrate. Because of their high melamine resin content, colorthrough HPDLs can buckle when temperature or humidity shifts. See "Plastics" in Chapter 3 for further discussion on plastic laminates.

Solid surfacing material can be shaped like solid wood, creating almost limitless variety in countertop edge profiles. It is sometimes referred to by the trade name of one of the first solid surfacing products on the market — Corian, manufactured by Du Pont. Unlike the thin veneer of HPDLs, this material has a uniform pattern and color uniform through its depth. Worn surfaces may go unnoticed.

Annotated Specification Checklist for Casework

PART 1 GENERAL

SUBMITTALS

Casework Shop Drawings
Countertop Shop Drawings
Samples: Casework finish face.
Samples: Countertop material.

QUALITY ASSURANCE

Plastic Laminate Countertops: ANSI A161.1. *This standard is specified in Part 1 because it includes HPDL, substrate, and workmanship. Only those standards that refer to a material alone are specified in Part 2.*

PROJECT CONDITIONS

Environmental Requirements: Comply with manufacturer's written requirements. *Custom casework can be especially sensitive to fluctuations in humidity and temperature.*

Field Measurements: Verify casework and countertop dimensions before fabrication.

PART 2 PRODUCTS

MATERIALS

Prebuilt Casework: ANSI A161.1.

　　Manufacturer: _____.
　　Model: _____.

Plastic Laminate Countertop: ANSI A161.2.

High Pressure Decorative Laminate: NEMA LD 3.

　　Color: _____.
　　Pattern: _____.

Thermoset Decorative Panels: ALA-1988.

　　Color: _____.
　　Pattern: _____.

FABRICATION

Custom Casework: AWI, *Architectural Woodwork Quality Standards*, Section 400, Architectural Cabinets.

　　Premium grade.
　　Custom grade.
　　Economy grade.

PART 3 EXECUTION

INSTALLATION

Install casework and countertops level and plumb.
Install casework so that doors and drawers are fully operational.

ADJUSTING

Adjust hardware so that doors and drawers operate smoothly without racking.

FILE CABINETS

Even though the advent of the paperless office has been heralded, meeting the demand for file storage remains a priority. File cabinets can be categorized in two basic types: the traditional vertical files and the more contemporary lateral files. Vertical file cabinets are one drawer wide and range in height from two to five drawers (Figure 5.2). A lateral file is defined as a file cabinet whose width is greater than its depth (Figure 5.3). Because of their proportions, lateral files are often integrated into the office setting as credenzas or space dividers.

Good quality commercial grade files have several features that make for a durable, safely operating cabinet. Interlock devices ensure that only one file drawer can be opened at a time. This safety feature protects the stability of the cabinet and prevents it from falling over because of an unbalanced load. Leveling feet are an important feature in a file cabinet. File cabinets are sometimes leveled after they are filled with files in case the floor deflects slightly under the load. If it is not level and plumb, a fully loaded cabinet can twist over time, causing structural damage to the cabinet frame.

File cabinets are often anchored to the wall, floor, or adjacent cabinets to increase their stability when the top drawers are fully extended. Counterweights, located in the bottom rear of a cabinet are also available to prevent it from tipping over.

Figure 5.2 Four-high vertical files. Steelcase.

Figure 5.3 A wall of lateral files of various heights. Steelcase.

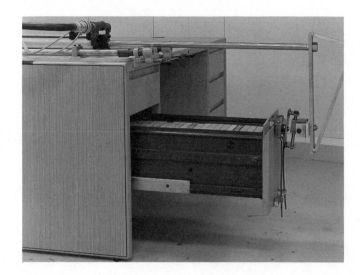

Figure 5.4 File drawer being tested. Steelcase.

The Business and Institutional Furniture Manufacturers Association (BIFMA) sponsors two standards for file cabinets: ANSI X5.2 *Lateral Files Tests* and ANSI X5.3 *Vertical Files Tests*. These standards test a file cabinet in its least stable position. The top drawer is fully extended and loaded to determine whether the cabinet could tip over and possibly injure someone (Figure 5.4). Other tests include static load applications, to determine whether structural damage could occur to the cabinet frame, and life-cycle testing to demonstrate endurance.

Annotated Specification Checklist for File Cabinets

PART 1 GENERAL

SUBMITTALS

Samples: File cabinet finish.

Samples: Countertop finish. *Include this requirement if countertops are specified on top of lateral files.*

QUALITY ASSURANCE

Performance Requirements for Lateral Files: ANSI X5.2.

Performance Requirements for Vertical Files: ANSI X5.3.

PROJECT CONDITIONS

Field Measurements: Verify and coordinate with installation of file cabinets. *Require field measurements where file cabinets are designed as built-ins; for example, if they will be flush with a corridor wall.*

PART 2 PRODUCTS

MANUFACTURED UNITS

Item Code: _____. *The item code is used on the drawings and schedules to indicate a particular chair.*

Manufacturer:_____.

Model Name:_____.

Model Number:_____.

Color:_____.

Height:_____.

Width:_____.

Depth: _____.

ACCESSORIES

Inserts:_____.

Counterweights: _____.

Keys: _____.

PART 3 EXECUTION

INSTALLATION

Install level and plumb.

ADJUSTING

Level after cabinet has been fully loaded..

The chair has been singled out as the most critical comfort factor in the contemporary workplace. Back and arm aches, fatigue, and decreased productivity have all been associated with inadequately designed seating. No other piece of office furniture has been the subject of more lawsuits and insurance claims.

The contemporary office chair is a complicated piece of equipment. It accommodates the movement of its user in one of two ways: with a traditional swivel/tilt mechanism or a synchronized tilt mechanism. The standard swivel/tilt allows the seat to spin on its base and to tilt backward for comfort. In a synchronized tilt chair, the back and seat operate independently at different ratios of motion.

There is no single ideal posture for the performance of work. Each user has to find his or her own individual comfort level. Thus, the most important feature of any chair is adjustability. Separate seat and back assemblies are increasingly popular because they allow for maximum adjustability. There are four basic adjustments that allow the user to customize the fit of a chair:

Seat height
Seat tilt
Back height
Back tilt

SEATING

Seating for Work

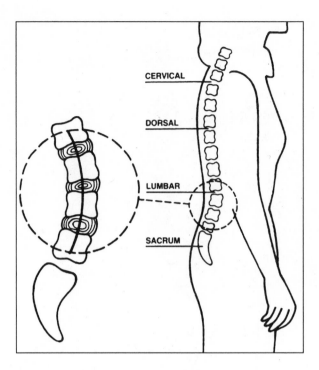

Figure 5.5a The natural curve of the standing spine. The lumbar vertebrae are the five spinal segments above the tailbone. The lumbar region is commonly referred to as the lower back. Fixtures Furniture, KCMO.

CERVICAL

DORSAL

LUMBAR

SACRUM

Seat height adjustments are made either pneumatically or with a mechanical rachet. Automatically adjusting chairs use the weight of the user to lower the seat once the pneumatic cylinder is engaged. The ease with which a pneumatic cylinder can be replaced should be considered in selecting this type of chair. Mechanically adjusted seats are twirled clockwise to lower them and counterclockwise to raise them. An adjustable seat height ensures that the seat is the right height from the floor, the user has enough knee clearance, and the user's eyes and elbows are at the right heights for the work surface.

Seat tilt, in conjunction with back tilt, works to maintain an angle of up to 135° between the torso and the thigh. This angle promotes the natural curvature of the lower spine in which the pressure is evenly distributed on the lumbar vertebrae (Figure 5.5). The use of a "waterfall" front seat edge helps promote circulation in the lower thigh and leg.

Back height adjustments allow the user to position the backrest to properly and comfortably support the lumbar area. Some chairs allow for the adjustment of the seat depth by moving the backrest inward.

Back tilt flexibility allows the user to lean back in the chair and stretch. The Human Factors Society (see "Performance and Design Standards," page 220) recommends an adjustable back that ranges from 90° to 105°. The back tilt tension is often adjustable.

TYPES OF OFFICE SEATING

Office seating lines are usually available in several design variations. The same visual characteristics are incorporated into a variety of styles that reflect different levels of management. The terms used to describe these differences vary among manufacturers. The categories generally include a

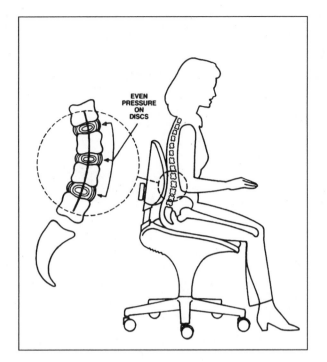

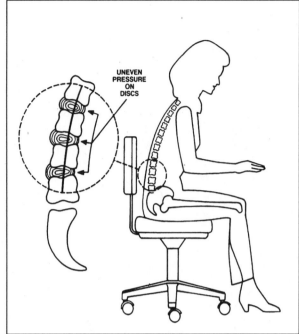

Figure 5.5b The sitting spine. The natural curve of the lower spine is maintained with a forward tilt seat and lumbar support. Fixtures Furniture, KCMO.

Figure 5.5c The nontiltable seat and straight back flatten the spine, exerting excessive pressure on the spinal discs. Fixtures Furniture, KCMO.

side or guest chair, task chair, one or two levels of seating for managers, and an executive chair.

1. A *side chair* or *guest chair* is placed in an office for the use of visitors. It is designed with the expectation that the time a person is seated will be brief and that no tasks requiring posture support will be performed. A side chair does not have casters. A pedestal, four-legged, or glide base are the typical options for the chair base. Side chairs do not have adjustable features.

2. *Task seating* (sometimes referred to as "secretarial" or "operational" seating) is designed to support typing and clerical tasks requiring extensive upper body movement, such as filing. A chair of this type usually has detachable arms and a low back (Figures 5.6a, 5.6b, and 5.6c).

3. A *management* chair may have a low or high back and a wider, thicker seat than one used for task seating. Arms are almost always standard for a management chair. It is designed to support entry- through mid-level managers who spend part of a day working at their desk or keyboard and part of their day conferring (Figure 5.6d).

4. An *executive* chair is a larger-scale chair with arms. It has a wider, thicker seat and higher back to impart an image of authority. Leather is a common upholstery option. Such chairs are not designed for the continuous, repetitive, movements of the average worker; they support computing, conferring, and telephoning. They are also appropriate for use in conference and boardrooms (Figure 5.6e).

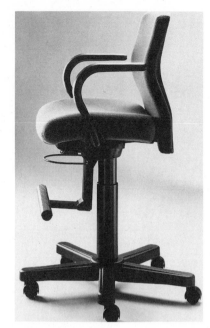

Figure 5.6a High task chair with arms. The Bulldog Chair, courtesy of The Knoll Group.

Figure 5.6b Task chair. The Bulldog Chair, courtesy of The Knoll Group.

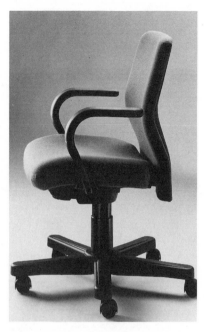

Figure 5.6c Operational armchair. The Bulldog Chair, courtesy of The Knoll Group.

Figure 5.6d Management chair. The Bulldog Chair, courtesy of The Knoll Group.

Figure 5.6e Executive chair with leather upholstery. The Bulldog Chair, courtesy of The Knoll Group.

CASTER AND GLIDE SELECTION

Two types of casters are popular for use on chair bases: dual wheel and hooded (Figures 5.7a and 5.7b). The caster wheel is made of either hard or soft plastic, typically nylon. The selection of caster material is based in part on the type of flooring that will be used under the chair.

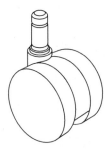

Figure 5.7a Dual wheel casters have two independent wheels to increase mobility and decrease wear on the flooring. Courtesy Herman Miller, Inc., TMI.

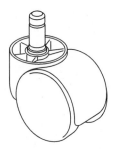

Figure 5.7b Hooded casters offer protection from dust and impact. Courtesy Herman Miller, Inc., TMI.

 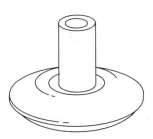 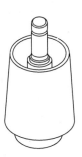

Figure 5.8a, b, c Permanent indentation of the flooring material can be minimized with the use of wide-based glides. Courtesy Herman Miller, Inc.

Hard casters are used on soft floorings such as carpet or carpet tile. The use of a rigid caster increases the chair's mobility on a carpeted surface. When selecting casters that will be used only on carpet floors, keep the following guidelines in mind: hard casters with slightly rounded wheel edge profiles tend to have better carpet wear characteristics than those with square edges, and hard rubber casters tend to mark a carpet more than plastic casters. Soft casters are used on hard or resilient floorings to help control the roll of the chair.

Glides are typically specified for chairs that will not be moved repeatedly or are required to remain stationary. Wide-based glides help distribute the weight of the chair and prevent the permanent indentation of a floor finish (Figures 5.8a, 5.8b, and 5.8c). Glides may reduce the height of the chair.

PERFORMANCE AND DESIGN STANDARDS

BIFMA X5.1 *Test for General-Purpose Office Chairs* evaluates the safety, durability, and structural adequacy of office seating (Figure 5.9). It tests the chair's ability to withstand the load of its user dropping into it, caster durability, swivel cycling, and tilt mechanism. It is a minimum standard; chairs either pass or fail. The standard does not grade or rank chairs.

Figure 5.9 BIFMA X5.1 *Test for General-Purpose Office Chairs* evaluates the durability of office seating. Steelcase.

The Human Factors Society sponsors ANSI 100 *Human Factors Engineering of Visual Display Terminal Workstations*. Among the seating features required by this standard are the following:

Adjustable task arms to support the user's forearms and a distance between armrests of at least 462 mm (18.2 in)

Adjustable seat height range of 406 mm to 520 mm (16 in to 20½ in)

Seat depth that permits contact with the seat back in the lumbar region

Seat cushion at least 462 mm (18.2 in) wide

A fixed back angle of 90° or more, or an adjustable back that ranges from 90° to 105°

Upholstered Seating

An upholstered armchair, love seat, or sofa can warm a commercial interior with an invitation to sit, spend a moment, and relax. Commonly used in reception areas and executive offices, upholstered seating provides comfort and style. There are four construction components that must be considered when evaluating upholstered seating: the frame, the suspension system, the cushions, and the upholstery material.

FRAME

The frame gives an upholstered piece its structure and form. Kiln-dried hardwood provides a dimensionally stable frame foundation. The frame can be assembled with screws, nails, staples, and glue; however, a combination of mortise and tenon and double-doweled joints is often used in the most durable seating construction. Seat joints should be reinforced with corner blocks that are glued and screwed in place for added strength. For finer seating units, the portions of the frame that will be exposed are machine sanded and then hand sanded to ensure a smooth, scratch-free surface (Figure 5.10).

Some furniture manufacturers prestain the sanded wood frame to verify that there are no scratches. The prestain must be completely sanded off before the desired stain is applied by hand with either a rag or a brush (Figure 5.11). Sealer is applied after the wood is stained, preparing the surface to receive the finish coats. Catalyzed urethane is a popular choice for fine wood finishes, because it is extremely hard and resistant to water, alcohol, and scratches (Figure 5.12). Between each coat, the wood may be scuff sanded to raise the grain of the wood and to ensure good adhesion.

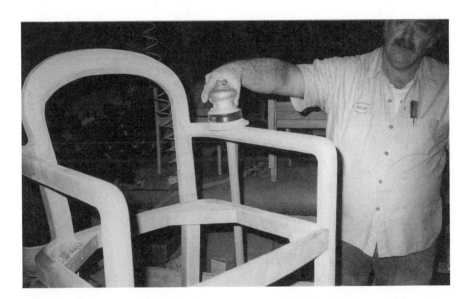

Figure 5.10 The first step in finishing a fine piece of wood furniture is machine sanding. Glued and screwed corner blocks provide additional strength where the seat meets the legs. David Edward, Baltimore, MD.

Figure 5.11 Stain is hand applied with a rag. David Edward, Baltimore, MD.

Figure 5.12 The finish coat is spray applied in a ventilated finishing booth. David Edward, Baltimore, MD.

SUSPENSION SYSTEMS

Much as a box spring is crucial to the proper support of a mattress, a chair's suspension system provides a firm foundation for the cushions. Several types of springing and webbing systems are combined to achieve the desired support in the seat and back.

Springing systems are used in conjunction with webbing to provide greater resilience and longer wear. There are two common springing systems—coil spring and Marshall units—each of which is supported by a webbing system. Eight-way hand-tied coil springs (Figure 5.13) is the most expensive, labor-intensive, and durable springing system. The springs are held together with springing twine that is laced through the top of the spring and tied to adjacent springs in eight directions (Figure 5.14). This integrates the coils, forming a uniform surface of support. Marshall, or innerspring, units are springs that are contained inside individual pockets of muslin or burlap. Marshall units are purchased joined together, ready to be used as a springing system (Figure 5.21).

There are five webbing systems that are commonly used for commercial seating: woven decking, webbing tape, corrugated steel, wire mesh, and sinuous spring. Rubberized, woven decking is stretched taut across the frame and stapled in place, providing a firm but resilient base for cushions (Figure 5.15). Interwoven webbing tape, made of jute, cotton, or rubber, provides support directly for cushions or for coil springs (Figure 5.16). Corrugated steel bands are often used to support coil springs in an eight-way hand-tied suspension system (Figure 5.17). Plastic-covered wire mesh grids can be stretched across the seating frame for a more affordable suspension system. One of the most popular webbing systems is sagless, or sinuous, springs. This "wiggle wire" is linked together by small helical springs (Figure 5.18).

CUSHIONS

Polyurethane foam is the first choice for seating cushions. Multiple grades and densities of foam are usually bonded together to achieve the desired

Figure 5.13 Eight-way hand-tied coil springs. David Edward, Baltimore, MD.

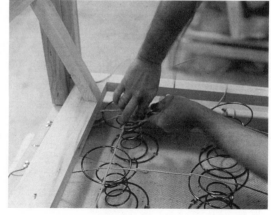

Figure 5.14 Coil springs are tied together in eight directions with springing twine. David Edward, Baltimore, MD.

Figure 5.15 Chair back and sides with rubberized, woven decking and an eight-way hand-tied seat. David Edward, Baltimore, MD.

Figure 5.16 Webbing tape is interwoven as a suspension systems for coil springs or for cushions. David Edward, Baltimore, MD.

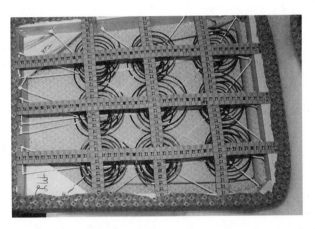

Figure 5.17 Corrugated steel bands are used to support coil springs in an eight-way hand-tied suspension system. David Edward, Baltimore, MD.

Figure 5.18 Sinuous springs are connected by small helical springs.

feel. For example, softer foams may be laminated to harder foams to provide surface softness along with firm support. Cushions can be preupholstered in muslin or bonded polyester to increase the life of the upholstery material. There are three basic properties that affect the performance of a polyurethane foam: density, the Indentation Force Deflection, and the Compression Modulus.

1. **Density** is a measurement of the mass per unit volume, expressed in kg/m^3 (lb/ft^3) (Figure 5.19). Density is the most important foam property and determines the durability and support of the foam. The greater the foam density is, the greater is the support. Density is not a measurement of firmness; high-density foams can be quite soft. Water, for example, has a high density. Typically, higher-density foams are more expensive than low-density foams.

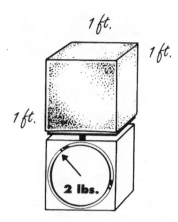

Figure 5.19 Foam density calculation. Flexible polyurethane foam density is measured in pounds per cubic foot. Copyright © 1995 Polyurethane Foam Association.

$$\text{Density} = \frac{\text{Weight (mass)}}{\text{Length} \times \text{Width} \times \text{Height (volume)}}$$

2. The **Indentation Force Deflection (IFD)** is a measure of the foam firmness and is independent of density. It is determined by indenting the foam a percentage of its original height and noting the required force. IFD is an indication of comfort. A 25% IFD (indenting the foam 25% of its original height) is used to measure the surface feel of a foam. The less force required to compress the foam, the softer it is. For upholstery, 25% IFD can range from 2.2 kg to 22 kg (5 lb to 50 lb).

3. The **Compression Modulus**, or support factor, is an indication of the foam's support and is primarily a function of the type of foam. The Compression Modulus is calculated by taking a second IFD measurement by indenting the foam 65% of its original height and dividing it by the 25% IFD (Figure 5.20). Typically, the greater the difference between the 25% IFD and the 65% IFD, the more ability the foam has to support weight. To put it another way, the higher the support factor, the better the foam's ability to provide support. In most cases, the higher the foam density, the greater the Compression Modulus.

$$\text{Compression Modulus} = \frac{65\% \text{ IFD}}{25\% \text{ IFD}}$$

Figure 5.20 Foam compression modulus (support factor). The support factor is the ratio of 65% IFD (indentation force deflection) divided by 25% IFD. Copyright © 1995 Polyurethane Foam Association.

UPHOLSTERY MATERIAL

The seating frame, suspension system, and cushions (Figure 5.21) form the foundation that is wrapped in an upholstery material. The direction in which the upholstery fabric is to be applied over the cushions should be specified. A "railroad" application is usually the most efficient use of a fabric. The cushions are upholstered with the selvage edge of the fabric parallel to the seat cushion edge (Figure 5.22). *Run right* and *up-the-bolt* are terms used to describe the traditional method of upholstery application (Figure 5.23).

For fabrics with large patterns, the motif should be centered on each seat and back cushion, and should be continuous down the seat front and sides. Fabrics with a **repeat** (a repeated pattern) or narrower width fabrics will require more yardage than a standard 1370-mm- (54-in-) wide piece of upholstery material. Table 5.2 is a guide to determining approximate yardage. See "Flammability Standards for Furniture" in Chapter 2 for seating fire-test-response characteristics and "Textiles and Materials" in Chapter 3 for fiber and performance criteria of upholstery material.

C.O.M. AND C.O.L.

Seating manufacturers typically supply upholstery fabric options for their chairs. The fabric selections have been tested on their seating and have

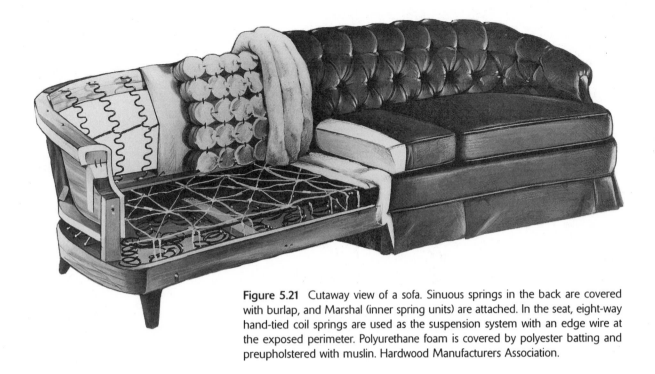

Figure 5.21 Cutaway view of a sofa. Sinuous springs in the back are covered with burlap, and Marshal (inner spring units) are attached. In the seat, eight-way hand-tied coil springs are used as the suspension system with an edge wire at the exposed perimeter. Polyurethane foam is covered by polyester batting and preupholstered with muslin. Hardwood Manufacturers Association.

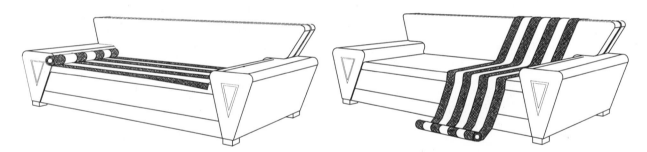

Figure 5.22 Railroaded upholstery fabric.

Figure 5.23 Vertically run upholstery fabric.

TABLE 5.2   APPROXIMATE YARDAGE CALCULATIONS FOR UPHOLSTERY MATERIAL

Fabric Width	Plain Fabric	50 mm–100 mm (2 in–14 in) Repeat	380 mm–480 mm (15 in–19 in) Repeat	510 mm–680 mm (20 in–27 in) Repeat	700 mm–900 mm (28 in–36 in) Repeat
1370 mm (54 in)	0%	10%	15%	20%	25%
1350 mm–1270 mm (53 in - 50 in)	16%	20%	25%	30%	35%
1220 mm (48 in)	16%	25%	30%	35%	40%
1140 mm (45 in)	40%	50%	55%	60%	65%
910 mm (36 in)	50%	60%	65%	70%	75%

Source: David Edward, Baltimore, Maryland.

performed satisfactorily with regard to wear and flammability. Often a designer will find the upholstery selection limiting and will select a fabric from a textile manufacturer. Upholstery material that is not supplied by the seating manufacturer is referred to as "C.O.M." Written approval from the furniture manufacturer is usually required for the use of C.O.M. The furniture manufacturer must verify that the material is acceptable as an upholstery fabric.

C.O.M. is the abbreviation for "customer's own material." (C.O.L. means "customer's own leather.") "Customer" does not refer to the designer's customer. It refers to the manufacturer's customer—the party placing the order—which is the FF&E (furniture, furnishings, and equipment) contractor. The material is purchased separately from the seating and supplied to the furniture manufacturer for application. The FF&E contractor (usually the furniture dealer) is responsible for the acquisition and coordination of C.O.M.

Annotated Specification Checklist
for Seating

PART 1 GENERAL

SUBMITTALS

Samples: Upholstery material.

QUALITY ASSURANCE

Regulatory Requirements: (See "Flammability Standards for Furniture" in Chapter 2.)

MAINTENANCE

Extra Materials: Packaged and labeled, full-width upholstery material. *Extra upholstery material (and possibly casters or pneumatic cylinders) may be required, especially if the material is custom-made or special ordered. Be specific about how much extra material will be required and where it will be stored.*

PART 2 PRODUCTS

MANUFACTURED UNITS

Item Code: _____. *The item code is used on the drawings and schedules to indicate a particular chair.*

    Manufacturer:_____.

    Model Name:_____.

    Model Number:_____.

    Base:_____.

        Casters: _____.

        Glides: _____.

Upholstery Material

*Textile Manufacturer:*_____. *If C.O.M. is selected, verify its applicability with the furniture manufacturer.*

    Textile Designation: _____.
    Fiber Content: _____.
    Colorway: _____.
    Pattern: _____.

Leather Supplier: _____. *If C.O.L. is selected, verify its applicability with the furniture manufacturer.*

    Leather: _____.
    Color: _____.

FABRICATION

Upholstery Material Application: _____. If the upholstery material is patterned, specify how the fabric is to be applied. For example, "railroad fabric"; "match stripes"; or "center motif on seat, back, and arms."

PART 3 EXECUTION

SCHEDULES

The schedule of furniture is usually included either in the specifications or on the drawings.

SYSTEMS FURNITURE

Automated office technologies demand the sophistication of systems furniture. Technology-intensive workstations and the increasing demand for flexibility have made systems furniture the standard for the modern workplace. Telephone, computer, and electrical cables are accessible, facilitating the modifications required as the task or the employee changes. The popularity of systems furniture has been further boosted because, although its panels can function like walls for visual, acoustic, and wiring purposes, it is considered furniture—not construction—and as such can be depreciated for tax purposes.

There are two basic types of systems furniture: free standing and panel-supported. Free-standing systems are independent of surrounding panels and function like floor-supported desks. Furniture components, like screens, can be attached to the worksurface (Figure 5.24) or can be supported by a structural beam (Figure 5.25). Free-standing systems can be surrounded by panels or installed in a space with constructed walls.

Panel-supported systems, the most popular type of systems furniture, hang the worksurfaces, accessories, and other furniture components from panels that form the boundaries of the workstation (Figure 5.26). Wall-

Figure 5.24 Free-standing system utilizing screens that are supported by the desk. Steelcase Context shown. Steelcase.

Figure 5.25 Free-standing beam-based system supports work surfaces, drawers, telephone tables, and other accessories from a structural beam. Herman Miller Burdick Group shown. Courtesy Herman Miller, Inc. Photo: Nick Merrick, Hedrich-Blessing.

Figure 5.26 Panel-supported system utilizes structural panels from which worksurfaces, overhead storage bins, and accessories are hung. Herman Miller Action Office Series 1 shown. Courtesy Herman Miller, Inc. Photo: Jonathan Hillyer.

TABLE 5.3   PANEL CONNECTION METHODS

Type	Disadvantages	Advantages
Nonprogressive	Requires more hardware	Modifications can be made without disturbing adjacent workstations.
Progressive	Shift, or "Creep"	Panel connections are less complicated.

mounted slotted standards are also available so that these systems can be hung on a traditional gypsum wallboard wall. BIFMA has authored a standard for panel-based systems furniture; ANSI X5.6 *Standard for Office Furnishings – Panel Systems* tests the safety of panels and panel-mounted components.

The connection methods for panel-supported systems have ramifications in the design and future modification of workstations. Panel-supported systems furniture is considered either progressive or nonprogressive with regard to the panel-to-panel attachment method (see Table 5.3).

Progressive systems shift, or "creep," when additional panels are added. Panel thicknesses must be accounted for at each connection (Figure 5.27). Perpendicular panel connections require the insertion of a connector, resulting in a shift of all subsequent adjacent panels.

Changes to the configuration of nonprogressive systems can be made without moving existing panels. Because every panel connection requires a connector post, perpendicular panels can be added or removed without disturbing adjacent workstations. Panel widths in nonprogressive systems are measured from centerline to centerline of the connector posts (Figure 5.28).

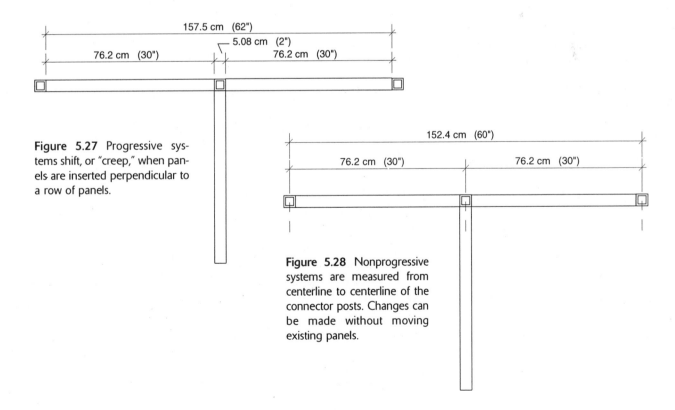

Figure 5.27 Progressive systems shift, or "creep," when panels are inserted perpendicular to a row of panels.

Figure 5.28 Nonprogressive systems are measured from centerline to centerline of the connector posts. Changes can be made without moving existing panels.

Figure 5.29a Panel base power in. Steelcase.

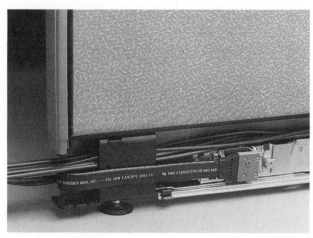

Figure 5.29b Panel base power in with base plate removed. Steelcase Avenir shown. Steelcase.

Wire and Cable

Two types of metallic conductors carrying signals are accommodated by systems furniture raceways: electrical wiring and communications cabling. Wire and cable are distributed from the base building source through the systems furniture to the workstation equipment.

ELECTRICAL WIRING

As equipment costs decrease and the amount of hardware required by each workstation increases, properly assessing the power requirements of a systems furniture installation is of considerable importance. Systems furniture manufacturers provide power in assemblies so that all that is required is the hook up of the panel's electrical wiring conduit, commonly called a "pigtail," to the building's electrical supply (Figures 5.29a and 5.29b). Connections between panels are snapped together, making them easy to install and reconfigure.

Some electrical equipment is vulnerable to disturbances or interferences from other electrical sources. **Dedicated circuits** are used to keep power "clean" or free from these interferences, which can cause problems with sensitive equipment. Although "dedicated" is not defined by the National Electrical Code, the expression is widely used to describe a circuit that does not share a neutral wire, as many three-phase wiring systems do. The use of common neutrals in commercial and industrial situations is standard practice. The neutral return wire carries unbalanced current back to the power source. This can generate interference. Not sharing neutral wires reduces electromagnetic interference, which is caused by a power line acting as an antenna receiving electromagnetic field signals. These electromagnet fields generate an electric current that flows through wiring, creating electrical "noise." **Designated circuits** are circuits reserved for use by specific equipment. These circuits are often used for important equipment that requires a heavy electrical load or that is best isolated from other equipment in case of a power outage.

COMMUNICATIONS CABLING

Clear communication is an important part of success in the business arena. While phone lines are typically stranded wire, computer systems use a variety of other cable types, including twisted pair, coaxial, and shielded cable.

Twisted pair is the traditional, economical type of cable for voice and lower-speed data communication (Figure 5.30a). Each pair of insulated copper wires connects a single signal from one point to another. Twisted pair cables are not suitable for high-speed and video transmissions.

Coaxial cable consists of a single copper wire surrounded by an insulator encased in a metal shell, which acts as a ground return (Figure 5.30b). The insulated return is surrounded by a braided wire or foil shield. This shielding makes coaxial cable relatively immune to interference. Coaxial cable transmits a large amount of data at very high speeds with relatively little signal loss. Broadband coaxial cable systems are used by the cable television industry.

Shielded cable is covered with metal foil to keep out electromagnetic interference (Figure 5.30c). Twisted pair cables are often shielded for improved performance.

Technology continues to evolve, and new developments in communications include fiber optics and wireless networks (radio and infrared transmissions).

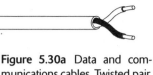

Figure 5.30a Data and communications cables. Twisted pair.

Figure 5.30b Coaxial cable.

Figure 5.30c Shielded cable.

WIRE AND CABLE CONNECTIONS TO SYSTEMS FURNITURE

Wire and cable connections from the base building source to the equipment at the workstation can be made in a variety of ways, depending on the structure of the base building.

Wall receptacles connect wire and cable services from the building to the panel raceway (Figure 5.31a). This connection type severely restricts the system's flexibility. Workstation location relies on proximity to power and data supplies. Relocating wall-mounted junction boxes is labor-intensive and generates a comparatively large amount of construction debris.

Underfloor steel ducts are separate, continuous steel channels cast in the concrete floor slab (Figure 5.31b).

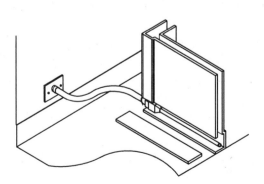

Figure 5.31a Wall receptacles connect wire and cable services from the building to the systems furniture.

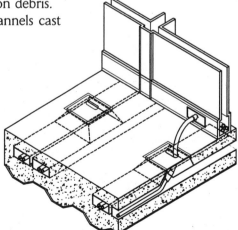

Figure 5.31b Underfloor steel ducts route power and communication cables.

Cellular floors systems separate wire and cable to protect against electromagnetic interference. Outlets are typically concealed, and the floor finish is level without the interruption of floor monuments, or "tombstones," as they are sometimes called (Figure 5.31c).

Access flooring is a structural system of removable floor panels 100 mm to 760 mm (4 in to 30 in) above the structural floor (Figure 5.31d). These floor systems, commonly used for computer rooms, can handle the largest capacities. This is the most flexible distribution system, because virtually every inch of wire and cable can be accessed by the removal of a floor panel. However, it requires adequate ceiling heights to allow for a raised floor.

Poke-through systems access wire and cable sources in the ceiling cavity below the floor (Figure 5.31e). Modifying a poke-through system

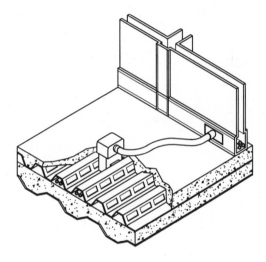

Figure 5.31c Cellular floor systems incorporate raceways in the structural metal deck.

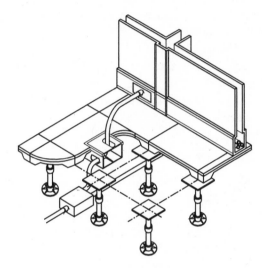

Figure 5.31d Access floors offer direct access for easy reconfiguration of power and communication system connections.

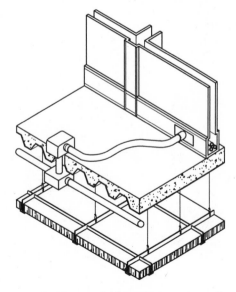

Figure 5.31e Poke-through systems access wire and cable in the ceiling below the floor.

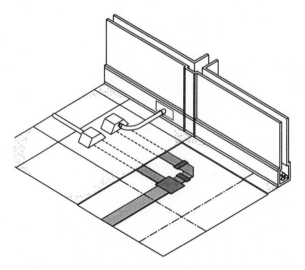

Figure 5.31f Flat wire power distribution is installed directly under carpet tile.

requires the disruption of activities on both floors. Fire-rated assemblies and floor monuments must be used to maintain the fire resistance rating of the floor.

Flat wire is a thin, flexible conductor cable that is so thin that it can be placed directly under the finish flooring (Figure 5.31f). It can be folded or easily joined and there is virtually no disruption to the workplace. Carpet tile is the only finish flooring permitted by the National Electric Code (NEC) for use over flat wire. Flat wire is a new technology and is relatively expensive.

Whereas windows provide daylight, a view, and sometimes ventilation, window treatments function to control light and glare, provide privacy, and act as acoustic buffers. Window treatments are important design elements that can soften a space and bring the outside in.

Window treatments also play a significant role in the energy performance of a building and must be coordinated with heating and cooling load calculations. The energy efficiency of the building and the comfort of its inhabitants are heavily reliant on the proper selection of window treatments. They can be categorized according to two energy-saving functions: shading from solar heat gain in the summer and insulation from building heat loss in the winter. Because these are two very different functions, most treatments are more effective at one than the other.

WINDOW TREATMENTS

Solar radiation is the primary heat source in a commercial building. When sunlight strikes a window, some of the heat energy is reflected and the rest is either absorbed by the glass or transmitted to the interior (Figure 5.32). **Reflected** solar radiation bounces off the surface and does not penetrate the glass. **Absorbed** solar radiation is soaked up by the glass and eventually is dissipated by convection or reradiation. **Transmitted** heat energy penetrates the glass and heats the building's interior.

In 1963, The American Society of Heating, Refrigerating and Air Conditioning Engineers (ASHRAE) established a procedure for estimating the solar heat gain of a window system. **Shading coefficient** (SC) is the term ASHRAE chose to describe a window system's ability to reduce heat gain. The three solar heat gain factors—reflection, absorption, and transmission—determine a window system's SC. The shading coefficient is a function of the entire window system, including the window treatment.

The SC is the ratio between the solar gain through a window system and the gain through clear glass 3 mm (⅛ in) thick under the same conditions. An SC of .22 means that a window system allows 22% of the heat energy transmitted through glass, 3 mm (⅛ in) thick, into the building's interior. The lower the shading coefficient, the better the window system's ability to reduce incoming solar radiation.

The effectiveness of a window treatment to protect against solar heat gain depends on its ability to reflect incoming solar radiation back through the window before it can be converted into heat within the building.

Shading from Solar Heat Gain

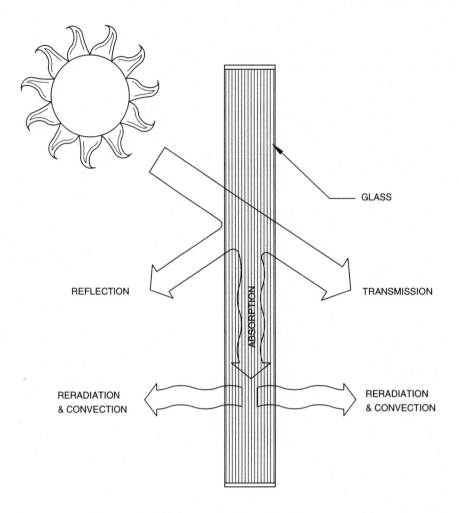

GLASS

REFLECTION

ABSORPTION

TRANSMISSION

RERADIATION
& CONVECTION

RERADIATION
& CONVECTION

Figure 5.32 Radiation = reflection + absorption + transmission.

Because reflectance is the most important property of a window treatment in reducing heat gain, color selection is an important factor. Dark colors tend to absorb heat and light colors reflect it; thus, white and light-colored window treatments are the first choice for reducing heat gain (Table 5.4).

Manufacturers typically provide SCs for window systems using blinds or shades. Probable SCs for unlined draperies with 100% fullness can be estimated by using a guide developed by ASHRAE. Drapery fabrics are classified in terms of their estimated weave density (openness) and yarn color (reflectance). This value is referred to as the Fabric Designator. A Fabric Designator may be, but is not usually, provided by the drapery fabric manufacturer. Visual estimations of openness and reflectance can be made by using Figure 5.33 to classify a drapery material. The Fabric Designator and the type of window glazing are used to estimate the SC of a window system with draperies. These values are approximate, and other factors may have to be considered. The ASHRAE Handbook, *Fundamentals,* and an HVAC engineer should be consulted in determining the SC of a window system.

Emissivity can be thought of as the counterpart to reflectivity. If a surface has high reflectivity, it has low emissivity. **Low emissivity** (low-E) surfaces allow the visible spectrum of light through while reflecting back a

TABLE 5.4 SHADING COEFFICIENTS FOR INSULATING GLASS WITH INDOOR SHADING BY VENETIAN BLINDS OR ROLLER SHADES

Notice that for insulating glass with a heat-absorbing outer pane and a clear inner pane (the second row in the table) a white opaque roller shade is significantly more effective in reducing solar heat gain than a dark-colored one.

Type of Glass	Nominal Thickness Each Light	Solar Transmittance[a] Outer Pane	Inner Pane	Venetian Blinds[b] Medium	Light	Roller Shade Opaque Dark	White	Translucent Light
Clear out	³⁄₃₂, ⅛ in.	0.87	0.87	0.62[c]	0.58[e]	0.71	0.35	0.40
Clear in				(0.63)[d]	(0.58)[d]			
Clear in	¼ in.	0.80	0.80					
Heat-absorbing[e] out	¼ in.	0.46	0.80	0.39	0.36	0.40	0.22	0.30
Clear in								
Reflective coated glass	SC = 0.20[f]			0.19	0.18			
	= 0.30			0.27	0.26			
	= 0.40			0.34	0.33			

Table refers to factory-fabricated units with ³⁄₁₆, ¼, or ½-in. air space, or to prime windows plus storm windows.

[a] Refer to manufacturers' literature for exact values.
[b] For vertical blinds with opaque white or beige louvers, tightly closed, SC is approximately the same as for opaque white roller shades.

[c] From Van Dyck and Konen (1982), for 45° open venetian blinds, 35° solar incidence, and 35° profile angle.
[d] Values for closed venetian blinds. Use these values only when operation is automated for solar gain reduction (as opposed to day-light use).
[e] Refers to bronze, or green tinted, heat-absorbing glass.
[f] SC for glass with no shading device.

Source: Reprinted by permission of the American Society of Heating, Refrigerating and Air-Conditioning Engineers, Atlanta, Georgia, from the 1993 ASHRAE *Handbook—Fundamentals.*

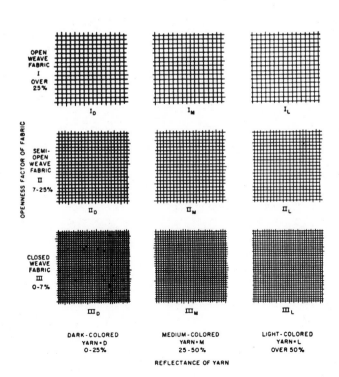

Figure 5.33 ASHRAE Classification of drapery fabrics. Reprinted by permission of the American Society of Heating, Refrigerating and Air-Conditioning Engineers, Atlanta, GA, from the 1993 ASHRAE *Handbook—Fundamentals.*

large portion of the thermal radiation, which makes them popular for use as glass coatings. Light comes through, but most of the heat does not. Horizontal louver blind slats and roller shade fabrics are available with low-E coatings that increase the energy performance of a window system.

Insulation from Heat Loss

Heat energy moves from a warmer to a colder substance by conduction, convection, or radiation (Figure 5.34).

Conduction is the transfer of heat energy through a substance. Glass is an excellent conductor, which means that heat or cold is quickly and efficiently conveyed through it. **Convection** is the transfer of heat energy through air. The human body loses and gains heat primarily through the air. **Radiation** is the transmission of energy by invisible light waves independent of a substance or air. For example, solar radiation travels through space (a vacuum) to reach the earth in this manner (Figure 5.35). Most window treatments do not effectively prevent heat loss, because they are inferior insulators.

These three factors—conduction, convection, and radiation—determine a material's thermal resistance, referred to as its R-value. The **R-value** measures the insulating effect of a material, the material's resistance to the

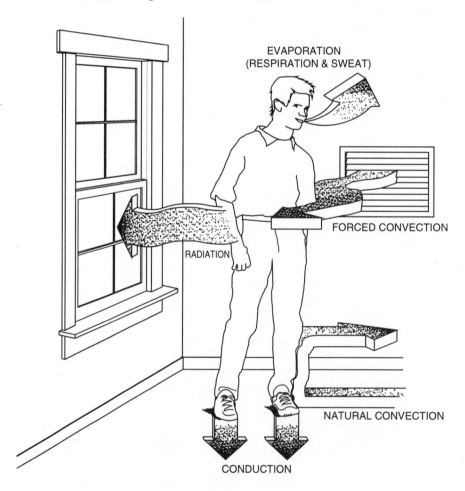

Figure 5.34 Methods of body heat loss.

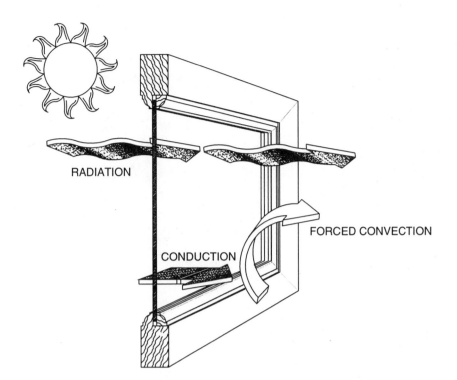

Figure 5.35 Conduction, convection, and radiation.

flow of heat. The larger the R-value, the greater the resistance and the better the insulating value. The effectiveness of a window treatment as an insulator depends on its ability to reduce the conductive transfer of heat to the interior.

The R-values of window treatments such as blinds and shades may be quite low. However, in a fully lowered position they form an insulating air space next to the window, which somewhat improves the R-value of the window system.

HORIZONTAL LOUVER BLINDS

Blinds

Horizontal louver blinds are the traditional, cost-effective solution to controlling glare. Horizontal louver blinds are tremendously versatile and are often the only window treatment suitable for unusually shaped windows (Figure 5.36).

Horizontal louver blinds are available in slat widths of up to 50 mm (nominally 2 in), but the most popular sizes for commercial applications are miniblinds and microblinds. Miniblinds have a slat width of 25 mm (nominally 1 in); microblinds have a slat width of 15 mm to 16 mm (nominally ½ in) (Figure 5.37). Although microblinds have a narrower slat width than miniblinds, they are typically heavier because more slats are required for the same size blind. This added weight can contribute to a shorter lifespan for the hardware of microblinds.

Size limitations for horizontal louver blinds vary among manufacturers and styles. The maximum width of a blind is about 3.6 m (12 ft). The maximum area of a microblind is about 6.5 sq m (70 sq ft), and of a miniblind, about 9.3 sq m (100 sq ft).

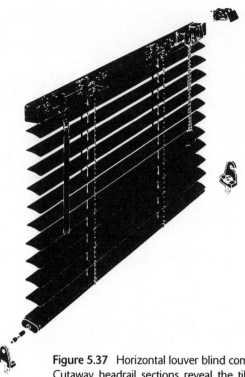

Figure 5.37 Horizontal louver blind components. Cutaway headrail sections reveal the tilt mechanism, ladder drum, and cord lock. Two types of hold-down brackets are shown at the bottom rail. Springs Window Fashions Division Inc.

Figure 5.36 Horizontal louver blinds are often the only window treatment suitable for unusually shaped windows. Levolor Home Fashions Contract Division.

For blinds with slats 25 mm (1 in) wide or wider and having an overall size of 3 m × 3 m (10 ft × 10 ft) or less, The American Window Covering Manufacturers Association (AWCMA) Document 1029 establishes minimum performance criteria. Most blinds manufactured in the United States comply with this test. The AWCMA standard also calls for the uniform location of the cord lock on the right side of the head channel and the tilting mechanism (typically a wand) on the left side of the head channel. If other locations are required because of inaccessibility, this should be specified or indicated on the drawings.

Perforated slats preserve the view while reducing glare, conserving energy, and providing privacy. Evenly spaced tiny holes allow light through while protecting the interior from solar heat gain. The openness factor for horizontal louver blinds is typically limited to 6% of the area of the slat so that the strength of the slat is not diminished.

If tilt wand and lift cord lengths are not specified, manufacturers usually assume the window sill height to be 900 mm (36 in) above the finish floor. In commercial applications where pets or children may be involved, accidental strangulation with the traditional end loop and cord equalizer is of concern. Break-through lift cord ends are available as a safety feature. The attached ends of the lift cord separate easily when force is applied.

To maintain a uniform appearance in a building's exterior, the base building standard may require blinds with certain features. Top-locking cord locks offer only two blind positions—fully raised and fully lowered. Slat tilt limiters may also be required. These devices limit the slat angle

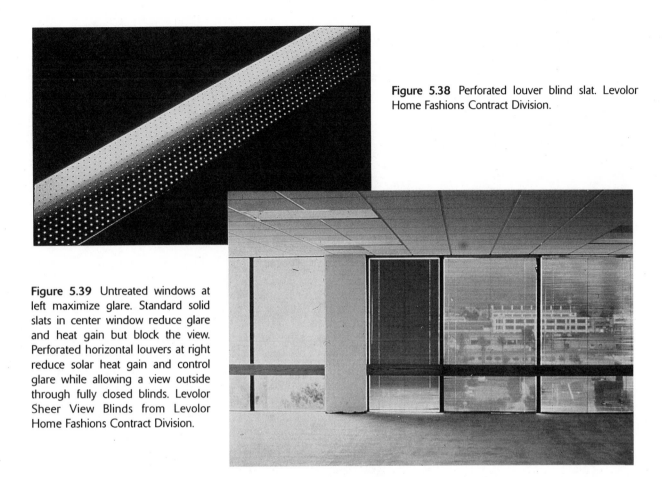

Figure 5.38 Perforated louver blind slat. Levolor Home Fashions Contract Division.

Figure 5.39 Untreated windows at left maximize glare. Standard solid slats in center window reduce glare and heat gain but block the view. Perforated horizontal louvers at right reduce solar heat gain and control glare while allowing a view outside through fully closed blinds. Levolor Sheer View Blinds from Levolor Home Fashions Contract Division.

position, allowing tilt only within a narrow range. Tilt limiters also keep the blind from being fully closed and thus preventing inadvertent damage to the glazing caused by heat build-up between the face of the glass and the face of the blind. A uniform blind color on the building exterior can be maintained, while using a variety of colors on the interior, by specifying slats with different finishes on the concave and convex sides. Where a dark-colored slat is the required design statement, the reflectance of the window system can be improved with a light-colored or low-E coated concave slat side. The color and openness factor of blinds will affect the perception of the view (Figures 5.38 and 5.39). Perforated, dark window treatments minimize glare and appear to be more transparent. These features are most critical where windows face direct sunlight.

In comparing horizontal louver blinds, an increased slat count (number of slats per given dimension) or decreased pitch (rung spacing) usually indicates a better quality blind.

VERTICAL LOUVER BLINDS

Vertical louver blinds are among the easiest window treatments to clean and repair (Figures 5.40 and 5.41). The vanes collect no more dust than walls or other vertical surfaces. Vertical louver vanes are also easier to replace

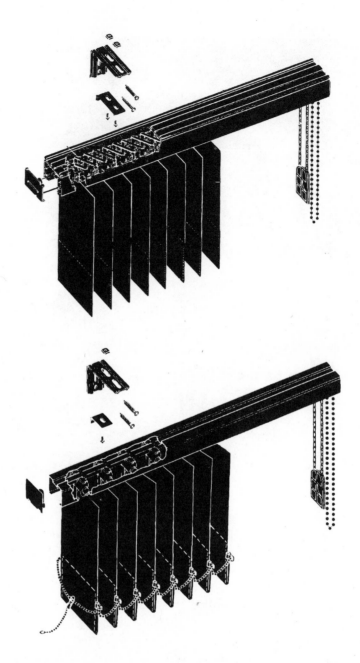

Figure 5.40 Vertical louver blind components (pantograph traversing system). A wall bracket (above) and a ceiling bracket (below) are shown. Weights are sewn into pockets at the bottom of the louver. Springs Window Fashions Division Inc.

Figure 5.41 Vertical louver blind components (linked carrier traversing system). Bottom chain constrains louver movement. Traverse and rotation cords are typically located on the right unless specified otherwise. Springs Window Fashions Division Inc.

than horizontal louver blind slats. Unlike horizontal louver blinds, vertical louver blinds can be specified where curved track applications are required. Similar to draperies, stack back dimensions (the width of a window treatment in a fully open position at the side of the window) must be considered if the full window is to be exposed when the blinds are fully opened.

Vane widths of 50.8 mm (2 in), 88.9 mm (3½ in), and 127 mm (5 in) are commonly available. Vane materials for commercial use include fabric, polyvinyl chloride (PVC), and aluminum, the most popular being fabric and PVC.

The fiber content of fabric vanes is typically polyester; however, cotton, acrylic, fiberglass, and rayon are also available. The fabric can be woven or nonwoven. This vane type can be free-hanging, or the fabric can be inserted into an extruded PVC sleeve to add rigidity and durability.

Fabric vanes can be treated with soil repellant or fire retardant finishes. Sealed or sewn-in bottom weights, or bottom chains linking the vanes together, are often recommended to stabilize this relatively light-weight type of vane.

PVC can be extruded into a variety of vane profiles. These vanes typically contain titanium dioxide (a common light block found in some sunscreen lotions) for opaqueness. PVC vanes should be treated with an anti-static solution to prevent dirt attraction and static cling. Because of this vane type's rigidity and weight, bottom chains linking the vanes together are not required.

Several factors can indicate the relative differences in quality between various vertical louver blinds under consideration. Self-synchronizing vanes can be realigned without tools while the blind is installed in its opening. Those without the self-synchronizing feature must be returned to the factory for repair when a vane is out of alignment. Vane hook replacement may also require removal of the window treatment, unless a blind is selected with hooks that can be replaced on-site.

Because the structural integrity of a vane is not as crucial as that of a horizontal louver, a much larger openness factor (ranging from about 6% to 13%) is possible for vertical louver blinds than for horizontal louver blinds.

ROLLER SHADES

Shades

The most effective type of interior protection against heat gain through a window is a light-colored, opaque **roller shade**. Flat roller shades are categorized by two methods of operation: those that are drawn up onto a roller at the top and those that roll up from the bottom. Bottom-up shades offer privacy while allowing light in. Rollers may be reverse mounted, which means installing the roller behind the shade rather than in front (Figure 5.42). Reverse roll should be specified for print shade fabrics, as it

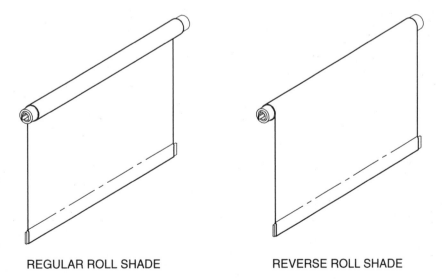

REGULAR ROLL SHADE   REVERSE ROLL SHADE

Figure 5.42 Regular and reverse roll shades.

allows only the finish face, not the back of the material, to be exposed to the interior.

Openness factors for shade materials range from about 3% to 17%. Fabrics for shades with higher openness factors are usually woven from vinyl-covered fiberglass (because of its dimensional stability), as opposed to vinyl-covered polyester. Room darkening and blackout shades are typically made of fiberglass covered with a PVC film.

Bead-chain-operated shades are more easily kept clean, because the shades are not touched during operation. They are also ideal for applications where the bottom of a shade is difficult to reach.

PLEATED SHADES

Polyester with an antistatic treatment is the standard fabric for **pleated shades**. However, shades fabricated from C.O.M. are available. The problem with this type of shade is that the pleats tend to deform, sagging at the top and compressing at the bottom. However, shades with pleats that retain their shape are available (Figure 5.43). Pleat size is determined by measuring from valley to peak of the pleat (Figure 5.44).

Reflective backings are available for pleated shades to increase the shading performance of the window system and the opacity in blackout applications. However, to effectively increase the window system's reflectivity, the shade must be kept fully lowered.

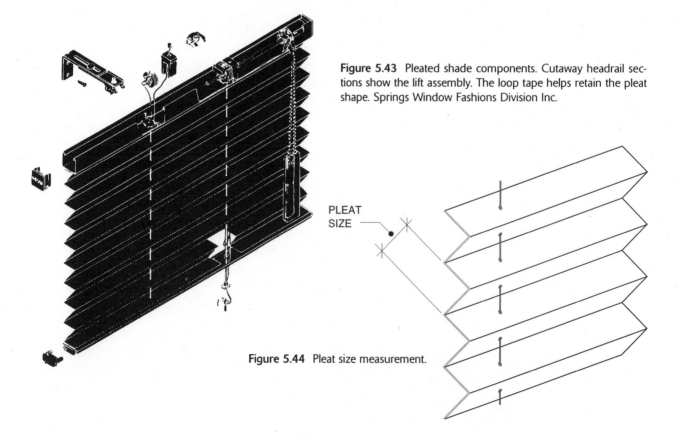

Figure 5.43 Pleated shade components. Cutaway headrail sections show the lift assembly. The loop tape helps retain the pleat shape. Springs Window Fashions Division Inc.

PLEAT SIZE

Figure 5.44 Pleat size measurement.

Draperies

Although there are no strict industry definitions, the term **draperies** usually refers to lined treatments with a stiffened, constructed heading requiring a traversing rod and carriers; **curtains**, on the other hand, are unlined and have a gathered or shirred heading. Curtains are often not intended to be opened. Common curtain headings are shown in Figure 5.45. A **panel** is a single drapery unit of one or more fabric widths.

Casements are usually sheer or semisheer fabrics, often used with operable over-drapes or fixed side panels. Extra wide fabrics [up to 299.72 cm (118 in)], are available to be railroaded, thus eliminating the obvious seams inherent in sheer materials.

Swags are draped in soft folds at the tops of drapery headings. They can be used alone as a window treatment or as valances over drapes, shades, or blinds. Swags are typically lined to add body and shape to the draped effect. **Cascades** are folds of fabric hanging from the tops of drap-

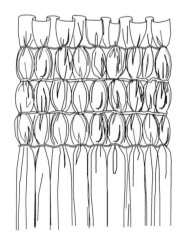

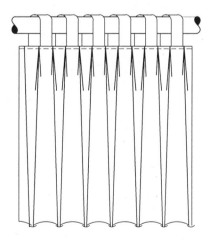

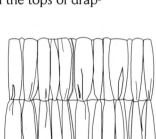

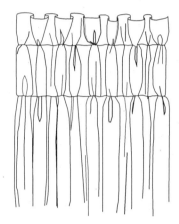

RUFFLED SHIRRED HEADING ON
A WIDE ROD OR ROUND POLE

RUFFLELESS SHIRRED HEADING
ON A WIDE ROD

TRIPLE SHIRRED HEADING WITH RUFFLE.
THREE NARROW RODS ARE USED.

TAB HEADING

Figure 5.45 Common curtain headings.

Figure 5.46 Swag and cascade.

ery headings. Cascades are lined so that the wrong side of the fabric is not exposed in the folds (Figure 5.46).

A **lining** is a fabric backing that can enhance the draping qualities of a fabric, increase the energy performance of the window system, and protect the drapery fabric from ultraviolet (UV) radiation. Linings can be sewn to the face fabric if they have compatible cleaning requirements, or they can hang on a separate track. Metallic lings in various weights can increase a window system's reflectivity, and insulative linings can boost the thermal performance. Ultraviolet inhibitors can be added to lining fabrics to help protect the drapery fabric against deterioration caused by sunlight. Water repellant finishes protect linings from unsightly staining and streaking from resulting condensation. A **blackout lining** can be used to darken a room completely; such linings are popular in hospitality applications or in meeting rooms where the use of a slide or movie projector is anticipated.

DRAPERY OPERATION

A drapery panel with **one-way draw** operation is one that opens entirely to one side. A one-way draw is designated as either *full left* or *full right*, indicating the direction in which the drapery stacks as you face it. For example, if you are looking at an open drapery stacked on the right, it is a right draw. **Two-way draw** or bipart draw means that the drapery panels meet in the center and open to either side.

The master carrier holds the drapery end that traverses the rod. **Butt master** carriers are often used in roll pleat and stack pleat draperies. **Overlap master** carriers are commonly the choice for conventional pleated drapes (Figure 5.47). For standard master overlap carriers the overlap is 75 mm (3 in) per panel, and the right panel overlaps the left.

The **return** is the distance from the traversing rod to the wall or the depth of the projection. When casements and over-drapes are used in the same window opening, the depths of the returns should provide adequate clearance for unencumbered operation. The dimensions of the return and the overlap must be added to the dimension of the opening to determine the drapery panel width (Figure 5.48). The stack space dimension, or stack back, is the drapery width when fully opened. The stack back must be considered when determining the traversing rod length and may determine the traversing direction.

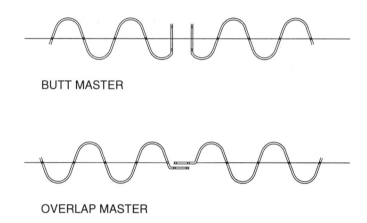

BUTT MASTER

OVERLAP MASTER

Figure 5.47 Butt and overlap master carriers.

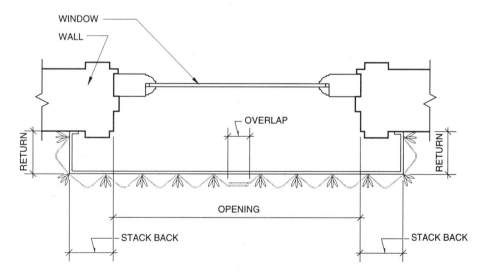

Figure 5.48 Finished drapery panel width for biparting draperies = return + stack back + 1/2 opening + overlap.

Drapery **fullness** is the ratio of the total fabric used, less allowances for side hems and seams, to the finished drapery width. For example, a drapery with a 100% fullness is 100% wider than the width of the drapery in a closed position, or twice the finished drapery width; a drapery with 225% fullness is 3¼ times the finished drapery width.

DRAPERY HEADING STYLES

Pleated heading styles vary considerably (Figure 5.49), but the three most popular headings for commercial applications are stack pleat, roll pleat, and pinch pleat (Figure 5.50). Stack pleat and roll pleat are popular because, especially in healthcare installations, they can be machine-washed. They also appear the same from either side of the window and consequently do not need to be lined for appearance sake. Pinch pleats, sometimes referred to as **French pleats**, remain the most popular. Although the terms *French* and *pinch* are often used interchangeably, there is a subtle difference. A French pleat is a softer, rounded pleat that is not permanently creased. A pinch pleat is pressed into sharp folds. Fullness for a conventional pleated drapery is typically 225% and can range up to 250%, making the stack back dimension the largest among the drapery types (Table 5.5).

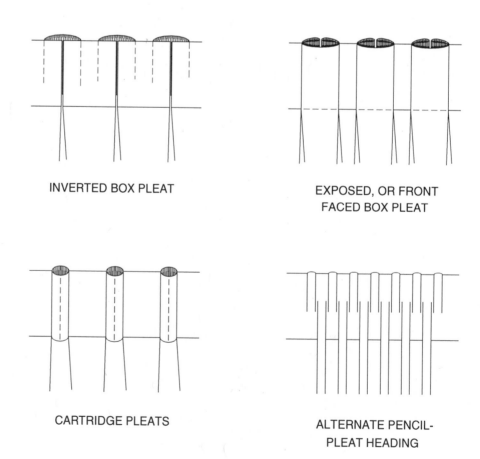

INVERTED BOX PLEAT

EXPOSED, OR FRONT
FACED BOX PLEAT

CARTRIDGE PLEATS

ALTERNATE PENCIL-
PLEAT HEADING

Figure 5.49 Pleated heading styles.

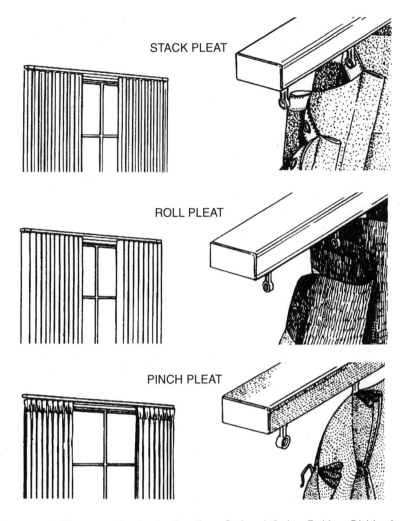

STACK PLEAT

ROLL PLEAT

PINCH PLEAT

Figure 5.50 Three popular drapery headings. Springs Window Fashions Division Inc.

TABLE 5.5   CONVENTIONAL PLEAT STACK BACK WIDTHS

Conventional pleat stack back requirements are calculated for medium-weight fabric with one-way draw (or one-half of a biparting pair) using 225% fullness and overlap masters. If draperies are lined, add a minimum of 20% to the stack back space. Return dimensions are not included.

Width of Rod (including stack back)	Stack Back Width
510–810 mm (20–32")	250–300 mm (10–12")
810–1120 mm (32–44")	300–360 mm (12–14")
1120–1420 mm (44–56")	360–400 mm (14–16")
1420–1730 mm (56–68")	400–460 mm (16–18")
1730–2060 mm (68–81")	460–510 mm (18–20")
2060–2540 mm (81–100")	510–560 mm (20–22")
2540–2840 mm (100–112")	560–610 mm (22–24")
2840–3180 mm (112–125")	610–660 mm (24–26")
3180–3660 mm (125–144")	660–710 mm (26–28")
3660–3960 mm (144–156")	710–760 mm (28–30")
3960–4300 mm (156–169")	760–810 mm (30–32")
4300–4600 mm (169–181")	810–860 mm (32–34")
4600–4880 mm (181–192")	860–910 mm (34–36")

Source: Benten Brothers.

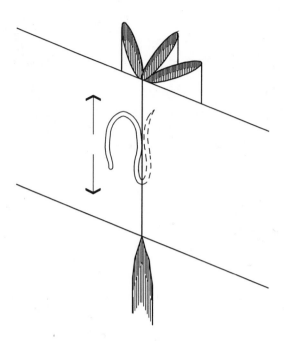

Figure 5.51 Conventional pleated draperies can be raised or lowered by repositioning the drapery hooks.

Pleated headings are reinforced with buckram or other stiffening materials and special care must be taken in dry cleaning and pressing the pleats. Of all the drapery headings, these are the most readily adaptable at a project site. Minor adjustments can be made in the length after fabrication by varying the insertion points of the drapery hooks (Figure 5.51). A required drapery fullness can be accommodated by adjusting the depth and the distance between the pleats.

The **pleat to** dimension is the width of the drapery after it has been pleated. For example, if a 121.92 cm (48 in) width of fabric is 48.26 cm (19 in) after it has been pleated, it is specified as "pleat to 48.26 cm (19 in)."

Roll pleats provide a soft, rounded pleating pattern. This is a low-maintenance drapery type. The draperies are fabricated in a flat panel and can be machine washed and pressed flat, making them a popular choice for healthcare facilities. Because there is less fullness, there is also less stack back required for roll pleats than for conventional pleats. Fullness is achieved by varying the spacing between the snaps or grommets on the drapery heading. Fullnesses of 60%, 80%, and 120% are also available. Standard fullness is 100%. Like stack pleats, this heading style looks the same from both sides of the opening it covers (Table 5.6).

Stack pleats are a creased drapery with the pleat crease sewn front and back for the length of the drapery. Stack pleat draperies require the smallest stack back dimension and can stack as tightly as one sixth of the drapery width. Fullness and the depth of the pleat are interdependent, which is not the case with conventional pleated headings. The standard fullness for stack pleats is 100%. Fullnesses of 40%, 60%, 80%, and 120% are also available (Table 5.7).

TABLE 5.6   ROLL PLEAT STACK BACK WIDTHS

Roll pleat stack back requirements are calculated for medium-weight fabric with one-way draw (or one-half of a biparting pair) using 100% fullness and butt master carriers. Overlap master carriers require approximately 50 mm (2") additional space. Return dimensions are not included.

Width of Rod (including stack back)	Stack Back Width
300–580 mm (12–23")	130–180 mm (5–7")
580–910 mm (23–36")	180–250 mm (7–10")
910–1220 mm (36–48")	250–330 mm (10–13")
1220–1550 mm (48–61")	330–380 mm (13–15")
1550–1880 mm (61–74")	380–460 mm (15–18")
1880–2210 mm (74–87")	460–510 mm (18–20")
2210–2410 mm (87–95")	510–560 mm (20–22")
2410–2740 mm (95–108")	560–640 mm (22–25")
2740–3070 mm (108–121")	640–710 mm (25–28")
3070–3380 mm (121–133")	710–760 mm (28–30")
3380–3710 mm (133–146")	760–840 mm (30–33")
3710–3960 mm (146–156")	840–890 mm (33–35")
3960–4270 mm (156–168")	890–970 mm (35–38")
4270–4570 mm (168–180")	970–1020 mm (38–40")
4570–4877 mm (180–192")	1020–1090 mm (40–43")

Source: Benton Brothers.

TABLE 5.7   STACK PLEAT STACK BACK WIDTHS

Stack pleat stack back requirements are calculated for medium-weight fabric with one-way draw (or one-half of a biparting pair) using 100% fullness and overlap master carriers. Butt master carriers require approximately 50 mm (2") less space. Return dimensions are not included.

Width of Rod (including stack back)	Stack Back Width
330–610 mm (13–24")	180–200 mm (7–8")
610–910 mm (24–36")	200–230 mm (8–9")
910–1220 mm (36–48")	230–250 mm (9–10")
1220–1520 mm (48–60")	250–300 mm (10–12")
1520–1830 mm (60–72")	300–330 mm (12–13")
1830–2130 mm (72–84")	330–350 mm (13–14")
2130–2440 mm (84–96")	350–410 mm (14–16")
2440–2740 mm (95–108")	410–430 mm (16–17")
2740–3050 mm (108–120")	430–460 mm (17–18")
3050–3350 mm (120–132")	460–510 mm (18–20")
3350–3660 mm (132–144")	510–530 mm (20–21")
3660–3960 mm (144–156")	530–560 mm (21–22")
3960–4270 mm (156–168")	560–610 mm (22–24")
4270–4570 mm (168–180")	610–640 mm (24–25")
4570–4880 mm (180–192")	640–660 mm (25–26")

Source: Benton Brothers.

Annotated Specification Checklist
for Window Treatment

PART 1 GENERAL

SUBMITTALS

Shop Drawings: Show location of each window treatment and operation controls.

Samples: Louver. *For horizontal or vertical louver blinds.*

Samples: Fabric with right side and selvage marked and all specified treatments applied. *Fire and stain resistant treatments can alter the draping qualities of a fabric. For lined draperies, request a 0.9 m (1 yd) of both the lining and drapery fabrics so that the drapability of the combined fabrics can be assessed.*

QUALITY ASSURANCE

Regulatory Requirements: NFPA 701.

Mock-ups: Mock-ups can be particularly helpful when multiple window treatments will be used on a window, to verify the appropriate depth and hardware operation; for example, a combination of horizontal louver blinds, casement, drapes, and a valance.

PROJECT CONDITIONS

Environmental Requirements: Comply with manufacturer's written requirements. *Window treatments should not be installed until after the relative humidity and temperature in a space are at the levels at which they will be maintained during installation and occupancy.*

Field Measurements: Verify and coordinate with fabrication of window treatments.

MAINTENANCE

Extra Materials: Packaged and labeled, full-width material. *Extra drapery material should be required, especially if the material is custom-made or special-ordered. Be specific about how much extra material will be required and where it will be stored.*

PART 2 PRODUCTS

FABRICATION

Tolerances: Width 12 mm (½ in) less than opening. *Include for blinds and shades installed within an opening, between window jambs, to ensure that the treatment fills the opening.*

PART 3 EXECUTION

SCHEDULES

The schedule of wall coverings is usually given on a finish schedule included either in the specifications or, more commonly, on the drawings.

APPENDIX **A**

Referenced Associations and Organizations

Acoustical Society of America (ASA)
500 Sunnyside Boulevard
Woodbury, NY 11797
(516) 349-7800

Aluminum Association (AA)
900 19th Street, NW, Suite 300
Washington, DC 20002
(202) 862-5100

American Architectural Metal Manufacturer's Association
(AAMMA)
2700 River Road, Suite 118
Des Plaines, IL 60018
(312) 699-7310

American Association of Textile Chemists and Colorists
(AATCC)
P.O. Box 12215
Research Triangle Park, NC 27709
(919) 549-8141

American Council of Independent Laboratories (ACIL)
1725 K Street, NW
Washington, DC 20006
(202) 887-5872

American Fiber Manufacturers Association, Inc.
(AFMA)
1150 Seventeenth Street, NW, Suite 310
Washington, DC 20036
(202) 296-6508

American Hardboard Association (ACPA)
520 N. Hicks Road
Palatine, IL 60067
(312) 934-8800

American Institute of Architects (AIA)
1735 New York Avenue, NW
Washington, DC 20006
(202) 626-7300

American Institute of Architects
Master Systems
332 East 500 South
Salt Lake City, UT 84111
(800) 424-5080; (801) 521-9161

American Iron and Steel Institute (AISI)
1101 Seventeenth Street, NW
Suite 1300
Washington, DC 20036
(202) 452-7100

American Lumber Standards Committee (ALSC)
P.O. Box 210
Germantown, MD 20874
(301) 972-1700

American National Standards Institute (ANSI)
11 West 42nd Street, 13th Floor
New York, NY 10036
(212) 642-4900

American Parquet Association (APA)
P.O. Box 87
Magnolia, AR 71753
(800) 234-2510; (501) 234-2310
member of National Wood Flooring Association

American Plywood Association (APA)
P.O. Box 11700
Tacoma, WA 98411
(206) 565-6600

American Society of Heating, Refrigerating and Air-
Conditioning Engineers (ASHRAE)
1791 Tullie Circle, NE
Atlanta, GA 30329
(404) 636-8400

American Society of Interior Designers (ASID)
608 Massachusetts Avenue, NE
Washington, DC 20002
(202) 546-3480

American Society for Testing and Materials (ASTM)
100 Barr Harbor Dr.
West Conshohocken, PA 19428
(610) 832-9500

Architectural Woodwork Institute (AWI)
1952 Isaac Newton Square
Reston, VA 22090
(703) 671-9100

Builders Hardware Manufacturers Association
    (BHMA)
355 Lexington Avenue, 17th Floor
New York, NY 10017
(212) 661-4261

Building Officials and Code Administrators International
    (BOCA)
4051 West Flossmoor Road
Country Club Hills, IL 60478-5795
(708) 799-2300

Building Owners and Managers Association International
    (BOMA)
1201 New York Avenue, NW
Suite 300
Washington, DC 20005
(202) 408-2662

Business and Institutional Furniture Manufacturers
    Association (BIFMA)
2335 Burton Street, SE
Grand Rapids, MI 49506
(616) 243-1681

Carpet Cushion Council (CCC)
P.O. Box 546
Riverside, CT 06878
(203) 637-1312

Carpet and Rug Institute (CRI)
Box 2048
Dalton, GA 30722
(706) 278-3176

Ceiling and Interior Systems Construction Association
    (CISCA)
579 W. North Avenue, Suite 301
Elmhurst, IL 60126
(708) 833-1919

Ceramic Tile Institute of America (CTI)
700 N. Virgil Avenue
Los Angeles, CA 90029
(213) 660-1911

Chemical Fabrics & Film Association, Inc. (CFFA)
1230 Keith Building
Cleveland, OH 44115
(216) 241-7333

Code of Federal Regulations (CFR)
Superintendent of Documents
P.O. Box 371954
Pittsburgh, PA 15250
(202) 512-1800

Construction Specifications Institute (CSI)
601 Madison Street
Alexandria, VA 22314
(800) 689-2900; (703) 684-0300

Consumer Product Safety Commission (CPSC)
CPSC Publications
Washington, DC 20207
(800) 638-2772

Copper Development Association (CDA)
Box 1840, Greenwich Office Park 2
Greenwich, CT 06836
(203) 625-8210

Council of American Building Officials (CABO)
5203 Leesburg Pike
Suite 708
Falls Church, VA 22041
(703) 931-4533

Decorative Laminate Products Association (DLPA)
600 S. Federal Street, Suite 400
Chicago, IL 60605
(312) 922-6222

Department of Commerce (DOC)
14th Street and Constitution Avenue, NW
Washington, DC 20230
(202) 482-2000

Door and Hardware Institute (DHI)
7711 Old Springhouse Road
McLean, VA 22102
(703) 556-3990

Environmental Protection Agency (EPA)
401 M Street, SW
Washington, DC 20460
(202) 260-2090

ETL Testing Laboratories, Inc. (ETL)
P.O. Box 2040
Route 11, Industrial Park
Cortland, NY 13045
(607) 753-6711

Factory Mutual Engineering
and Research Organization (FM)
1151 Boston-Providence Turnpike
Norwood, MA 02062
(617) 762-4300

Floor Covering Installation Board (FCIB)
310 Holiday Avenue
Dalton, GA 30720
(800) 235-2420; (706) 226-5488

Glass Association of North America (GANA)
(formerly the Flat Glass Manufacturer's Association)
White Lakes Professional Building
3310 Harrison
Topeka, KS 66611
(913) 266-7013

Hardwood Manufacturers Association (HMA)
2831 Airways Boulevard, Suite 205, Building B
Memphis, TN 38132
(901) 346-2222

Hardwood Plywood Manufacturers Association (HPMA)
1825 Michael Farraday Drive
P.O. Box 2789
Reston, VA 22090
(703) 435-2900

International Conference of Building Officials (ICBO)
5360 South Workman Mill Road
Whittier, CA 90601
(213) 699-0541

International Facilities Management Association (IFMA)
1 East Greenway Plaza
Suite 1100
Houston, TX 77046
(713) 629-6753

International Interior Designers Association (IIDA)
341 Merchandise Mart
Chicago, IL 60654
(312) 467-1950

Iron and Steel Society (ISS)
410 Commonwealth Drive
Warrendale, PA 15086
(412) 776-9460

Maple Flooring Manufacturers Association (MFMA)
60 Revere Drive, Suite 500
Northbrook, IL 60062
(708) 480-9138

Marble Institute of America (MIA)
30 Eden Alley, Suite 201
Columbus, OH 43215
(614) 228-6194

National Association of Architectural Metal
Manufacturers (NAAMM)
600 S. Federal Street, Suite 400
Chicago, IL 60605
(312) 922-6222

National Conference of States on Building Codes and
Standards, Inc. (NCSBCS)
505 Huntmar Park Drive, Suite 210
Herndon, VA 22070
(703) 437-0100

National Electrical Manufacturers Association (NEMA)
2101 L Street NW, Suite 300
Washington, DC 20037
(202) 457-8400

National Fire Protection Association (NFPA)
Batterymarch Park
Quincy, MA 02169
(617) 770-3000

National Forest Products Association (NFPA)
1250 Connecticut Avenue NW, Suite 200
Washington, DC 20036
(202) 463-2700

National Hardwood Lumber Association (NFPA)
P.O. Box 34518
Memphis, TN 38184
(901) 377-1818

National Institute of Standards and Technology (NIST)
U.S. Department of Commerce
Gaithersburg, MD 20899
(301) 975-2000

National Kitchen Cabinet Association (NKCA)
P.O. Box 6830
Falls Church, VA 22046
(703) 237-7580

National Oak Flooring Manufacturers Association
(NOFMA)
P.O. Box 3009
Memphis, TN 38173
(901) 526-5016

National Paint and Coatings Association (NPCA)
1500 Rhode Island Avenue, NW
Washington, DC 20005
(202) 462-6272

National Particleboard Association (NPA)
18928 Premiere Court
Gaithersburg, MD 20879
(301) 670-0604

National Terrazzo and Mosaic Association (NTMA)
3166 Des Plaines Avenue, Suite 132
Des Plaines, IL 60018
(800) 323-9736; (708) 635-7744

National Wood Flooring Association (NWFA)
233 Old Meramec Station Road
Manchester, MO 63021
(800) 422-4556; (314) 391-5161

Nickel Development Institute (NiDI)
214 King Street West, Suite 510
Toronto, Ontario, Canada M5H 3S6
(416) 491-7999

Occupational Safety and Health Administration (OSHA)
  U.S. Department of Labor, Government Printing Office
Washington, DC 20402
(202) 219-8148

Resilient Floor Covering Institute (RFCI)
966 Hungerford Drive, Suite 12-B
Rockville, MD 20805
(301) 340-8580

Safety Glazing Certification Council (SGCC)
(c/o ETL Testing Laboratories)
Route 11, Industrial Park
Cortland, NY 13045
(607) 753-6711

Sheet Metal and Air Conditioning Contractors National
  Association (SMACNA)
4201 Lafayette Center Drive
Chantilly, VA 22021
(703) 803-2980

Southern Building Code Congress International
  (SBCCI)
900 Montclair Road
Birmingham, AL 35213
(205) 591-1853

Tile Council of America (TCA)
P.O. Box 326
Princeton, NJ 08542
(609) 921-7050

Underwriters Laboratories (UL)
333 Pfingsten Road
Northbrook, IL 60062
(312) 272-8800

Wallcovering Manufacturers Association (WCMA)
355 Lexington Avenue
New York, NY 10017
(212) 661-4261

Western Wood Products Association (WWPA)
522 S.W. 5th Avenue, Yeon Building
Portland, OR 97204
(503) 224-3930

Wood and Synthetic Flooring Institute (WSFI)
4415 W. Harrison Street, Suite 242 C
Hillside, IL 60162
(312) 449-2933

Woodwork Institute of California (WIC)
P.O. Box 11428
Fresno, CA 93773
(209) 233-9035

APPENDIX B

AIA Document 270

General Conditions of the Contract for Construction

*THIS DOCUMENT HAS IMPORTANT LEGAL CONSEQUENCES, CONSULTATION
WITH AN ATTORNEY IS ENCOURAGED WITH RESPECT TO ITS MODIFICATION*

1987 EDITION
TABLE OF ARTICLES

This document has been approved and endorsed by the Associated General Contractors of America.

AIA DOCUMENT A201 • GENERAL CONDITIONS OF THE CONTRACT FOR CONSTRUCTION • FOURTEENTH EDITION
AIA® • ©1987 THE AMERICAN INSTITUTE OF ARCHITECTS, 1735 NEW YORK AVENUE, N.W., WASHINGTON, D.C. 20006   A201-1987   1

AIA DOCUMENT A201 • GENERAL CONDITIONS OF THE CONTRACT FOR CONSTRUCTION • FOURTEENTH EDITION
AIA® • ©1987 THE AMERICAN INSTITUTE OF ARCHITECTS, 1735 NEW YORK AVENUE, N.W., WASHINGTON, D.C. 20006

ARTICLE 1

GENERAL PROVISIONS

1.1 BASIC DEFINITIONS

1.1.1 THE CONTRACT DOCUMENTS

The Contract Documents consist of the Agreement between Owner and Contractor (hereinafter the Agreement), Conditions of the Contract (General, Supplementary and other Conditions), Drawings, Specifications, addenda issued prior to execution of the Contract, other documents listed in the Agreement and Modifications issued after execution of the Contract. A Modification is (1) a written amendment to the Contract signed by both parties, (2) a Change Order, (3) a Construction Change Directive or (4) a written order for a minor change in the Work issued by the Architect. Unless specifically enumerated in the Agreement, the Contract Documents do not include other documents such as bidding requirements (advertisement or invitation to bid, Instructions to Bidders, sample forms, the Contractor's bid or portions of addenda relating to bidding requirements).

1.1.2 THE CONTRACT

The Contract Documents form the Contract for Construction. The Contract represents the entire and integrated agreement between the parties hereto and supersedes prior negotiations, representations or agreements, either written or oral. The Contract may be amended or modified only by a Modification. The Contract Documents shall not be construed to create a contractual relationship of any kind (1) between the Architect and Contractor, (2) between the Owner and a Subcontractor or Sub-subcontractor or (3) between any persons or entities other than the Owner and Contractor. The Architect shall, however, be entitled to performance and enforcement of obligations under the Contract intended to facilitate performance of the Architect's duties.

1.1.3 THE WORK

The term "Work" means the construction and services required by the Contract Documents, whether completed or partially completed, and includes all other labor, materials, equipment and services provided or to be provided by the Contractor to fulfill the Contractor's obligations. The Work may constitute the whole or a part of the Project.

1.1.4 THE PROJECT

The Project is the total construction of which the Work performed under the Contract Documents may be the whole or a part and which may include construction by the Owner or by separate contractors.

1.1.5 THE DRAWINGS

The Drawings are the graphic and pictorial portions of the Contract Documents, wherever located and whenever issued, showing the design, location and dimensions of the Work, generally including plans, elevations, sections, details, schedules and diagrams.

1.1.6 THE SPECIFICATIONS

The Specifications are that portion of the Contract Documents consisting of the written requirements for materials, equip-

ment, construction systems, standards and workmanship for the Work, and performance of related services.

1.1.7 THE PROJECT MANUAL

The Project Manual is the volume usually assembled for the Work which may include the bidding requirements, sample forms, Conditions of the Contract and Specifications.

1.2 EXECUTION, CORRELATION AND INTENT

1.2.1 The Contract Documents shall be signed by the Owner and Contractor as provided in the Agreement. If either the Owner or Contractor or both do not sign all the Contract Documents, the Architect shall identify such unsigned Documents upon request.

1.2.2 Execution of the Contract by the Contractor is a representation that the Contractor has visited the site, become familiar with local conditions under which the Work is to be performed and correlated personal observations with requirements of the Contract Documents.

1.2.3 The intent of the Contract Documents is to include all items necessary for the proper execution and completion of the Work by the Contractor. The Contract Documents are complementary, and what is required by one shall be as binding as if required by all; performance by the Contractor shall be required only to the extent consistent with the Contract Documents and reasonably inferable from them as being necessary to produce the intended results.

1.2.4 Organization of the Specifications into divisions, sections and articles, and arrangement of Drawings shall not control the Contractor in dividing the Work among Subcontractors or in establishing the extent of Work to be performed by any trade.

1.2.5 Unless otherwise stated in the Contract Documents, words which have well-known technical or construction industry meanings are used in the Contract Documents in accordance with such recognized meanings.

1.3 OWNERSHIP AND USE OF ARCHITECT'S DRAWINGS, SPECIFICATIONS AND OTHER DOCUMENTS

1.3.1 The Drawings, Specifications and other documents prepared by the Architect are instruments of the Architect's service through which the Work to be executed by the Contractor is described. The Contractor may retain one contract record set. Neither the Contractor nor any Subcontractor, Sub-subcontractor or material or equipment supplier shall own or claim a copyright in the Drawings, Specifications and other documents prepared by the Architect, and unless otherwise indicated the Architect shall be deemed the author of them and will retain all common law, statutory and other reserved rights, in addition to the copyright. All copies of them, except the Contractor's record set, shall be returned or suitably accounted for to the Architect, on request, upon completion of the Work. The Drawings, Specifications and other documents prepared by the Architect, and copies thereof furnished to the Contractor, are for use solely with respect to this Project. They are not to be used by the Contractor or any Subcontractor, Sub-subcontractor or material or equipment supplier on other projects or for additions to this Project outside the scope of the

Work without the specific written consent of the Owner and Architect. The Contractor, Subcontractors, Sub-subcontractors and material or equipment suppliers are granted a limited license to use and reproduce applicable portions of the Drawings, Specifications and other documents prepared by the Architect appropriate to and for use in the execution of their Work under the Contract Documents. All copies made under this license shall bear the statutory copyright notice, if any, shown on the Drawings, Specifications and other documents prepared by the Architect. Submittal or distribution to meet official regulatory requirements or for other purposes in connection with this Project is not to be construed as publication in derogation of the Architect's copyright or other reserved rights.

1.4 CAPITALIZATION

1.4.1 Terms capitalized in these General Conditions include those which are (1) specifically defined, (2) the titles of numbered articles and identified references to Paragraphs, Subparagraphs and Clauses in the document or (3) the titles of other documents published by the American Institute of Architects.

1.5 INTERPRETATION

1.5.1 In the interest of brevity the Contract Documents frequently omit modifying words such as "all" and "any" and articles such as "the" and "an," but the fact that a modifier or an article is absent from one statement and appears in another is not intended to affect the interpretation of either statement.

ARTICLE 2

OWNER

2.1 DEFINITION

2.1.1 The Owner is the person or entity identified as such in the Agreement and is referred to throughout the Contract Documents as if singular in number. The term "Owner" means the Owner or the Owner's authorized representative.

2.1.2 The Owner upon reasonable written request shall furnish to the Contractor in writing information which is necessary and relevant for the Contractor to evaluate, give notice of or enforce mechanic's lien rights. Such information shall include a correct statement of the record legal title to the property on which the Project is located, usually referred to as the site, and the Owner's interest therein at the time of execution of the Agreement and, within five days after any change, information of such change in title, recorded or unrecorded.

2.2 INFORMATION AND SERVICES REQUIRED OF THE OWNER

2.2.1 The Owner shall, at the request of the Contractor, prior to execution of the Agreement and promptly from time to time thereafter, furnish to the Contractor reasonable evidence that financial arrangements have been made to fulfill the Owner's obligations under the Contract. *[Note: Unless such reasonable evidence were furnished on request prior to the execution of the Agreement, the prospective contractor would not be required to execute the Agreement or to commence the Work.]*

2.2.2 The Owner shall furnish surveys describing physical characteristics, legal limitations and utility locations for the site of the Project, and a legal description of the site.

2.2.3 Except for permits and fees which are the responsibility of the Contractor under the Contract Documents, the Owner shall secure and pay for necessary approvals, easements, assess-

ments and charges required for construction, use or occupancy of permanent structures or for permanent changes in existing facilities.

2.2.4 Information or services under the Owner's control shall be furnished by the Owner with reasonable promptness to avoid delay in orderly progress of the Work.

2.2.5 Unless otherwise provided in the Contract Documents, the Contractor will be furnished, free of charge, such copies of Drawings and Project Manuals as are reasonably necessary for execution of the Work.

2.2.6 The foregoing are in addition to other duties and responsibilities of the Owner enumerated herein and especially those in respect to Article 6 (Construction by Owner or by Separate Contractors), Article 9 (Payments and Completion) and Article 11 (Insurance and Bonds).

2.3 OWNER'S RIGHT TO STOP THE WORK

2.3.1 If the Contractor fails to correct Work which is not in accordance with the requirements of the Contract Documents as required by Paragraph 12.2 or persistently fails to carry out Work in accordance with the Contract Documents, the Owner, by written order signed personally or by an agent specifically so empowered by the Owner in writing, may order the Contractor to stop the Work, or any portion thereof, until the cause for such order has been eliminated; however, the right of the Owner to stop the Work shall not give rise to a duty on the part of the Owner to exercise this right for the benefit of the Contractor or any other person or entity, except to the extent required by Subparagraph 6.1.3.

2.4 OWNER'S RIGHT TO CARRY OUT THE WORK

2.4.1 If the Contractor defaults or neglects to carry out the Work in accordance with the Contract Documents and fails within a seven-day period after receipt of written notice from the Owner to commence and continue correction of such default or neglect with diligence and promptness, the Owner may after such seven-day period give the Contractor a second written notice to correct such deficiencies within a second seven-day period. If the Contractor within such second seven-day period after receipt of such second notice fails to commence and continue to correct any deficiencies, the Owner may, without prejudice to other remedies the Owner may have, correct such deficiencies. In such case an appropriate Change Order shall be issued deducting from payments then or thereafter due the Contractor the cost of correcting such deficiencies, including compensation for the Architect's additional services and expenses made necessary by such default, neglect or failure. Such action by the Owner and amounts charged to the Contractor are both subject to prior approval of the Architect. If payments then or thereafter due the Contractor are not sufficient to cover such amounts, the Contractor shall pay the difference to the Owner.

ARTICLE 3

CONTRACTOR

3.1 DEFINITION

3.1.1 The Contractor is the person or entity identified as such in the Agreement and is referred to throughout the Contract Documents as if singular in number. The term "Contractor" means the Contractor or the Contractor's authorized representative.

3.2 REVIEW OF CONTRACT DOCUMENTS AND FIELD CONDITIONS BY CONTRACTOR

3.2.1 The Contractor shall carefully study and compare the Contract Documents with each other and with information furnished by the Owner pursuant to Subparagraph 2.2.2 and shall at once report to the Architect errors, inconsistencies or omissions discovered. The Contractor shall not be liable to the Owner or Architect for damage resulting from errors, inconsistencies or omissions in the Contract Documents unless the Contractor recognized such error, inconsistency or omission and knowingly failed to report it to the Architect. If the Contractor performs any construction activity knowing it involves a recognized error, inconsistency or omission in the Contract Documents without such notice to the Architect, the Contractor shall assume appropriate responsibility for such performance and shall bear an appropriate amount of the attributable costs for correction.

3.2.2 The Contractor shall take field measurements and verify field conditions and shall carefully compare such field measurements and conditions and other information known to the Contractor with the Contract Documents before commencing activities. Errors, inconsistencies or omissions discovered shall be reported to the Architect at once.

3.2.3 The Contractor shall perform the Work in accordance with the Contract Documents and submittals approved pursuant to Paragraph 3.12.

3.3 SUPERVISION AND CONSTRUCTION PROCEDURES

3.3.1 The Contractor shall supervise and direct the Work using the Contractor's best skill and attention. The Contractor shall be solely responsible for and have control over construction means, methods, techniques, sequences and procedures and for coordinating all portions of the Work under the Contract, unless Contract Documents give other specific instructions concerning these matters.

3.3.2 The Contractor shall be responsible to the Owner for acts and omissions of the Contractor's employees, Subcontractors and their agents and employees, and other persons performing portions of the Work under a contract with the Contractor.

3.3.3 The Contractor shall not be relieved of obligations to perform the Work in accordance with the Contract Documents either by activities or duties of the Architect in the Architect's administration of the Contract, or by tests, inspections or approvals required or performed by persons other than the Contractor.

3.3.4 The Contractor shall be responsible for inspection of portions of Work already performed under this Contract to determine that such portions are in proper condition to receive subsequent Work.

3.4 LABOR AND MATERIALS

3.4.1 Unless otherwise provided in the Contract Documents, the Contractor shall provide and pay for labor, materials, equipment, tools, construction equipment and machinery, water, heat, utilities, transportation, and other facilities and services necessary for proper execution and completion of the Work, whether temporary or permanent and whether or not incorporated or to be incorporated in the Work.

3.4.2 The Contractor shall enforce strict discipline and good order among the Contractor's employees and other persons carrying out the Contract. The Contractor shall not permit employment of unfit persons or persons not skilled in tasks assigned to them.

3.5 WARRANTY

3.5.1 The Contractor warrants to the Owner and Architect that materials and equipment furnished under the Contract will be of good quality and new unless otherwise required or permitted by the Contract Documents, that the Work will be free from defects not inherent in the quality required or permitted, and that the Work will conform with the requirements of the Contract Documents. Work not conforming to these requirements, including substitutions not properly approved and authorized, may be considered defective. The Contractor's warranty excludes remedy for damage or defect caused by abuse, modifications not executed by the Contractor, improper or insufficient maintenance, improper operation, or normal wear and tear under normal usage. If required by the Architect, the Contractor shall furnish satisfactory evidence as to the kind and quality of materials and equipment.

3.6 TAXES

3.6.1 The Contractor shall pay sales, consumer, use and similar taxes for the Work or portions thereof provided by the Contractor which are legally enacted when bids are received or negotiations concluded, whether or not yet effective or merely scheduled to go into effect.

3.7 PERMITS, FEES AND NOTICES

3.7.1 Unless otherwise provided in the Contract Documents, the Contractor shall secure and pay for the building permit and other permits and governmental fees, licenses and inspections necessary for proper execution and completion of the Work which are customarily secured after execution of the Contract and which are legally required when bids are received or negotiations concluded.

3.7.2 The Contractor shall comply with and give notices required by laws, ordinances, rules, regulations and lawful orders of public authorities bearing on performance of the Work.

3.7.3 It is not the Contractor's responsibility to ascertain that the Contract Documents are in accordance with applicable laws, statutes, ordinances, building codes, and rules and regulations. However, if the Contractor observes that portions of the Contract Documents are at variance therewith, the Contractor shall promptly notify the Architect and Owner in writing, and necessary changes shall be accomplished by appropriate Modification.

3.7.4 If the Contractor performs Work knowing it to be contrary to laws, statutes, ordinances, building codes, and rules and regulations without such notice to the Architect and Owner, the Contractor shall assume full responsibility for such Work and shall bear the attributable costs.

3.8 ALLOWANCES

3.8.1 The Contractor shall include in the Contract Sum all allowances stated in the Contract Documents. Items covered by allowances shall be supplied for such amounts and by such persons or entities as the Owner may direct, but the Contractor shall not be required to employ persons or entities against which the Contractor makes reasonable objection.

3.8.2 Unless otherwise provided in the Contract Documents:

.1 materials and equipment under an allowance shall be selected promptly by the Owner to avoid delay in the Work;

.2 allowances shall cover the cost to the Contractor of materials and equipment delivered at the site and all required taxes, less applicable trade discounts;

AIA DOCUMENT A201 • GENERAL CONDITIONS OF THE CONTRACT FOR CONSTRUCTION • FOURTEENTH EDITION
AIA® • ©1987 THE AMERICAN INSTITUTE OF ARCHITECTS, 1735 NEW YORK AVENUE, N.W., WASHINGTON, D.C. 20006

.3 Contractor's costs for unloading and handling at the site, labor, installation costs, overhead, profit and other expenses contemplated for stated allowance amounts shall be included in the Contract Sum and not in the allowances;

.4 whenever costs are more than or less than allowances, the Contract Sum shall be adjusted accordingly by Change Order. The amount of the Change Order shall reflect (1) the difference between actual costs and the allowances under Clause 3.8.2.2 and (2) changes in Contractor's costs under Clause 3.8.2.3.

3.9 SUPERINTENDENT

3.9.1 The Contractor shall employ a competent superintendent and necessary assistants who shall be in attendance at the Project site during performance of the Work. The superintendent shall represent the Contractor, and communications given to the superintendent shall be as binding as if given to the Contractor. Important communications shall be confirmed in writing. Other communications shall be similarly confirmed on written request in each case.

3.10 CONTRACTOR'S CONSTRUCTION SCHEDULES

3.10.1 The Contractor, promptly after being awarded the Contract, shall prepare and submit for the Owner's and Architect's information a Contractor's construction schedule for the Work. The schedule shall not exceed time limits current under the Contract Documents, shall be revised at appropriate intervals as required by the conditions of the Work and Project, shall be related to the entire Project to the extent required by the Contract Documents, and shall provide for expeditious and practicable execution of the Work.

3.10.2 The Contractor shall prepare and keep current, for the Architect's approval, a schedule of submittals which is coordinated with the Contractor's construction schedule and allows the Architect reasonable time to review submittals.

3.10.3 The Contractor shall conform to the most recent schedules.

3.11 DOCUMENTS AND SAMPLES AT THE SITE

3.11.1 The Contractor shall maintain at the site for the Owner one record copy of the Drawings, Specifications, addenda, Change Orders and other Modifications, in good order and marked currently to record changes and selections made during construction, and in addition approved Shop Drawings, Product Data, Samples and similar required submittals. These shall be available to the Architect and shall be delivered to the Architect for submittal to the Owner upon completion of the Work.

3.12 SHOP DRAWINGS, PRODUCT DATA AND SAMPLES

3.12.1 Shop Drawings are drawings, diagrams, schedules and other data specially prepared for the Work by the Contractor or a Subcontractor, Sub-subcontractor, manufacturer, supplier or distributor to illustrate some portion of the Work.

3.12.2 Product Data are illustrations, standard schedules, performance charts, instructions, brochures, diagrams and other information furnished by the Contractor to illustrate materials or equipment for some portion of the Work.

3.12.3 Samples are physical examples which illustrate materials, equipment or workmanship and establish standards by which the Work will be judged.

3.12.4 Shop Drawings, Product Data, Samples and similar submittals are not Contract Documents. The purpose of their submittal is to demonstrate for those portions of the Work for which submittals are required the way the Contractor proposes to conform to the information given and the design concept expressed in the Contract Documents. Review by the Architect is subject to the limitations of Subparagraph 4.2.7.

3.12.5 The Contractor shall review, approve and submit to the Architect Shop Drawings, Product Data, Samples and similar submittals required by the Contract Documents with reasonable promptness and in such sequence as to cause no delay in the Work or in the activities of the Owner or of separate contractors. Submittals made by the Contractor which are not required by the Contract Documents may be returned without action.

3.12.6 The Contractor shall perform no portion of the Work requiring submittal and review of Shop Drawings, Product Data, Samples or similar submittals until the respective submittal has been approved by the Architect. Such Work shall be in accordance with approved submittals.

3.12.7 By approving and submitting Shop Drawings, Product Data, Samples and similar submittals, the Contractor represents that the Contractor has determined and verified materials, field measurements and field construction criteria related thereto, or will do so, and has checked and coordinated the information contained within such submittals with the requirements of the Work and of the Contract Documents.

3.12.8 The Contractor shall not be relieved of responsibility for deviations from requirements of the Contract Documents by the Architect's approval of Shop Drawings, Product Data, Samples or similar submittals unless the Contractor has specifically informed the Architect in writing of such deviation at the time of submittal and the Architect has given written approval to the specific deviation. The Contractor shall not be relieved of responsibility for errors or omissions in Shop Drawings, Product Data, Samples or similar submittals by the Architect's approval thereof.

3.12.9 The Contractor shall direct specific attention, in writing or on resubmitted Shop Drawings, Product Data, Samples or similar submittals, to revisions other than those requested by the Architect on previous submittals.

3.12.10 Informational submittals upon which the Architect is not expected to take responsive action may be so identified in the Contract Documents.

3.12.11 When professional certification of performance criteria of materials, systems or equipment is required by the Contract Documents, the Architect shall be entitled to rely upon the accuracy and completeness of such calculations and certifications.

3.13 USE OF SITE

3.13.1 The Contractor shall confine operations at the site to areas permitted by law, ordinances, permits and the Contract Documents and shall not unreasonably encumber the site with materials or equipment.

3.14 CUTTING AND PATCHING

3.14.1 The Contractor shall be responsible for cutting, fitting or patching required to complete the Work or to make its parts fit together properly.

3.14.2 The Contractor shall not damage or endanger a portion of the Work or fully or partially completed construction of the Owner or separate contractors by cutting, patching or otherwise altering such construction, or by excavation. The Contractor shall not cut or otherwise alter such construction by the

Owner or a separate contractor except with written consent of the Owner and of such separate contractor; such consent shall not be unreasonably withheld. The Contractor shall not unreasonably withhold from the Owner or a separate contractor the Contractor's consent to cutting or otherwise altering the Work.

3.15 CLEANING UP

3.15.1 The Contractor shall keep the premises and surrounding area free from accumulation of waste materials or rubbish caused by operations under the Contract. At completion of the Work the Contractor shall remove from and about the Project waste materials, rubbish, the Contractor's tools, construction equipment, machinery and surplus materials.

3.15.2 If the Contractor fails to clean up as provided in the Contract Documents, the Owner may do so and the cost thereof shall be charged to the Contractor.

3.16 ACCESS TO WORK

3.16.1 The Contractor shall provide the Owner and Architect access to the Work in preparation and progress wherever located.

3.17 ROYALTIES AND PATENTS

3.17.1 The Contractor shall pay all royalties and license fees. The Contractor shall defend suits or claims for infringement of patent rights and shall hold the Owner and Architect harmless from loss on account thereof, but shall not be responsible for such defense or loss when a particular design, process or product of a particular manufacturer or manufacturers is required by the Contract Documents. However, if the Contractor has reason to believe that the required design, process or product is an infringement of a patent, the Contractor shall be responsible for such loss unless such information is promptly furnished to the Architect.

3.18 INDEMNIFICATION

3.18.1 To the fullest extent permitted by law, the Contractor shall indemnify and hold harmless the Owner, Architect, Architect's consultants, and agents and employees of any of them from and against claims, damages, losses and expenses, including but not limited to attorneys' fees, arising out of or resulting from performance of the Work, provided that such claim, damage, loss or expense is attributable to bodily injury, sickness, disease or death, or to injury to or destruction of tangible property (other than the Work itself) including loss of use resulting therefrom, but only to the extent caused in whole or in part by negligent acts or omissions of the Contractor, a Subcontractor, anyone directly or indirectly employed by them or anyone for whose acts they may be liable, regardless of whether or not such claim, damage, loss or expense is caused in part by a party indemnified hereunder. Such obligation shall not be construed to negate, abridge, or reduce other rights or obligations of indemnity which would otherwise exist as to a party or person described in this Paragraph 3.18.

3.18.2 In claims against any person or entity indemnified under this Paragraph 3.18 by an employee of the Contractor, a Subcontractor, anyone directly or indirectly employed by them or anyone for whose acts they may be liable, the indemnification obligation under this Paragraph 3.18 shall not be limited by a limitation on amount or type of damages, compensation or benefits payable by or for the Contractor or a Subcontractor under workers' or workmen's compensation acts, disability benefit acts or other employee benefit acts.

3.18.3 The obligations of the Contractor under this Paragraph 3.18 shall not extend to the liability of the Architect, the Architect's consultants, and agents and employees of any of them arising out of (1) the preparation or approval of maps, drawings, opinions, reports, surveys, Change Orders, designs or specifications, or (2) the giving of or the failure to give directions or instructions by the Architect, the Architect's consultants, and agents and employees of any of them provided such giving or failure to give is the primary cause of the injury or damage.

ARTICLE 4

ADMINISTRATION OF THE CONTRACT

4.1 ARCHITECT

4.1.1 The Architect is the person lawfully licensed to practice architecture or an entity lawfully practicing architecture identified as such in the Agreement and is referred to throughout the Contract Documents as if singular in number. The term "Architect" means the Architect or the Architect's authorized representative.

4.1.2 Duties, responsibilities and limitations of authority of the Architect as set forth in the Contract Documents shall not be restricted, modified or extended without written consent of the Owner, Contractor and Architect. Consent shall not be unreasonably withheld.

4.1.3 In case of termination of employment of the Architect, the Owner shall appoint an architect against whom the Contractor makes no reasonable objection and whose status under the Contract Documents shall be that of the former architect.

4.1.4 Disputes arising under Subparagraphs 4.1.2 and 4.1.3 shall be subject to arbitration.

4.2 ARCHITECT'S ADMINISTRATION OF THE CONTRACT

4.2.1 The Architect will provide administration of the Contract as described in the Contract Documents, and will be the Owner's representative (1) during construction, (2) until final payment is due and (3) with the Owner's concurrence, from time to time during the correction period described in Paragraph 12.2. The Architect will advise and consult with the Owner. The Architect will have authority to act on behalf of the Owner only to the extent provided in the Contract Documents, unless otherwise modified by written instrument in accordance with other provisions of the Contract.

4.2.2 The Architect will visit the site at intervals appropriate to the stage of construction to become generally familiar with the progress and quality of the completed Work and to determine in general if the Work is being performed in a manner indicating that the Work, when completed, will be in accordance with the Contract Documents. However, the Architect will not be required to make exhaustive or continuous on-site inspections to check quality or quantity of the Work. On the basis of on-site observations as an architect, the Architect will keep the Owner informed of progress of the Work, and will endeavor to guard the Owner against defects and deficiencies in the Work.

4.2.3 The Architect will not have control over or charge of and will not be responsible for construction means, methods, techniques, sequences or procedures, or for safety precautions and programs in connection with the Work, since these are solely the Contractor's responsibility as provided in Paragraph 3.3. The Architect will not be responsible for the Contractor's failure to carry out the Work in accordance with the Contract Documents. The Architect will not have control over or charge of and will not be responsible for acts or omissions of the Con-

AIA DOCUMENT A201 • GENERAL CONDITIONS OF THE CONTRACT FOR CONSTRUCTION • FOURTEENTH EDITION
AIA® • ©1987 THE AMERICAN INSTITUTE OF ARCHITECTS, 1735 NEW YORK AVENUE, N.W., WASHINGTON, D.C. 20006

tractor, Subcontractors, or their agents or employees, or of any other persons performing portions of the Work.

4.2.4 Communications Facilitating Contract Administration.
Except as otherwise provided in the Contract Documents or when direct communications have been specially authorized, the Owner and Contractor shall endeavor to communicate through the Architect. Communications by and with the Architect's consultants shall be through the Architect. Communications by and with Subcontractors and material suppliers shall be through the Contractor. Communications by and with separate contractors shall be through the Owner.

4.2.5 Based on the Architect's observations and evaluations of the Contractor's Applications for Payment, the Architect will review and certify the amounts due the Contractor and will issue Certificates for Payment in such amounts.

4.2.6 The Architect will have authority to reject Work which does not conform to the Contract Documents. Whenever the Architect considers it necessary or advisable for implementation of the intent of the Contract Documents, the Architect will have authority to require additional inspection or testing of the Work in accordance with Subparagraphs 13.5.2 and 13.5.3, whether or not such Work is fabricated, installed or completed. However, neither this authority of the Architect nor a decision made in good faith either to exercise or not to exercise such authority shall give rise to a duty or responsibility of the Architect to the Contractor, Subcontractors, material and equipment suppliers, their agents or employees, or other persons performing portions of the Work.

4.2.7 The Architect will review and approve or take other appropriate action upon the Contractor's submittals such as Shop Drawings, Product Data and Samples, but only for the limited purpose of checking for conformance with information given and the design concept expressed in the Contract Documents. The Architect's action will be taken with such reasonable promptness as to cause no delay in the Work or in the activities of the Owner, Contractor or separate contractors, while allowing sufficient time in the Architect's professional judgment to permit adequate review. Review of such submittals is not conducted for the purpose of determining the accuracy and completeness of other details such as dimensions and quantities, or for substantiating instructions for installation or performance of equipment or systems, all of which remain the responsibility of the Contractor as required by the Contract Documents. The Architect's review of the Contractor's submittals shall not relieve the Contractor of the obligations under Paragraphs 3.3, 3.5 and 3.12. The Architect's review shall not constitute approval of safety precautions or, unless otherwise specifically stated by the Architect, of any construction means, methods, techniques, sequences or procedures. The Architect's approval of a specific item shall not indicate approval of an assembly of which the item is a component.

4.2.8 The Architect will prepare Change Orders and Construction Change Directives, and may authorize minor changes in the Work as provided in Paragraph 7.4.

4.2.9 The Architect will conduct inspections to determine the date or dates of Substantial Completion and the date of final completion, will receive and forward to the Owner for the Owner's review and records written warranties and related documents required by the Contract and assembled by the Contractor, and will issue a final Certificate for Payment upon compliance with the requirements of the Contract Documents.

4.2.10 If the Owner and Architect agree, the Architect will provide one or more project representatives to assist in carrying out the Architect's responsibilities at the site. The duties, responsibilities and limitations of authority of such project representatives shall be as set forth in an exhibit to be incorporated in the Contract Documents.

4.2.11 The Architect will interpret and decide matters concerning performance under and requirements of the Contract Documents on written request of either the Owner or Contractor. The Architect's response to such requests will be made with reasonable promptness and within any time limits agreed upon. If no agreement is made concerning the time within which interpretations required of the Architect shall be furnished in compliance with this Paragraph 4.2, then delay shall not be recognized on account of failure by the Architect to furnish such interpretations until 15 days after written request is made for them.

4.2.12 Interpretations and decisions of the Architect will be consistent with the intent of and reasonably inferable from the Contract Documents and will be in writing or in the form of drawings. When making such interpretations and decisions, the Architect will endeavor to secure faithful performance by both Owner and Contractor, will not show partiality to either and will not be liable for results of interpretations or decisions so rendered in good faith.

4.2.13 The Architect's decisions on matters relating to aesthetic effect will be final if consistent with the intent expressed in the Contract Documents.

4.3 CLAIMS AND DISPUTES

4.3.1 Definition. A Claim is a demand or assertion by one of the parties seeking, as a matter of right, adjustment or interpretation of Contract terms, payment of money, extension of time or other relief with respect to the terms of the Contract. The term "Claim" also includes other disputes and matters in question between the Owner and Contractor arising out of or relating to the Contract. Claims must be made by written notice. The responsibility to substantiate Claims shall rest with the party making the Claim.

4.3.2 Decision of Architect. Claims, including those alleging an error or omission by the Architect, shall be referred initially to the Architect for action as provided in Paragraph 4.4. A decision by the Architect, as provided in Subparagraph 4.4.4, shall be required as a condition precedent to arbitration or litigation of a Claim between the Contractor and Owner as to all such matters arising prior to the date final payment is due, regardless of (1) whether such matters relate to execution and progress of the Work or (2) the extent to which the Work has been completed. The decision by the Architect in response to a Claim shall not be a condition precedent to arbitration or litigation in the event (1) the position of Architect is vacant, (2) the Architect has not received evidence or has failed to render a decision within agreed time limits, (3) the Architect has failed to take action required under Subparagraph 4.4.4 within 30 days after the Claim is made, (4) 45 days have passed after the Claim has been referred to the Architect or (5) the Claim relates to a mechanic's lien.

4.3.3 Time Limits on Claims. Claims by either party must be made within 21 days after occurrence of the event giving rise to such Claim or within 21 days after the claimant first recognizes the condition giving rise to the Claim, whichever is later. Claims must be made by written notice. An additional Claim made after the initial Claim has been implemented by Change Order will not be considered unless submitted in a timely manner.

4.3.4 Continuing Contract Performance. Pending final resolution of a Claim including arbitration, unless otherwise agreed in writing the Contractor shall proceed diligently with performance of the Contract and the Owner shall continue to make payments in accordance with the Contract Documents.

4.3.5 Waiver of Claims: Final Payment. The making of final payment shall constitute a waiver of Claims by the Owner except those arising from:

.1 liens, Claims, security interests or encumbrances arising out of the Contract and unsettled;

.2 failure of the Work to comply with the requirements of the Contract Documents; or

.3 terms of special warranties required by the Contract Documents.

4.3.6 Claims for Concealed or Unknown Conditions. If conditions are encountered at the site which are (1) subsurface or otherwise concealed physical conditions which differ materially from those indicated in the Contract Documents or (2) unknown physical conditions of an unusual nature, which differ materially from those ordinarily found to exist and generally recognized as inherent in construction activities of the character provided for in the Contract Documents, then notice by the observing party shall be given to the other party promptly before conditions are disturbed and in no event later than 21 days after first observance of the conditions. The Architect will promptly investigate such conditions and, if they differ materially and cause an increase or decrease in the Contractor's cost of, or time required for, performance of any part of the Work, will recommend an equitable adjustment in the Contract Sum or Contract Time, or both. If the Architect determines that the conditions at the site are not materially different from those indicated in the Contract Documents and that no change in the terms of the Contract is justified, the Architect shall so notify the Owner and Contractor in writing, stating the reasons. Claims by either party in opposition to such determination must be made within 21 days after the Architect has given notice of the decision. If the Owner and Contractor cannot agree on an adjustment in the Contract Sum or Contract Time, the adjustment shall be referred to the Architect for initial determination, subject to further proceedings pursuant to Paragraph 4.4.

4.3.7 Claims for Additional Cost. If the Contractor wishes to make Claim for an increase in the Contract Sum, written notice as provided herein shall be given before proceeding to execute the Work. Prior notice is not required for Claims relating to an emergency endangering life or property arising under Paragraph 10.3. If the Contractor believes additional cost is involved for reasons including but not limited to (1) a written interpretation from the Architect, (2) an order by the Owner to stop the Work where the Contractor was not at fault, (3) a written order for a minor change in the Work issued by the Architect, (4) failure of payment by the Owner, (5) termination of the Contract by the Owner, (6) Owner's suspension or (7) other reasonable grounds, Claim shall be filed in accordance with the procedure established herein.

4.3.8 Claims for Additional Time

4.3.8.1 If the Contractor wishes to make Claim for an increase in the Contract Time, written notice as provided herein shall be given. The Contractor's Claim shall include an estimate of cost and of probable effect of delay on progress of the Work. In the case of a continuing delay only one Claim is necessary.

4.3.8.2 If adverse weather conditions are the basis for a Claim for additional time, such Claim shall be documented by data substantiating that weather conditions were abnormal for the period of time and could not have been reasonably anticipated, and that weather conditions had an adverse effect on the scheduled construction.

4.3.9 Injury or Damage to Person or Property. If either party to the Contract suffers injury or damage to person or property because of an act or omission of the other party, of any of the other party's employees or agents, or of others for whose acts such party is legally liable, written notice of such injury or damage, whether or not insured, shall be given to the other party within a reasonable time not exceeding 21 days after first observance. The notice shall provide sufficient detail to enable the other party to investigate the matter. If a Claim for additional cost or time related to this Claim is to be asserted, it shall be filed as provided in Subparagraphs 4.3.7 or 4.3.8.

4.4 RESOLUTION OF CLAIMS AND DISPUTES

4.4.1 The Architect will review Claims and take one or more of the following preliminary actions within ten days of receipt of a Claim: (1) request additional supporting data from the claimant, (2) submit a schedule to the parties indicating when the Architect expects to take action, (3) reject the Claim in whole or in part, stating reasons for rejection, (4) recommend approval of the Claim by the other party or (5) suggest a compromise. The Architect may also, but is not obligated to, notify the surety, if any, of the nature and amount of the Claim.

4.4.2 If a Claim has been resolved, the Architect will prepare or obtain appropriate documentation.

4.4.3 If a Claim has not been resolved, the party making the Claim shall, within ten days after the Architect's preliminary response, take one or more of the following actions: (1) submit additional supporting data requested by the Architect, (2) modify the initial Claim or (3) notify the Architect that the initial Claim stands.

4.4.4 If a Claim has not been resolved after consideration of the foregoing and of further evidence presented by the parties or requested by the Architect, the Architect will notify the parties in writing that the Architect's decision will be made within seven days, which decision shall be final and binding on the parties but subject to arbitration. Upon expiration of such time period, the Architect will render to the parties the Architect's written decision relative to the Claim, including any change in the Contract Sum or Contract Time or both. If there is a surety and there appears to be a possibility of a Contractor's default, the Architect may, but is not obligated to, notify the surety and request the surety's assistance in resolving the controversy.

4.5 ARBITRATION

4.5.1 Controversies and Claims Subject to Arbitration. Any controversy or Claim arising out of or related to the Contract, or the breach thereof, shall be settled by arbitration in accordance with the Construction Industry Arbitration Rules of the American Arbitration Association, and judgment upon the award rendered by the arbitrator or arbitrators may be entered in any court having jurisdiction thereof, except controversies or Claims relating to aesthetic effect and except those waived as provided for in Subparagraph 4.3.5. Such controversies or Claims upon which the Architect has given notice and rendered a decision as provided in Subparagraph 4.4.4 shall be subject to arbitration upon written demand of either party. Arbitration may be commenced when 45 days have passed after a Claim has been referred to the Architect as provided in Paragraph 4.3 and no decision has been rendered.

4.5.2 Rules and Notices for Arbitration. Claims between the Owner and Contractor not resolved under Paragraph 4.4 shall, if subject to arbitration under Subparagraph 4.5.1, be decided by arbitration in accordance with the Construction Industry Arbitration Rules of the American Arbitration Association currently in effect, unless the parties mutually agree otherwise. Notice of demand for arbitration shall be filed in writing with the other party to the Agreement between the Owner and Contractor and with the American Arbitration Association, and a copy shall be filed with the Architect.

4.5.3 Contract Performance During Arbitration. During arbitration proceedings, the Owner and Contractor shall comply with Subparagraph 4.3.4.

4.5.4 When Arbitration May Be Demanded. Demand for arbitration of any Claim may not be made until the earlier of (1) the date on which the Architect has rendered a final written decision on the Claim, (2) the tenth day after the parties have presented evidence to the Architect or have been given reasonable opportunity to do so, if the Architect has not rendered a final written decision by that date, or (3) any of the five events described in Subparagraph 4.3.2.

4.5.4.1 When a written decision of the Architect states that (1) the decision is final but subject to arbitration and (2) a demand for arbitration of a Claim covered by such decision must be made within 30 days after the date on which the party making the demand receives the final written decision, then failure to demand arbitration within said 30 days' period shall result in the Architect's decision becoming final and binding upon the Owner and Contractor. If the Architect renders a decision after arbitration proceedings have been initiated, such decision may be entered as evidence, but shall not supersede arbitration proceedings unless the decision is acceptable to all parties concerned.

4.5.4.2 A demand for arbitration shall be made within the time limits specified in Subparagraphs 4.5.1 and 4.5.4 and Clause 4.5.4.1 as applicable, and in other cases within a reasonable time after the Claim has arisen, and in no event shall it be made after the date when institution of legal or equitable proceedings based on such Claim would be barred by the applicable statute of limitations as determined pursuant to Paragraph 13.7.

4.5.5 Limitation on Consolidation or Joinder. No arbitration arising out of or relating to the Contract Documents shall include, by consolidation or joinder or in any other manner, the Architect, the Architect's employees or consultants, except by written consent containing specific reference to the Agreement and signed by the Architect, Owner, Contractor and any other person or entity sought to be joined. No arbitration shall include, by consolidation or joinder or in any other manner, parties other than the Owner, Contractor, a separate contractor as described in Article 6 and other persons substantially involved in a common question of fact or law whose presence is required if complete relief is to be accorded in arbitration. No person or entity other than the Owner, Contractor or a separate contractor as described in Article 6 shall be included as an original third party or additional third party to an arbitration whose interest or responsibility is insubstantial. Consent to arbitration involving an additional person or entity shall not constitute consent to arbitration of a dispute not described therein or with a person or entity not named or described therein. The foregoing agreement to arbitrate and other agreements to arbitrate with an additional person or entity duly consented to by parties to the Agreement shall be specifically enforceable under applicable law in any court having jurisdiction thereof.

4.5.6 Claims and Timely Assertion of Claims. A party who files a notice of demand for arbitration must assert in the demand all Claims then known to that party on which arbitration is permitted to be demanded. When a party fails to include a Claim through oversight, inadvertence or excusable neglect, or when a Claim has matured or been acquired subsequently, the arbitrator or arbitrators may permit amendment.

4.5.7 Judgment on Final Award. The award rendered by the arbitrator or arbitrators shall be final, and judgment may be entered upon it in accordance with applicable law in any court having jurisdiction thereof.

ARTICLE 5

SUBCONTRACTORS

5.1 DEFINITIONS

5.1.1 A Subcontractor is a person or entity who has a direct contract with the Contractor to perform a portion of the Work at the site. The term "Subcontractor" is referred to throughout the Contract Documents as if singular in number and means a Subcontractor or an authorized representative of the Subcontractor. The term "Subcontractor" does not include a separate contractor or subcontractors of a separate contractor.

5.1.2 A Sub-subcontractor is a person or entity who has a direct or indirect contract with a Subcontractor to perform a portion of the Work at the site. The term "Sub-subcontractor" is referred to throughout the Contract Documents as if singular in number and means a Sub-subcontractor or an authorized representative of the Sub-subcontractor.

5.2 AWARD OF SUBCONTRACTS AND OTHER CONTRACTS FOR PORTIONS OF THE WORK

5.2.1 Unless otherwise stated in the Contract Documents or the bidding requirements, the Contractor, as soon as practicable after award of the Contract, shall furnish in writing to the Owner through the Architect the names of persons or entities (including those who are to furnish materials or equipment fabricated to a special design) proposed for each principal portion of the Work. The Architect will promptly reply to the Contractor in writing stating whether or not the Owner or the Architect, after due investigation, has reasonable objection to any such proposed person or entity. Failure of the Owner or Architect to reply promptly shall constitute notice of no reasonable objection.

5.2.2 The Contractor shall not contract with a proposed person or entity to whom the Owner or Architect has made reasonable and timely objection. The Contractor shall not be required to contract with anyone to whom the Contractor has made reasonable objection.

5.2.3 If the Owner or Architect has reasonable objection to a person or entity proposed by the Contractor, the Contractor shall propose another to whom the Owner or Architect has no reasonable objection. The Contract Sum shall be increased or decreased by the difference in cost occasioned by such change and an appropriate Change Order shall be issued. However, no increase in the Contract Sum shall be allowed for such change unless the Contractor has acted promptly and responsively in submitting names as required.

5.2.4 The Contractor shall not change a Subcontractor, person or entity previously selected if the Owner or Architect makes reasonable objection to such change.

5.3 SUBCONTRACTUAL RELATIONS

5.3.1 By appropriate agreement, written where legally required for validity, the Contractor shall require each Subcontractor, to the extent of the Work to be performed by the Subcontractor, to be bound to the Contractor by terms of the Contract Documents, and to assume toward the Contractor all the obligations and responsibilities which the Contractor, by these Documents, assumes toward the Owner and Architect. Each subcontract agreement shall preserve and protect the rights of the Owner and Architect under the Contract Documents with respect to the Work to be performed by the Subcontractor so that subcontracting thereof will not prejudice such rights, and shall allow to the Subcontractor, unless specifically provided otherwise in the subcontract agreement, the benefit of all rights, remedies and redress against the Contractor that the Contractor, by the Contract Documents, has against the Owner. Where appropriate, the Contractor shall require each Subcontractor to enter into similar agreements with Sub-sub-contractors. The Contractor shall make available to each proposed Subcontractor, prior to the execution of the subcontract agreement, copies of the Contract Documents to which the Subcontractor will be bound, and, upon written request of the Subcontractor, identify to the Subcontractor terms and conditions of the proposed subcontract agreement which may be at variance with the Contract Documents. Subcontractors shall similarly make copies of applicable portions of such documents available to their respective proposed Sub-subcontractors.

5.4 CONTINGENT ASSIGNMENT OF SUBCONTRACTS

5.4.1 Each subcontract agreement for a portion of the Work is assigned by the Contractor to the Owner provided that:

.1 assignment is effective only after termination of the Contract by the Owner for cause pursuant to Paragraph 14.2 and only for those subcontract agreements which the Owner accepts by notifying the Subcontractor in writing; and

.2 assignment is subject to the prior rights of the surety, if any, obligated under bond relating to the Contract.

5.4.2 If the Work has been suspended for more than 30 days, the Subcontractor's compensation shall be equitably adjusted.

ARTICLE 6

CONSTRUCTION BY OWNER OR BY SEPARATE CONTRACTORS

6.1 OWNER'S RIGHT TO PERFORM CONSTRUCTION AND TO AWARD SEPARATE CONTRACTS

6.1.1 The Owner reserves the right to perform construction or operations related to the Project with the Owner's own forces, and to award separate contracts in connection with other portions of the Project or other construction or operations on the site under Conditions of the Contract identical or substantially similar to these including those portions related to insurance and waiver of subrogation. If the Contractor claims that delay or additional cost is involved because of such action by the Owner, the Contractor shall make such Claim as provided elsewhere in the Contract Documents.

6.1.2 When separate contracts are awarded for different portions of the Project or other construction or operations on the site, the term "Contractor" in the Contract Documents in each case shall mean the Contractor who executes each separate Owner-Contractor Agreement.

6.1.3 The Owner shall provide for coordination of the activities of the Owner's own forces and of each separate contractor with the Work of the Contractor, who shall cooperate with them. The Contractor shall participate with other separate contractors and the Owner in reviewing their construction schedules when directed to do so. The Contractor shall make any revisions to the construction schedule and Contract Sum deemed necessary after a joint review and mutual agreement. The construction schedules shall then constitute the schedules to be used by the Contractor, separate contractors and the Owner until subsequently revised.

6.1.4 Unless otherwise provided in the Contract Documents, when the Owner performs construction or operations related to the Project with the Owner's own forces, the Owner shall be deemed to be subject to the same obligations and to have the same rights which apply to the Contractor under the Conditions of the Contract, including, without excluding others, those stated in Article 3, this Article 6 and Articles 10, 11 and 12.

6.2 MUTUAL RESPONSIBILITY

6.2.1 The Contractor shall afford the Owner and separate contractors reasonable opportunity for introduction and storage of their materials and equipment and performance of their activities and shall connect and coordinate the Contractor's construction and operations with theirs as required by the Contract Documents.

6.2.2 If part of the Contractor's Work depends for proper execution or results upon construction or operations by the Owner or a separate contractor, the Contractor shall, prior to proceeding with that portion of the Work, promptly report to the Architect apparent discrepancies or defects in such other construction that would render it unsuitable for such proper execution and results. Failure of the Contractor so to report shall constitute an acknowledgment that the Owner's or separate contractors' completed or partially completed construction is fit and proper to receive the Contractor's Work, except as to defects not then reasonably discoverable.

6.2.3 Costs caused by delays or by improperly timed activities or defective construction shall be borne by the party responsible therefor.

6.2.4 The Contractor shall promptly remedy damage wrongfully caused by the Contractor to completed or partially completed construction or to property of the Owner or separate contractors as provided in Subparagraph 10.2.5.

6.2.5 Claims and other disputes and matters in question between the Contractor and a separate contractor shall be subject to the provisions of Paragraph 4.3 provided the separate contractor has reciprocal obligations.

6.2.6 The Owner and each separate contractor shall have the same responsibilities for cutting and patching as are described for the Contractor in Paragraph 3.14.

6.3 OWNER'S RIGHT TO CLEAN UP

6.3.1 If a dispute arises among the Contractor, separate contractors and the Owner as to the responsibility under their respective contracts for maintaining the premises and surrounding area free from waste materials and rubbish as described in Paragraph 3.15, the Owner may clean up and allocate the cost among those responsible as the Architect determines to be just.

ARTICLE 7

CHANGES IN THE WORK

7.1 CHANGES

7.1.1 Changes in the Work may be accomplished after execution of the Contract, and without invalidating the Contract, by Change Order, Construction Change Directive or order for a minor change in the Work, subject to the limitations stated in this Article 7 and elsewhere in the Contract Documents.

7.1.2 A Change Order shall be based upon agreement among the Owner, Contractor and Architect; a Construction Change Directive requires agreement by the Owner and Architect and may or may not be agreed to by the Contractor; an order for a minor change in the Work may be issued by the Architect alone.

7.1.3 Changes in the Work shall be performed under applicable provisions of the Contract Documents, and the Contractor shall proceed promptly, unless otherwise provided in the Change Order, Construction Change Directive or order for a minor change in the Work.

7.1.4 If unit prices are stated in the Contract Documents or subsequently agreed upon, and if quantities originally contemplated are so changed in a proposed Change Order or Construction Change Directive that application of such unit prices to quantities of Work proposed will cause substantial inequity to the Owner or Contractor, the applicable unit prices shall be equitably adjusted.

7.2 CHANGE ORDERS

7.2.1 A Change Order is a written instrument prepared by the Architect and signed by the Owner, Contractor and Architect, stating their agreement upon all of the following:

.1 a change in the Work;

.2 the amount of the adjustment in the Contract Sum, if any; and

.3 the extent of the adjustment in the Contract Time, if any.

7.2.2 Methods used in determining adjustments to the Contract Sum may include those listed in Subparagraph 7.3.3.

7.3 CONSTRUCTION CHANGE DIRECTIVES

7.3.1 A Construction Change Directive is a written order prepared by the Architect and signed by the Owner and Architect, directing a change in the Work and stating a proposed basis for adjustment, if any, in the Contract Sum or Contract Time, or both. The Owner may by Construction Change Directive, without invalidating the Contract, order changes in the Work within the general scope of the Contract consisting of additions, deletions or other revisions, the Contract Sum and Contract Time being adjusted accordingly.

7.3.2 A Construction Change Directive shall be used in the absence of total agreement on the terms of a Change Order.

7.3.3 If the Construction Change Directive provides for an adjustment to the Contract Sum, the adjustment shall be based on one of the following methods:

.1 mutual acceptance of a lump sum properly itemized and supported by sufficient substantiating data to permit evaluation;

.2 unit prices stated in the Contract Documents or subsequently agreed upon;

.3 cost to be determined in a manner agreed upon by the parties and a mutually acceptable fixed or percentage fee; or

.4 as provided in Subparagraph 7.3.6.

7.3.4 Upon receipt of a Construction Change Directive, the Contractor shall promptly proceed with the change in the Work involved and advise the Architect of the Contractor's agreement or disagreement with the method, if any, provided in the Construction Change Directive for determining the proposed adjustment in the Contract Sum or Contract Time.

7.3.5 A Construction Change Directive signed by the Contractor indicates the agreement of the Contractor therewith, including adjustment in Contract Sum and Contract Time or the method for determining them. Such agreement shall be effective immediately and shall be recorded as a Change Order.

7.3.6 If the Contractor does not respond promptly or disagrees with the method for adjustment in the Contract Sum, the method and the adjustment shall be determined by the Architect on the basis of reasonable expenditures and savings of those performing the Work attributable to the change, including, in case of an increase in the Contract Sum, a reasonable allowance for overhead and profit. In such case, and also under Clause 7.3.3.3, the Contractor shall keep and present, in such form as the Architect may prescribe, an itemized accounting together with appropriate supporting data. Unless otherwise provided in the Contract Documents, costs for the purposes of this Subparagraph 7.3.6 shall be limited to the following:

.1 costs of labor, including social security, old age and unemployment insurance, fringe benefits required by agreement or custom, and workers' or workmen's compensation insurance;

.2 costs of materials, supplies and equipment, including cost of transportation, whether incorporated or consumed;

.3 rental costs of machinery and equipment, exclusive of hand tools, whether rented from the Contractor or others;

.4 costs of premiums for all bonds and insurance, permit fees, and sales, use or similar taxes related to the Work; and

.5 additional costs of supervision and field office personnel directly attributable to the change.

7.3.7 Pending final determination of cost to the Owner, amounts not in dispute may be included in Applications for Payment. The amount of credit to be allowed by the Contractor to the Owner for a deletion or change which results in a net decrease in the Contract Sum shall be actual net cost as confirmed by the Architect. When both additions and credits covering related Work or substitutions are involved in a change, the allowance for overhead and profit shall be figured on the basis of net increase, if any, with respect to that change.

7.3.8 If the Owner and Contractor do not agree with the adjustment in Contract Time or the method for determining it, the adjustment or the method shall be referred to the Architect for determination.

7.3.9 When the Owner and Contractor agree with the determination made by the Architect concerning the adjustments in the Contract Sum and Contract Time, or otherwise reach agreement upon the adjustments, such agreement shall be effective immediately and shall be recorded by preparation and execution of an appropriate Change Order.

7.4 MINOR CHANGES IN THE WORK

7.4.1 The Architect will have authority to order minor changes in the Work not involving adjustment in the Contract Sum or extension of the Contract Time and not inconsistent with the intent of the Contract Documents. Such changes shall be effected by written order and shall be binding on the Owner and Contractor. The Contractor shall carry out such written orders promptly.

ARTICLE 8

TIME

8.1 DEFINITIONS

8.1.1 Unless otherwise provided, Contract Time is the period of time, including authorized adjustments, allotted in the Contract Documents for Substantial Completion of the Work.

8.1.2 The date of commencement of the Work is the date established in the Agreement. The date shall not be postponed by the failure to act of the Contractor or of persons or entities for whom the Contractor is responsible.

8.1.3 The date of Substantial Completion is the date certified by the Architect in accordance with Paragraph 9.8.

8.1.4 The term "day" as used in the Contract Documents shall mean calendar day unless otherwise specifically defined.

8.2 PROGRESS AND COMPLETION

8.2.1 Time limits stated in the Contract Documents are of the essence of the Contract. By executing the Agreement the Contractor confirms that the Contract Time is a reasonable period for performing the Work.

8.2.2 The Contractor shall not knowingly, except by agreement or instruction of the Owner in writing, prematurely commence operations on the site or elsewhere prior to the effective date of insurance required by Article 11 to be furnished by the Contractor. The date of commencement of the Work shall not be changed by the effective date of such insurance. Unless the date of commencement is established by a notice to proceed given by the Owner, the Contractor shall notify the Owner in writing not less than five days or other agreed period before commencing the Work to permit the timely filing of mortgages, mechanic's liens and other security interests.

8.2.3 The Contractor shall proceed expeditiously with adequate forces and shall achieve Substantial Completion within the Contract Time.

8.3 DELAYS AND EXTENSIONS OF TIME

8.3.1 If the Contractor is delayed at any time in progress of the Work by an act or neglect of the Owner or Architect, or of an employee of either, or of a separate contractor employed by the Owner, or by changes ordered in the Work, or by labor disputes, fire, unusual delay in deliveries, unavoidable casualties or other causes beyond the Contractor's control, or by delay authorized by the Owner pending arbitration, or by other causes which the Architect determines may justify delay, then the Contract Time shall be extended by Change Order for such reasonable time as the Architect may determine.

8.3.2 Claims relating to time shall be made in accordance with applicable provisions of Paragraph 4.3.

8.3.3 This Paragraph 8.3 does not preclude recovery of damages for delay by either party under other provisions of the Contract Documents.

ARTICLE 9

PAYMENTS AND COMPLETION

9.1 CONTRACT SUM

9.1.1 The Contract Sum is stated in the Agreement and, including authorized adjustments, is the total amount payable by the Owner to the Contractor for performance of the Work under the Contract Documents.

9.2 SCHEDULE OF VALUES

9.2.1 Before the first Application for Payment, the Contractor shall submit to the Architect a schedule of values allocated to various portions of the Work, prepared in such form and supported by such data to substantiate its accuracy as the Architect may require. This schedule, unless objected to by the Architect, shall be used as a basis for reviewing the Contractor's Applications for Payment.

9.3 APPLICATIONS FOR PAYMENT

9.3.1 At least ten days before the date established for each progress payment, the Contractor shall submit to the Architect an itemized Application for Payment for operations completed in accordance with the schedule of values. Such application shall be notarized, if required, and supported by such data substantiating the Contractor's right to payment as the Owner or Architect may require, such as copies of requisitions from Subcontractors and material suppliers, and reflecting retainage if provided for elsewhere in the Contract Documents.

9.3.1.1 Such applications may include requests for payment on account of changes in the Work which have been properly authorized by Construction Change Directives but not yet included in Change Orders.

9.3.1.2 Such applications may not include requests for payment of amounts the Contractor does not intend to pay to a Subcontractor or material supplier because of a dispute or other reason.

9.3.2 Unless otherwise provided in the Contract Documents, payments shall be made on account of materials and equipment delivered and suitably stored at the site for subsequent incorporation in the Work. If approved in advance by the Owner, payment may similarly be made for materials and equipment suitably stored off the site at a location agreed upon in writing. Payment for materials and equipment stored on or off the site shall be conditioned upon compliance by the Contractor with procedures satisfactory to the Owner to establish the Owner's title to such materials and equipment or otherwise protect the Owner's interest, and shall include applicable insurance, storage and transportation to the site for such materials and equipment stored off the site.

9.3.3 The Contractor warrants that title to all Work covered by an Application for Payment will pass to the Owner no later than the time of payment. The Contractor further warrants that upon submittal of an Application for Payment all Work for which Certificates for Payment have been previously issued and payments received from the Owner shall, to the best of the Contractor's knowledge, information and belief, be free and clear of liens, claims, security interests or encumbrances in favor of the Contractor, Subcontractors, material suppliers, or other persons or entities making a claim by reason of having provided labor, materials and equipment relating to the Work.

9.4 CERTIFICATES FOR PAYMENT

9.4.1 The Architect will, within seven days after receipt of the Contractor's Application for Payment, either issue to the

AIA DOCUMENT A201 • GENERAL CONDITIONS OF THE CONTRACT FOR CONSTRUCTION • FOURTEENTH EDITION
AIA® • ©1987 THE AMERICAN INSTITUTE OF ARCHITECTS, 1735 NEW YORK AVENUE, N.W., WASHINGTON, D.C. 20006

Owner a Certificate for Payment, with a copy to the Contractor, for such amount as the Architect determines is properly due, or notify the Contractor and Owner in writing of the Architect's reasons for withholding certification in whole or in part as provided in Subparagraph 9.5.1.

9.4.2 The issuance of a Certificate for Payment will constitute a representation by the Architect to the Owner, based on the Architect's observations at the site and the data comprising the Application for Payment, that the Work has progressed to the point indicated and that, to the best of the Architect's knowledge, information and belief, quality of the Work is in accordance with the Contract Documents. The foregoing representations are subject to an evaluation of the Work for conformance with the Contract Documents upon Substantial Completion, to results of subsequent tests and inspections, to minor deviations from the Contract Documents correctable prior to completion and to specific qualifications expressed by the Architect. The issuance of a Certificate for Payment will further constitute a representation that the Contractor is entitled to payment in the amount certified. However, the issuance of a Certificate for Payment will not be a representation that the Architect has (1) made exhaustive or continuous on-site inspections to check the quality or quantity of the Work, (2) reviewed construction means, methods, techniques, sequences or procedures, (3) reviewed copies of requisitions received from Subcontractors and material suppliers and other data requested by the Owner to substantiate the Contractor's right to payment or (4) made examination to ascertain how or for what purpose the Contractor has used money previously paid on account of the Contract Sum.

9.5 DECISIONS TO WITHHOLD CERTIFICATION

9.5.1 The Architect may decide not to certify payment and may withhold a Certificate for Payment in whole or in part, to the extent reasonably necessary to protect the Owner, if in the Architect's opinion the representations to the Owner required by Subparagraph 9.4.2 cannot be made. If the Architect is unable to certify payment in the amount of the Application, the Architect will notify the Contractor and Owner as provided in Subparagraph 9.4.1. If the Contractor and Architect cannot agree on a revised amount, the Architect will promptly issue a Certificate for Payment for the amount for which the Architect is able to make such representations to the Owner. The Architect may also decide not to certify payment or, because of subsequently discovered evidence or subsequent observations, may nullify the whole or a part of a Certificate for Payment previously issued, to such extent as may be necessary in the Architect's opinion to protect the Owner from loss because of:

.1 defective Work not remedied;

.2 third party claims filed or reasonable evidence indicating probable filing of such claims;

.3 failure of the Contractor to make payments properly to Subcontractors or for labor, materials or equipment;

.4 reasonable evidence that the Work cannot be completed for the unpaid balance of the Contract Sum;

.5 damage to the Owner or another contractor;

.6 reasonable evidence that the Work will not be completed within the Contract Time, and that the unpaid balance would not be adequate to cover actual or liquidated damages for the anticipated delay; or

.7 persistent failure to carry out the Work in accordance with the Contract Documents.

9.5.2 When the above reasons for withholding certification are removed, certification will be made for amounts previously withheld.

9.6 PROGRESS PAYMENTS

9.6.1 After the Architect has issued a Certificate for Payment, the Owner shall make payment in the manner and within the time provided in the Contract Documents, and shall so notify the Architect.

9.6.2 The Contractor shall promptly pay each Subcontractor, upon receipt of payment from the Owner, out of the amount paid to the Contractor on account of such Subcontractor's portion of the Work, the amount to which said Subcontractor is entitled, reflecting percentages actually retained from payments to the Contractor on account of such Subcontractor's portion of the Work. The Contractor shall, by appropriate agreement with each Subcontractor, require each Subcontractor to make payments to Sub-subcontractors in similar manner.

9.6.3 The Architect will, on request, furnish to a Subcontractor, if practicable, information regarding percentages of completion or amounts applied for by the Contractor and action taken thereon by the Architect and Owner on account of portions of the Work done by such Subcontractor.

9.6.4 Neither the Owner nor Architect shall have an obligation to pay or to see to the payment of money to a Subcontractor except as may otherwise be required by law.

9.6.5 Payment to material suppliers shall be treated in a manner similar to that provided in Subparagraphs 9.6.2, 9.6.3 and 9.6.4.

9.6.6 A Certificate for Payment, a progress payment, or partial or entire use or occupancy of the Project by the Owner shall not constitute acceptance of Work not in accordance with the Contract Documents.

9.7 FAILURE OF PAYMENT

9.7.1 If the Architect does not issue a Certificate for Payment, through no fault of the Contractor, within seven days after receipt of the Contractor's Application for Payment, or if the Owner does not pay the Contractor within seven days after the date established in the Contract Documents the amount certified by the Architect or awarded by arbitration, then the Contractor may, upon seven additional days' written notice to the Owner and Architect, stop the Work until payment of the amount owing has been received. The Contract Time shall be extended appropriately and the Contract Sum shall be increased by the amount of the Contractor's reasonable costs of shut-down, delay and start-up, which shall be accomplished as provided in Article 7.

9.8 SUBSTANTIAL COMPLETION

9.8.1 Substantial Completion is the stage in the progress of the Work when the Work or designated portion thereof is sufficiently complete in accordance with the Contract Documents so the Owner can occupy or utilize the Work for its intended use.

9.8.2 When the Contractor considers that the Work, or a portion thereof which the Owner agrees to accept separately, is substantially complete, the Contractor shall prepare and submit to the Architect a comprehensive list of items to be completed or corrected. The Contractor shall proceed promptly to complete and correct items on the list. Failure to include an item on such list does not alter the responsibility of the Contractor to complete all Work in accordance with the Contract Documents. Upon receipt of the Contractor's list, the Architect will make an inspection to determine whether the Work or designated portion thereof is substantially complete. If the Architect's inspection discloses any item, whether or not included on the Contractor's list, which is not in accordance with the requirements of the Contract Documents, the Contractor shall, before issuance of the Certificate of Substantial Completion, complete or correct such item upon notification by the Architect. The Contractor shall then submit a request for another inspection by the Architect to determine Substantial Completion. When the Work or designated portion thereof is substantially complete, the Architect will prepare a Certificate of Substantial Completion which shall establish the date of Substantial Completion, shall establish responsibilities of the Owner and Contractor for security, maintenance, heat, utilities, damage to the Work and insurance, and shall fix the time within which the Contractor shall finish all items on the list accompanying the Certificate. Warranties required by the Contract Documents shall commence on the date of Substantial Completion of the Work or designated portion thereof unless otherwise provided in the Certificate of Substantial Completion. The Certificate of Substantial Completion shall be submitted to the Owner and Contractor for their written acceptance of responsibilities assigned to them in such Certificate.

9.8.3 Upon Substantial Completion of the Work or designated portion thereof and upon application by the Contractor and certification by the Architect, the Owner shall make payment, reflecting adjustment in retainage, if any, for such Work or portion thereof as provided in the Contract Documents.

9.9 PARTIAL OCCUPANCY OR USE

9.9.1 The Owner may occupy or use any completed or partially completed portion of the Work at any stage when such portion is designated by separate agreement with the Contractor, provided such occupancy or use is consented to by the insurer as required under Subparagraph 11.3.11 and authorized by public authorities having jurisdiction over the Work. Such partial occupancy or use may commence whether or not the portion is substantially complete, provided the Owner and Contractor have accepted in writing the responsibilities assigned to each of them for payments, retainage if any, security, maintenance, heat, utilities, damage to the Work and insurance, and have agreed in writing concerning the period for correction of the Work and commencement of warranties required by the Contract Documents. When the Contractor considers a portion substantially complete, the Contractor shall prepare and submit a list to the Architect as provided under Subparagraph 9.8.2. Consent of the Contractor to partial occupancy or use shall not be unreasonably withheld. The stage of the progress of the Work shall be determined by written agreement between the Owner and Contractor or, if no agreement is reached, by decision of the Architect.

9.9.2 Immediately prior to such partial occupancy or use, the Owner, Contractor and Architect shall jointly inspect the area to be occupied or portion of the Work to be used in order to determine and record the condition of the Work.

9.9.3 Unless otherwise agreed upon, partial occupancy or use of a portion or portions of the Work shall not constitute acceptance of Work not complying with the requirements of the Contract Documents.

9.10 FINAL COMPLETION AND FINAL PAYMENT

9.10.1 Upon receipt of written notice that the Work is ready for final inspection and acceptance and upon receipt of a final Application for Payment, the Architect will promptly make such inspection and, when the Architect finds the Work acceptable under the Contract Documents and the Contract fully performed, the Architect will promptly issue a final Certificate for Payment stating that to the best of the Architect's knowledge, information and belief, and on the basis of the Architect's observations and inspections, the Work has been completed in accordance with terms and conditions of the Contract Documents and that the entire balance found to be due the Contractor and noted in said final Certificate is due and payable. The Architect's final Certificate for Payment will constitute a further representation that conditions listed in Subparagraph 9.10.2 as precedent to the Contractor's being entitled to final payment have been fulfilled.

9.10.2 Neither final payment nor any remaining retained percentage shall become due until the Contractor submits to the Architect (1) an affidavit that payrolls, bills for materials and equipment, and other indebtedness connected with the Work for which the Owner or the Owner's property might be responsible or encumbered (less amounts withheld by Owner) have been paid or otherwise satisfied, (2) a certificate evidencing that insurance required by the Contract Documents to remain in force after final payment is currently in effect and will not be cancelled or allowed to expire until at least 30 days' prior written notice has been given to the Owner, (3) a written statement that the Contractor knows of no substantial reason that the insurance will not be renewable to cover the period required by the Contract Documents, (4) consent of surety, if any, to final payment and (5), if required by the Owner, other data establishing payment or satisfaction of obligations, such as receipts, releases and waivers of liens, claims, security interests or encumbrances arising out of the Contract, to the extent and in such form as may be designated by the Owner. If a Subcontractor refuses to furnish a release or waiver required by the Owner, the Contractor may furnish a bond satisfactory to the Owner to indemnify the Owner against such lien. If such lien remains unsatisfied after payments are made, the Contractor shall refund to the Owner all money that the Owner may be compelled to pay in discharging such lien, including all costs and reasonable attorneys' fees.

9.10.3 If, after Substantial Completion of the Work, final completion thereof is materially delayed through no fault of the Contractor or by issuance of Change Orders affecting final completion, and the Architect so confirms, the Owner shall, upon application by the Contractor and certification by the Architect, and without terminating the Contract, make payment of the balance due for that portion of the Work fully completed and accepted. If the remaining balance for Work not fully completed or corrected is less than retainage stipulated in the Contract Documents, and if bonds have been furnished, the written consent of surety to payment of the balance due for that portion of the Work fully completed and accepted shall be submitted by the Contractor to the Architect prior to certification of such payment. Such payment shall be made under terms and conditions governing final payment, except that it shall not constitute a waiver of claims. The making of final payment shall constitute a waiver of claims by the Owner as provided in Subparagraph 4.3.5.

9.10.4 Acceptance of final payment by the Contractor, a Subcontractor or material supplier shall constitute a waiver of claims by that payee except those previously made in writing and identified by that payee as unsettled at the time of final Application for Payment. Such waivers shall be in addition to the waiver described in Subparagraph 4.3.5.

ARTICLE 10

PROTECTION OF PERSONS AND PROPERTY

10.1 SAFETY PRECAUTIONS AND PROGRAMS

10.1.1 The Contractor shall be responsible for initiating, maintaining and supervising all safety precautions and programs in connection with the performance of the Contract.

10.1.2 In the event the Contractor encounters on the site material reasonably believed to be asbestos or polychlorinated biphenyl (PCB) which has not been rendered harmless, the Contractor shall immediately stop Work in the area affected and report the condition to the Owner and Architect in writing. The Work in the affected area shall not thereafter be resumed except by written agreement of the Owner and Contractor if in fact the material is asbestos or polychlorinated biphenyl (PCB) and has not been rendered harmless. The Work in the affected area shall be resumed in the absence of asbestos or polychlorinated biphenyl (PCB), or when it has been rendered harmless, by written agreement of the Owner and Contractor, or in accordance with final determination by the Architect on which arbitration has not been demanded, or by arbitration under Article 4.

10.1.3 The Contractor shall not be required pursuant to Article 7 to perform without consent any Work relating to asbestos or polychlorinated biphenyl (PCB).

10.1.4 To the fullest extent permitted by law, the Owner shall indemnify and hold harmless the Contractor, Architect, Architect's consultants and agents and employees of any of them from and against claims, damages, losses and expenses, including but not limited to attorneys' fees, arising out of or resulting from performance of the Work in the affected area if in fact the material is asbestos or polychlorinated biphenyl (PCB) and has not been rendered harmless, provided that such claim, damage, loss or expense is attributable to bodily injury, sickness, disease or death, or to injury to or destruction of tangible property (other than the Work itself) including loss of use resulting therefrom, but only to the extent caused in whole or in part by negligent acts or omissions of the Owner, anyone directly or indirectly employed by the Owner or anyone for whose acts the Owner may be liable, regardless of whether or not such claim, damage, loss or expense is caused in part by a party indemnified hereunder. Such obligation shall not be construed to negate, abridge, or reduce other rights or obligations of indemnity which would otherwise exist as to a party or person described in this Subparagraph 10.1.4.

10.2 SAFETY OF PERSONS AND PROPERTY

10.2.1 The Contractor shall take reasonable precautions for safety of, and shall provide reasonable protection to prevent damage, injury or loss to:

 .1 employees on the Work and other persons who may be affected thereby;

 .2 the Work and materials and equipment to be incorporated therein, whether in storage on or off the site, under care, custody or control of the Contractor or the Contractor's Subcontractors or Sub-subcontractors; and

 .3 other property at the site or adjacent thereto, such as trees, shrubs, lawns, walks, pavements, roadways, structures and utilities not designated for removal, relocation or replacement in the course of construction.

10.2.2 The Contractor shall give notices and comply with applicable laws, ordinances, rules, regulations and lawful orders of public authorities bearing on safety of persons or property or their protection from damage, injury or loss.

10.2.3 The Contractor shall erect and maintain, as required by existing conditions and performance of the Contract, reasonable safeguards for safety and protection, including posting danger signs and other warnings against hazards, promulgating safety regulations and notifying owners and users of adjacent sites and utilities.

10.2.4 When use or storage of explosives or other hazardous materials or equipment or unusual methods are necessary for execution of the Work, the Contractor shall exercise utmost care and carry on such activities under supervision of properly qualified personnel.

10.2.5 The Contractor shall promptly remedy damage and loss (other than damage or loss insured under property insurance required by the Contract Documents) to property referred to in Clauses 10.2.1.2 and 10.2.1.3 caused in whole or in part by the Contractor, a Subcontractor, a Sub-subcontractor, or anyone directly or indirectly employed by any of them, or by anyone for whose acts they may be liable and for which the Contractor is responsible under Clauses 10.2.1.2 and 10.2.1.3, except damage or loss attributable to acts or omissions of the Owner or Architect or anyone directly or indirectly employed by either of them, or by anyone for whose acts either of them may be liable, and not attributable to the fault or negligence of the Contractor. The foregoing obligations of the Contractor are in addition to the Contractor's obligations under Paragraph 3.18.

10.2.6 The Contractor shall designate a responsible member of the Contractor's organization at the site whose duty shall be the prevention of accidents. This person shall be the Contractor's superintendent unless otherwise designated by the Contractor in writing to the Owner and Architect.

10.2.7 The Contractor shall not load or permit any part of the construction or site to be loaded so as to endanger its safety.

10.3 EMERGENCIES

10.3.1 In an emergency affecting safety of persons or property, the Contractor shall act, at the Contractor's discretion, to prevent threatened damage, injury or loss. Additional compensation or extension of time claimed by the Contractor on account of an emergency shall be determined as provided in Paragraph 4.3 and Article 7.

ARTICLE 11

INSURANCE AND BONDS

11.1 CONTRACTOR'S LIABILITY INSURANCE

11.1.1 The Contractor shall purchase from and maintain in a company or companies lawfully authorized to do business in the jurisdiction in which the Project is located such insurance as will protect the Contractor from claims set forth below which may arise out of or result from the Contractor's operations under the Contract and for which the Contractor may be legally liable, whether such operations be by the Contractor or by a Subcontractor or by anyone directly or indirectly employed by any of them, or by anyone for whose acts any of them may be liable:

 .1 claims under workers' or workmen's compensation, disability benefit and other similar employee benefit acts which are applicable to the Work to be performed;

.2 claims for damages because of bodily injury, occupational sickness or disease, or death of the Contractor's employees;

.3 claims for damages because of bodily injury, sickness or disease, or death of any person other than the Contractor's employees;

.4 claims for damages insured by usual personal injury liability coverage which are sustained (1) by a person as a result of an offense directly or indirectly related to employment of such person by the Contractor, or (2) by another person;

.5 claims for damages, other than to the Work itself, because of injury to or destruction of tangible property, including loss of use resulting therefrom;

.6 claims for damages because of bodily injury, death of a person or property damage arising out of ownership, maintenance or use of a motor vehicle; and

.7 claims involving contractual liability insurance applicable to the Contractor's obligations under Paragraph 3.18.

11.1.2 The insurance required by Subparagraph 11.1.1 shall be written for not less than limits of liability specified in the Contract Documents or required by law, whichever coverage is greater. Coverages, whether written on an occurrence or claims-made basis, shall be maintained without interruption from date of commencement of the Work until date of final payment and termination of any coverage required to be maintained after final payment.

11.1.3 Certificates of Insurance acceptable to the Owner shall be filed with the Owner prior to commencement of the Work. These Certificates and the insurance policies required by this Paragraph 11.1 shall contain a provision that coverages afforded under the policies will not be cancelled or allowed to expire until at least 30 days' prior written notice has been given to the Owner. If any of the foregoing insurance coverages are required to remain in force after final payment and are reasonably available, an additional certificate evidencing continuation of such coverage shall be submitted with the final Application for Payment as required by Subparagraph 9.10.2. Information concerning reduction of coverage shall be furnished by the Contractor with reasonable promptness in accordance with the Contractor's information and belief.

11.2 OWNER'S LIABILITY INSURANCE

11.2.1 The Owner shall be responsible for purchasing and maintaining the Owner's usual liability insurance. Optionally, the Owner may purchase and maintain other insurance for self-protection against claims which may arise from operations under the Contract. The Contractor shall not be responsible for purchasing and maintaining this optional Owner's liability insurance unless specifically required by the Contract Documents.

11.3 PROPERTY INSURANCE

11.3.1 Unless otherwise provided, the Owner shall purchase and maintain, in a company or companies lawfully authorized to do business in the jurisdiction in which the Project is located, property insurance in the amount of the initial Contract Sum as well as subsequent modifications thereto for the entire Work at the site on a replacement cost basis without voluntary deductibles. Such property insurance shall be maintained, unless otherwise provided in the Contract Documents or otherwise agreed in writing by all persons and entities who are beneficiaries of such insurance, until final payment has been made as provided in Paragraph 9.10 or until no person or entity

other than the Owner has an insurable interest in the property required by this Paragraph 11.3 to be covered, whichever is earlier. This insurance shall include interests of the Owner, the Contractor, Subcontractors and Sub-subcontractors in the Work.

11.3.1.1 Property insurance shall be on an all-risk policy form and shall insure against the perils of fire and extended coverage and physical loss or damage including, without duplication of coverage, theft, vandalism, malicious mischief, collapse, falsework, temporary buildings and debris removal including demolition occasioned by enforcement of any applicable legal requirements, and shall cover reasonable compensation for Architect's services and expenses required as a result of such insured loss. Coverage for other perils shall not be required unless otherwise provided in the Contract Documents.

11.3.1.2 If the Owner does not intend to purchase such property insurance required by the Contract and with all of the coverages in the amount described above, the Owner shall so inform the Contractor in writing prior to commencement of the Work. The Contractor may then effect insurance which will protect the interests of the Contractor, Subcontractors and Sub-subcontractors in the Work, and by appropriate Change Order the cost thereof shall be charged to the Owner. If the Contractor is damaged by the failure or neglect of the Owner to purchase or maintain insurance as described above, without so notifying the Contractor, then the Owner shall bear all reasonable costs properly attributable thereto.

11.3.1.3 If the property insurance requires minimum deductibles and such deductibles are identified in the Contract Documents, the Contractor shall pay costs not covered because of such deductibles. If the Owner or insurer increases the required minimum deductibles above the amounts so identified or if the Owner elects to purchase this insurance with voluntary deductible amounts, the Owner shall be responsible for payment of the additional costs not covered because of such increased or voluntary deductibles. If deductibles are not identified in the Contract Documents, the Owner shall pay costs not covered because of deductibles.

11.3.1.4 Unless otherwise provided in the Contract Documents, this property insurance shall cover portions of the Work stored off the site after written approval of the Owner at the value established in the approval, and also portions of the Work in transit.

11.3.2 Boiler and Machinery Insurance. The Owner shall purchase and maintain boiler and machinery insurance required by the Contract Documents or by law, which shall specifically cover such insured objects during installation and until final acceptance by the Owner; this insurance shall include interests of the Owner, Contractor, Subcontractors and Sub-subcontractors in the Work, and the Owner and Contractor shall be named insureds.

11.3.3 Loss of Use Insurance. The Owner, at the Owner's option, may purchase and maintain such insurance as will insure the Owner against loss of use of the Owner's property due to fire or other hazards, however caused. The Owner waives all rights of action against the Contractor for loss of use of the Owner's property, including consequential losses due to fire or other hazards however caused.

11.3.4 If the Contractor requests in writing that insurance for risks other than those described herein or for other special hazards be included in the property insurance policy, the Owner shall, if possible, include such insurance, and the cost thereof shall be charged to the Contractor by appropriate Change Order.

11.3.5 If during the Project construction period the Owner insures properties, real or personal or both, adjoining or adjacent to the site by property insurance under policies separate from those insuring the Project, or if after final payment property insurance is to be provided on the completed Project through a policy or policies other than those insuring the Project during the construction period, the Owner shall waive all rights in accordance with the terms of Subparagraph 11.3.7 for damages caused by fire or other perils covered by this separate property insurance. All separate policies shall provide this waiver of subrogation by endorsement or otherwise.

11.3.6 Before an exposure to loss may occur, the Owner shall file with the Contractor a copy of each policy that includes insurance coverages required by this Paragraph 11.3. Each policy shall contain all generally applicable conditions, definitions, exclusions and endorsements related to this Project. Each policy shall contain a provision that the policy will not be cancelled or allowed to expire until at least 30 days' prior written notice has been given to the Contractor.

11.3.7 Waivers of Subrogation. The Owner and Contractor waive all rights against (1) each other and any of their subcontractors, sub-subcontractors, agents and employees, each of the other, and (2) the Architect, Architect's consultants, separate contractors described in Article 6, if any, and any of their subcontractors, sub-subcontractors, agents and employees, for damages caused by fire or other perils to the extent covered by property insurance obtained pursuant to this Paragraph 11.3 or other property insurance applicable to the Work, except such rights as they have to proceeds of such insurance held by the Owner as fiduciary. The Owner or Contractor, as appropriate, shall require of the Architect, Architect's consultants, separate contractors described in Article 6, if any, and the subcontractors, sub-subcontractors, agents and employees of any of them, by appropriate agreements, written where legally required for validity, similar waivers each in favor of other parties enumerated herein. The policies shall provide such waivers of subrogation by endorsement or otherwise. A waiver of subrogation shall be effective as to a person or entity even though that person or entity would otherwise have a duty of indemnification, contractual or otherwise, did not pay the insurance premium directly or indirectly, and whether or not the person or entity had an insurable interest in the property damaged.

11.3.8 A loss insured under Owner's property insurance shall be adjusted by the Owner as fiduciary and made payable to the Owner as fiduciary for the insureds, as their interests may appear, subject to requirements of any applicable mortgagee clause and of Subparagraph 11.3.10. The Contractor shall pay Subcontractors their just shares of insurance proceeds received by the Contractor, and by appropriate agreements, written where legally required for validity, shall require Subcontractors to make payments to their Sub-subcontractors in similar manner.

11.3.9 If required in writing by a party in interest, the Owner as fiduciary shall, upon occurrence of an insured loss, give bond for proper performance of the Owner's duties. The cost of required bonds shall be charged against proceeds received as fiduciary. The Owner shall deposit in a separate account proceeds so received, which the Owner shall distribute in accordance with such agreement as the parties in interest may reach, or in accordance with an arbitration award in which case the procedure shall be as provided in Paragraph 4.5. If after such loss no other special agreement is made, replacement of damaged property shall be covered by appropriate Change Order.

11.3.10 The Owner as fiduciary shall have power to adjust and settle a loss with insurers unless one of the parties in interest shall object in writing within five days after occurrence of loss to the Owner's exercise of this power; if such objection be made, arbitrators shall be chosen as provided in Paragraph 4.5. The Owner as fiduciary shall, in that case, make settlement with insurers in accordance with directions of such arbitrators. If distribution of insurance proceeds by arbitration is required, the arbitrators will direct such distribution.

11.3.11 Partial occupancy or use in accordance with Paragraph 9.9 shall not commence until the insurance company or companies providing property insurance have consented to such partial occupancy or use by endorsement or otherwise. The Owner and the Contractor shall take reasonable steps to obtain consent of the insurance company or companies and shall, without mutual written consent, take no action with respect to partial occupancy or use that would cause cancellation, lapse or reduction of insurance.

11.4 PERFORMANCE BOND AND PAYMENT BOND

11.4.1 The Owner shall have the right to require the Contractor to furnish bonds covering faithful performance of the Contract and payment of obligations arising thereunder as stipulated in bidding requirements or specifically required in the Contract Documents on the date of execution of the Contract.

11.4.2 Upon the request of any person or entity appearing to be a potential beneficiary of bonds covering payment of obligations arising under the Contract, the Contractor shall promptly furnish a copy of the bonds or shall permit a copy to be made.

ARTICLE 12

UNCOVERING AND CORRECTION OF WORK

12.1 UNCOVERING OF WORK

12.1.1 If a portion of the Work is covered contrary to the Architect's request or to requirements specifically expressed in the Contract Documents, it must, if required in writing by the Architect, be uncovered for the Architect's observation and be replaced at the Contractor's expense without change in the Contract Time.

12.1.2 If a portion of the Work has been covered which the Architect has not specifically requested to observe prior to its being covered, the Architect may request to see such Work and it shall be uncovered by the Contractor. If such Work is in accordance with the Contract Documents, costs of uncovering and replacement shall, by appropriate Change Order, be charged to the Owner. If such Work is not in accordance with the Contract Documents, the Contractor shall pay such costs unless the condition was caused by the Owner or a separate contractor in which event the Owner shall be responsible for payment of such costs.

12.2 CORRECTION OF WORK

12.2.1 The Contractor shall promptly correct Work rejected by the Architect or failing to conform to the requirements of the Contract Documents, whether observed before or after Substantial Completion and whether or not fabricated, installed or completed. The Contractor shall bear costs of correcting such rejected Work, including additional testing and inspections and compensation for the Architect's services and expenses made necessary thereby.

12.2.2 If, within one year after the date of Substantial Completion of the Work or designated portion thereof, or after the date for commencement of warranties established under Sub-paragraph 9.9.1, or by terms of an applicable special warranty required by the Contract Documents, any of the Work is found to be not in accordance with the requirements of the Contract Documents, the Contractor shall correct it promptly after receipt of written notice from the Owner to do so unless the Owner has previously given the Contractor a written acceptance of such condition. This period of one year shall be extended with respect to portions of Work first performed after Substantial Completion by the period of time between Substantial Completion and the actual performance of the Work. This obligation under this Subparagraph 12.2.2 shall survive acceptance of the Work under the Contract and termination of the Contract. The Owner shall give such notice promptly after discovery of the condition.

12.2.3 The Contractor shall remove from the site portions of the Work which are not in accordance with the requirements of the Contract Documents and are neither corrected by the Contractor nor accepted by the Owner.

12.2.4 If the Contractor fails to correct nonconforming Work within a reasonable time, the Owner may correct it in accordance with Paragraph 2.4. If the Contractor does not proceed with correction of such nonconforming Work within a reasonable time fixed by written notice from the Architect, the Owner may remove it and store the salvable materials or equipment at the Contractor's expense. If the Contractor does not pay costs of such removal and storage within ten days after written notice, the Owner may upon ten additional days' written notice sell such materials and equipment at auction or at private sale and shall account for the proceeds thereof, after deducting costs and damages that should have been borne by the Contractor, including compensation for the Architect's services and expenses made necessary thereby. If such proceeds of sale do not cover costs which the Contractor should have borne, the Contract Sum shall be reduced by the deficiency. If payments then or thereafter due the Contractor are not sufficient to cover such amount, the Contractor shall pay the difference to the Owner.

12.2.5 The Contractor shall bear the cost of correcting destroyed or damaged construction, whether completed or partially completed, of the Owner or separate contractors caused by the Contractor's correction or removal of Work which is not in accordance with the requirements of the Contract Documents.

12.2.6 Nothing contained in this Paragraph 12.2 shall be construed to establish a period of limitation with respect to other obligations which the Contractor might have under the Contract Documents. Establishment of the time period of one year as described in Subparagraph 12.2.2 relates only to the specific obligation of the Contractor to correct the Work, and has no relationship to the time within which the obligation to comply with the Contract Documents may be sought to be enforced, nor to the time within which proceedings may be commenced to establish the Contractor's liability with respect to the Contractor's obligations other than specifically to correct the Work.

12.3 ACCEPTANCE OF NONCONFORMING WORK

12.3.1 If the Owner prefers to accept Work which is not in accordance with the requirements of the Contract Documents, the Owner may do so instead of requiring its removal and correction, in which case the Contract Sum will be reduced as appropriate and equitable. Such adjustment shall be effected whether or not final payment has been made.

ARTICLE 13

MISCELLANEOUS PROVISIONS

13.1 GOVERNING LAW

13.1.1 The Contract shall be governed by the law of the place where the Project is located.

13.2 SUCCESSORS AND ASSIGNS

13.2.1 The Owner and Contractor respectively bind themselves, their partners, successors, assigns and legal representatives to the other party hereto and to partners, successors, assigns and legal representatives of such other party in respect to covenants, agreements and obligations contained in the Contract Documents. Neither party to the Contract shall assign the Contract as a whole without written consent of the other. If either party attempts to make such an assignment without such consent, that party shall nevertheless remain legally responsible for all obligations under the Contract.

13.3 WRITTEN NOTICE

13.3.1 Written notice shall be deemed to have been duly served if delivered in person to the individual or a member of the firm or entity or to an officer of the corporation for which it was intended, or if delivered at or sent by registered or certified mail to the last business address known to the party giving notice.

13.4 RIGHTS AND REMEDIES

13.4.1 Duties and obligations imposed by the Contract Documents and rights and remedies available thereunder shall be in addition to and not a limitation of duties, obligations, rights and remedies otherwise imposed or available by law.

13.4.2 No action or failure to act by the Owner, Architect or Contractor shall constitute a waiver of a right or duty afforded them under the Contract, nor shall such action or failure to act constitute approval of or acquiescence in a breach thereunder, except as may be specifically agreed in writing.

13.5 TESTS AND INSPECTIONS

13.5.1 Tests, inspections and approvals of portions of the Work required by the Contract Documents or by laws, ordinances, rules, regulations or orders of public authorities having jurisdiction shall be made at an appropriate time. Unless otherwise provided, the Contractor shall make arrangements for such tests, inspections and approvals with an independent testing laboratory or entity acceptable to the Owner, or with the appropriate public authority, and shall bear all related costs of tests, inspections and approvals. The Contractor shall give the Architect timely notice of when and where tests and inspections are to be made so the Architect may observe such procedures. The Owner shall bear costs of tests, inspections or approvals which do not become requirements until after bids are received or negotiations concluded.

13.5.2 If the Architect, Owner or public authorities having jurisdiction determine that portions of the Work require additional testing, inspection or approval not included under Subparagraph 13.5.1, the Architect will, upon written authorization from the Owner, instruct the Contractor to make arrangements for such additional testing, inspection or approval by an entity acceptable to the Owner, and the Contractor shall give timely notice to the Architect of when and where tests and inspections are to be made so the Architect may observe such procedures.

AIA DOCUMENT A201 • GENERAL CONDITIONS OF THE CONTRACT FOR CONSTRUCTION • FOURTEENTH EDITION
AIA® • ©1987 THE AMERICAN INSTITUTE OF ARCHITECTS, 1735 NEW YORK AVENUE, N.W., WASHINGTON, D.C. 20006

The Owner shall bear such costs except as provided in Sub-paragraph 13.5.3.

13.5.3 If such procedures for testing, inspection or approval under Subparagraphs 13.5.1 and 13.5.2 reveal failure of the portions of the Work to comply with requirements established by the Contract Documents, the Contractor shall bear all costs made necessary by such failure including those of repeated procedures and compensation for the Architect's services and expenses.

13.5.4 Required certificates of testing, inspection or approval shall, unless otherwise required by the Contract Documents, be secured by the Contractor and promptly delivered to the Architect.

13.5.5 If the Architect is to observe tests, inspections or approvals required by the Contract Documents, the Architect will do so promptly and, where practicable, at the normal place of testing.

13.5.6 Tests or inspections conducted pursuant to the Contract Documents shall be made promptly to avoid unreasonable delay in the Work.

13.6 INTEREST

13.6.1 Payments due and unpaid under the Contract Documents shall bear interest from the date payment is due at such rate as the parties may agree upon in writing or, in the absence thereof, at the legal rate prevailing from time to time at the place where the Project is located.

13.7 COMMENCEMENT OF STATUTORY LIMITATION PERIOD

13.7.1 As between the Owner and Contractor:

  .1 Before Substantial Completion. As to acts or failures to act occurring prior to the relevant date of Substantial Completion, any applicable statute of limitations shall commence to run and any alleged cause of action shall be deemed to have accrued in any and all events not later than such date of Substantial Completion;

  .2 Between Substantial Completion and Final Certificate for Payment. As to acts or failures to act occurring subsequent to the relevant date of Substantial Completion and prior to issuance of the final Certificate for Payment, any applicable statute of limitations shall commence to run and any alleged cause of action shall be deemed to have accrued in any and all events not later than the date of issuance of the final Certificate for Payment; and

  .3 After Final Certificate for Payment. As to acts or failures to act occurring after the relevant date of issuance of the final Certificate for Payment, any applicable statute of limitations shall commence to run and any alleged cause of action shall be deemed to have accrued in any and all events not later than the date of any act or failure to act by the Contractor pursuant to any warranty provided under Paragraph 3.5, the date of any correction of the Work or failure to correct the Work by the Contractor under Paragraph 12.2, or the date of actual commission of any other act or failure to perform any duty or obligation by the Contractor or Owner, whichever occurs last.

ARTICLE 14

TERMINATION OR SUSPENSION OF THE CONTRACT

14.1 TERMINATION BY THE CONTRACTOR

14.1.1 The Contractor may terminate the Contract if the Work is stopped for a period of 30 days through no act or fault of the Contractor or a Subcontractor, Sub-subcontractor or their agents or employees or any other persons performing portions of the Work under contract with the Contractor, for any of the following reasons:

  .1 issuance of an order of a court or other public authority having jurisdiction;

  .2 an act of government, such as a declaration of national emergency, making material unavailable;

  .3 because the Architect has not issued a Certificate for Payment and has not notified the Contractor of the reason for withholding certification as provided in Subparagraph 9.4.1, or because the Owner has not made payment on a Certificate for Payment within the time stated in the Contract Documents;

  .4 if repeated suspensions, delays or interruptions by the Owner as described in Paragraph 14.3 constitute in the aggregate more than 100 percent of the total number of days scheduled for completion, or 120 days in any 365-day period, whichever is less; or

  .5 the Owner has failed to furnish to the Contractor promptly, upon the Contractor's request, reasonable evidence as required by Subparagraph 2.2.1.

14.1.2 If one of the above reasons exists, the Contractor may, upon seven additional days' written notice to the Owner and Architect, terminate the Contract and recover from the Owner payment for Work executed and for proven loss with respect to materials, equipment, tools, and construction equipment and machinery, including reasonable overhead, profit and damages.

14.1.3 If the Work is stopped for a period of 60 days through no act or fault of the Contractor or a Subcontractor or their agents or employees or any other persons performing portions of the Work under contract with the Contractor because the Owner has persistently failed to fulfill the Owner's obligations under the Contract Documents with respect to matters important to the progress of the Work, the Contractor may, upon seven additional days' written notice to the Owner and the Architect, terminate the Contract and recover from the Owner as provided in Subparagraph 14.1.2.

14.2 TERMINATION BY THE OWNER FOR CAUSE

14.2.1 The Owner may terminate the Contract if the Contractor:

  .1 persistently or repeatedly refuses or fails to supply enough properly skilled workers or proper materials;

  .2 fails to make payment to Subcontractors for materials or labor in accordance with the respective agreements between the Contractor and the Subcontractors;

  .3 persistently disregards laws, ordinances, or rules, regulations or orders of a public authority having jurisdiction; or

  .4 otherwise is guilty of substantial breach of a provision of the Contract Documents.

14.2.2 When any of the above reasons exist, the Owner, upon certification by the Architect that sufficient cause exists to justify such action, may without prejudice to any other rights or remedies of the Owner and after giving the Contractor and the Contractor's surety, if any, seven days' written notice, terminate employment of the Contractor and may, subject to any prior rights of the surety:

  .1 take possession of the site and of all materials, equipment, tools, and construction equipment and machinery thereon owned by the Contractor;

  .2 accept assignment of subcontracts pursuant to Paragraph 5.4; and

  .3 finish the Work by whatever reasonable method the Owner may deem expedient.

14.2.3 When the Owner terminates the Contract for one of the reasons stated in Subparagraph 14.2.1, the Contractor shall not be entitled to receive further payment until the Work is finished.

14.2.4 If the unpaid balance of the Contract Sum exceeds costs of finishing the Work, including compensation for the Architect's services and expenses made necessary thereby, such excess shall be paid to the Contractor. If such costs exceed the unpaid balance, the Contractor shall pay the difference to the Owner. The amount to be paid to the Contractor or Owner, as the case may be, shall be certified by the Architect, upon application, and this obligation for payment shall survive termination of the Contract.

14.3 SUSPENSION BY THE OWNER FOR CONVENIENCE

14.3.1 The Owner may, without cause, order the Contractor in writing to suspend, delay or interrupt the Work in whole or in part for such period of time as the Owner may determine.

14.3.2 An adjustment shall be made for increases in the cost of performance of the Contract, including profit on the increased cost of performance, caused by suspension, delay or interruption. No adjustment shall be made to the extent:

  .1 that performance is, was or would have been so suspended, delayed or interrupted by another cause for which the Contractor is responsible; or

  .2 that an equitable adjustment is made or denied under another provision of this Contract.

14.3.3 Adjustments made in the cost of performance may have a mutually agreed fixed or percentage fee.

APPENDIX C

AIA Document 271

General Conditions of the Contract for Furniture, Furnishings and Equipment

THIS DOCUMENT HAS IMPORTANT LEGAL CONSEQUENCES; CONSULTATION WITH AN ATTORNEY IS ENCOURAGED WITH RESPECT TO ITS COMPLETION OR MODIFICATION.

1990 EDITION
TABLE OF ARTICLES

 CAUTION: You should use an original AIA document which has this caution printed in red. An original assures that changes will not be obscured as may occur when documents are reproduced.

ARTICLE 1

GENERAL PROVISIONS

1.1 BASIC DEFINITIONS

1.1.1 THE CONTRACT DOCUMENTS

The Contract Documents consist of the Agreement between Owner and Contractor (hereinafter the Agreement), Conditions of the Contract (General, Supplementary and other Conditions), Drawings, Specifications, addenda issued prior to execution of the Contract, other documents listed in the Agreement and Modifications issued after execution of the Contract. A Modification is (1) a written amendment to the Contract signed by both parties, (2) a Change Order, (3) a Change Directive or (4) a written order for a minor change in the Work issued by the Architect. Unless specifically enumerated in the Agreement, the Contract Documents do not include other documents such as bidding requirements (advertisement or invitation to bid, Instructions to Bidders, sample forms, the Contractor's bid or portions of addenda relating to bidding requirements).

1.1.2 THE CONTRACT

The Contract Documents form the Contract for Furniture, Furnishings and Equipment. The Contract represents the entire and integrated agreement between the parties hereto and supersedes prior negotiations, representations or agreements, either written or oral. The Contract may be amended or modified only by a Modification. The Contract Documents shall not be construed to create a contractual relationship of any kind (1) between the Architect and Contractor, (2) between the Owner and a Subcontractor or Sub-subcontractor or (3) between any persons or entities other than the Owner and Contractor. The Architect shall, however, be entitled to performance and enforcement of obligations under the Contract intended to facilitate performance of the Architect's duties.

1.1.3 THE WORK

The term "Work" means the furniture, furnishings and equipment required by the Contract Documents, whether completed or partially completed, and includes fabrication, transportation, installation, and all other services, labor and materials provided or to be provided by the Contractor to fulfill the Contractor's obligations. The Work may constitute the whole or a part of the Project.

1.1.4 THE PROJECT

The Project is the total furniture, furnishings and equipment of which the Work performed under the Contract Documents may be the whole or a part. The Project may include construction or related activities performed by the Owner's own forces or by separate contractors.

1.1.5 THE DRAWINGS

The Drawings are the graphic and pictorial portions of the Contract Documents, wherever located and whenever issued, showing the design, location and dimensions of the Work, generally including plans, elevations, sections, details, schedules and diagrams.

1.1.6 THE SPECIFICATIONS

The Specifications are that portion of the Contract Documents consisting of the written requirements for materials, furniture, furnishings, equipment, standards and workmanship for the Work, and performance of related services.

1.1.7 THE PROJECT MANUAL

The Project Manual is the volume usually assembled for the Work which may include the bidding requirements, sample forms, Conditions of the Contract and Specifications.

1.2 EXECUTION, CORRELATION AND INTENT

1.2.1 The Contract Documents shall be signed by the Owner and Contractor as provided in the Agreement. If either the Owner or Contractor or both do not sign all the Contract Documents, the Architect shall identify such unsigned Documents upon request.

1.2.2 Execution of the Contract by the Contractor is a representation that the Contractor has visited the Project premises or, if the Project premises have not yet been constructed, has reviewed the documents pertaining thereto, has become familiar with local conditions under which the Work is to be performed and correlated personal observations with requirements of the Contract Documents.

1.2.3 The intent of the Contract Documents is to include all items necessary for the proper execution and completion of the Work by the Contractor. The Contract Documents are complementary, and what is required by one shall be as binding as if required by all; performance by the Contractor shall be required only to the extent consistent with the Contract Documents and reasonably inferable from them as being necessary to produce the intended results.

1.2.4 Organization of the Specifications into divisions, sections and articles, and arrangement of Drawings shall not control the Contractor in dividing the Work among Subcontractors or in establishing the extent of Work to be performed by any trade.

1.2.5 Unless otherwise stated in the Contract Documents, words which have well-known technical or trade meanings are used in the Contract Documents in accordance with such recognized meanings.

1.3 OWNERSHIP AND USE OF ARCHITECT'S DRAWINGS, SPECIFICATIONS AND OTHER DOCUMENTS

1.3.1 The Drawings, Specifications and other documents prepared by the Architect are instruments of the Architect's service through which the Work to be executed by the Contractor is described. The Contractor may retain one contract record set. Neither the Contractor nor any Subcontractor or Sub-subcontractor shall own or claim a copyright in the Drawings, Specifications and other documents prepared by the Architect, and unless otherwise indicated the Architect shall be deemed the author of them and will retain all common law, statutory and other reserved rights, in addition to the copyright. All copies of them, except the Contractor's record

AIA DOCUMENT A271 • GENERAL CONDITIONS OF THE CONTRACT FOR FURNITURE, FURNISHINGS AND EQUIPMENT
1990 EDITION • AIA® • ©1990 • THE AMERICAN INSTITUTE OF ARCHITECTS, 1735 NEW YORK AVENUE, N.W., WASHINGTON,
D.C. 20006-5209 • ASID® • ©1990 • THE AMERICAN SOCIETY OF INTERIOR DESIGNERS, 608 MASSACHUSETTS AVENUE, N.E.,
WASHINGTON, D.C. 20002

A271-1990   2

for such order has been eliminated; however, the right of the Owner to stop the Work shall not give rise to a duty on the part of the Owner to exercise this right for the benefit of the Contractor or any other person or entity, except to the extent required by Subparagraph 6.1.3.

2.6 OWNER'S RIGHT TO CARRY OUT THE WORK

2.6.1 If the Contractor fails to provide assurances as provided in Paragraph 2.4 or defaults or neglects to carry out the Work in accordance with the Contract Documents and fails within a seven-day period after receipt of written notice from the Owner to commence and continue correction of such default or neglect with diligence and promptness, the Owner may after such seven-day period give the Contractor a second written notice to correct such deficiencies within a second seven-day period. If the Contractor within such second seven-day period after receipt of such second notice fails to commence and continue to correct any deficiences, the Owner may, without prejudice to other remedies the Owner may have, correct such deficiencies. In such case an appropriate Change Order shall be issued deducting from payments then or thereafter due the Contractor the cost of correcting such deficiencies, including compensation for the Architect's additional services and expenses made necessary by such default, neglect or failure. Such action by the Owner and amounts charged to the Contractor are both subject to prior approval of the Architect. If payments then or thereafter due the Contractor are not sufficient to cover such amounts, the Contractor shall pay the difference to the Owner.

ARTICLE 3

CONTRACTOR

3.1 DEFINITION

3.1.1 The Contractor is the person or entity identified as such in the Agreement and is referred to throughout the Contract Documents as if singular in number. The term "Contractor" means the Contractor or the Contractor's authorized representative.

3.2 REVIEW OF CONTRACT DOCUMENTS AND INSPECTION OF PREMISES BY CONTRACTOR

3.2.1 The Contractor shall carefully study and compare the Contract Documents with each other and with information furnished by the Owner pursuant to Subparagraph 2.2.2 and shall at once report to the Architect errors, inconsistencies or omissions discovered. The Contractor shall not be liable to the Owner or Architect for damage resulting from errors, inconsistencies or omissions in the Contract Documents unless the Contractor recognized such error, inconsistency or omission and knowingly failed to report it to the Architect. If the Contractor performs any activity knowing it involves a recognized error, inconsistency or omission in the Contract Documents without such notice to the Architect, the Contractor shall assume appropriate responsibility for such performance and shall bear an appropriate amount of the attributable costs for correction.

3.2.2 In addition to the Contractor's representations under Subparagraph 1.2.2, the Contractor shall, prior to shipment, delivery and installation, visit and inspect the Project premises in order to confirm the conditions under which the Work is to be performed, verify the stage of completion of the premises and the Project, determine availability of facilities for access, delivery, transportation and storage, determine physical restrictions imposed by the Owner, separate con-

tractors and building trades, and correlate these observations with the requirements of the Contract Documents. The Contractor shall promptly report to the Owner difficulties observed during such inspection or thereafter, and shall not be responsible for correcting difficulties not reasonably anticipatable at the time of execution of the Contract.

3.2.3 The Contractor shall take field measurements and verify field conditions and shall carefully compare such field measurements and conditions and other information known to the Contractor with the Contract Documents before commencing activities. Errors, inconsistencies or omissions discovered shall be reported to the Architect at once. If the Contractor performs any activity knowing it involves a recognized error, inconsistency or omission without such notice to the Architect, the Contractor shall assume appropriate responsibility for such performance and shall bear an appropriate amount of the attributable costs for correction.

3.2.4 The Contractor shall perform the Work in accordance with the Contract Documents and submittals approved pursuant to Paragraph 3.12.

3.3 SUPERVISION AND PROCEDURES

3.3.1 The Contractor shall supervise and direct the Work, using the Contractor's best skill and attention. The Contractor shall be solely responsible for and have control over the means, methods, techniques, sequences and procedures of fabrication, transportation and installation and for coordinating all portions of the Work under the Contract, unless Contract Documents give other specific instructions concerning these matters.

3.3.2 The Contractor shall be responsible to the Owner for acts and omissions of the Contractor's employees, Subcontractors and their agents and employees, and other persons performing portions of the Work under a contract with the Contractor.

3.3.3 The Contractor shall not be relieved of obligations to perform the Work in accordance with the Contract Documents either by activities or duties of the Architect in the Architect's administration of the Contract, or by tests, inspections or approvals required or performed by persons other than the Contractor.

3.3.4 The Contractor shall be responsible for inspection of portions of Work already performed under this Contract to determine that such portions are in proper condition to receive subsequent Work.

3.4 LABOR AND MATERIALS

3.4.1 Unless otherwise provided in the Contract Documents, the Contractor shall provide and pay for labor, materials, furniture, furnishings and equipment, tools, installation equipment and machinery, transportation, and other facilities and services necessary for proper execution and completion of the Work, whether temporary or permanent and whether or not incorporated or to be incorporated in the Work.

3.4.2 The Contractor shall enforce strict discipline and good order among the Contractor's employees and other persons carrying out the Contract. The Contractor shall not permit employment of unfit persons or persons not skilled in tasks assigned to them.

3.5 WARRANTY

3.5.1 The Contractor warrants to the Owner and Architect that materials, furniture, furnishings and equipment supplied under the Contract will be of good quality and new unless otherwise required or permitted by the Contract Documents,

A271-1990 4

3.12.4 Shop Drawings, Product Data, Samples and similar submittals are not Contract Documents. The purpose of their submittal is to demonstrate for those portions of the Work for which submittals are required the way the Contractor proposes to conform to the information given and the design concept expressed in the Contract Documents and to establish standards by which the Work will be judged. Review by the Architect is subject to the limitations of Subparagraph 4.2.9.

3.12.5 The Contractor shall review, approve and submit to the Architect Shop Drawings, Product Data, Samples and similar submittals required by the Contract Documents with reasonable promptness and in such sequence as to cause no delay in the Work or in the activities of the Owner or of separate contractors. Submittals made by the Contractor which are not required by the Contract Documents may be returned without action.

3.12.6 The Contractor shall perform no portion of the Work requiring submittal and review of Shop Drawings, Product Data, Samples or similar submittals until the respective submittal has been approved by the Architect. Such Work shall be in accordance with approved submittals.

3.12.7 By approving and submitting Shop Drawings, Product Data, Samples and similar submittals, the Contractor represents that the Contractor has determined and verified field measurements and field installation criteria related thereto, or will do so, and has checked and coordinated the information contained within such submittals with the requirements of the Work and of the Contract Documents.

3.12.8 The Contractor shall not be relieved of responsibility for deviations from requirements of the Contract Documents by the Architect's approval of Shop Drawings, Product Data, Samples or similar submittals unless the Contractor has specifically informed the Architect in writing of such deviation at the time of submittal and the Architect has given written approval to the specific deviation. The Contractor shall not be relieved of responsibility for errors or omissions in Shop Drawings, Product Data, Samples or similar submittals by the Architect's approval thereof.

3.12.9 The Contractor shall direct specific attention, in writing or on resubmitted Shop Drawings, Product Data, Samples or similar submittals, to revisions other than those requested by the Architect on previous submittals.

3.12.10 Informational submittals upon which the Architect is not expected to take responsive action may be so identified in the Contract Documents.

3.12.11 When professional certification of performance criteria of furniture, furnishings and equipment is required by the Contract Documents, the Architect shall be entitled to rely upon the accuracy and completeness of such certifications.

3.13 USE OF PREMISES

3.13.1 The Contractor shall confine operations at the Project premises to areas permitted by law, ordinances, permits and the Contract Documents and shall not unreasonably encumber the premises with materials or equipment.

3.14 CLEANING UP

3.14.1 The Contractor shall keep the premises and surrounding area free from accumulation of waste materials or rubbish caused by operations under the Contract. At completion of the Work the Contractor shall remove from and about the Project premises waste materials, rubbish, the Con-

tractor's tools, installation equipment, machinery and surplus materials.

3.14.2 If the Contractor fails to clean up as provided in the Contract Documents, the Owner may do so and the cost thereof shall be charged to the Contractor.

3.15 ACCESS TO WORK

3.15.1 The Contractor shall provide the Owner and Architect access to the Work wherever it is in preparation and progress, before, during and after delivery to the premises and in any stage of completion. The Contractor shall provide facilities necessary for such access for the Owner and Architect to perform their functions under the Contract Documents.

3.16 ROYALTIES AND PATENTS

3.16.1 The Contractor shall pay all royalties and license fees. The Contractor shall defend suits or claims for infringement of patent rights and shall hold the Owner and the Architect harmless from loss on account thereof, but shall not be responsible for such defense or loss when a particular design, process or product of a particular manufacturer or manufacturers is required by the Contract Documents. However, if the Contractor has reason to believe that the required design, process or product is an infringement of a patent, the Contractor shall be responsible for such loss unless such information is promptly furnished to the Architect.

3.17 INDEMNIFICATION

3.17.1 To the fullest extent permitted by law, the Contractor shall indemnify and hold harmless the Owner, Architect, Architect's consultants, and agents and employees of any of them from and against claims, damages, losses and expenses, including but not limited to attorneys' fees, arising out of or resulting from performance of the Work, provided that such claim, damage, loss or expense is attributable to bodily injury, sickness, disease or death, or to injury to or destruction of tangible property (other than the Work itself) including loss of use resulting therefrom, but only to the extent caused in whole or in part by negligent acts or omissions of the Contractor, a Subcontractor, anyone directly or indirectly employed by them or anyone for whose acts they may be liable, regardless of whether or not such claim, damage, loss or expense is caused in part by a party indemnified hereunder. Such obligation shall not be construed to negate, abridge or reduce other rights or obligations of indemnity which would otherwise exist as to a party or person described in this Paragraph 3.17.

3.17.2 In claims against any person or entity indemnified under this Paragraph 3.17 by an employee of the Contractor, a Subcontractor, anyone directly or indirectly employed by them or anyone for whose acts they may be liable, the indemnification obligation under this Paragraph 3.17 shall not be limited by a limitation on amount or type of damages, compensation or benefits payable by or for the Contractor or a Subcontractor under workers' or workmen's compensation acts, disability benefit acts or other employee benefit acts.

3.17.3 The obligations of the Contractor under this Paragraph 3.17 shall not extend to the liability of the Architect, the Architect's consultants, and agents and employees of any of them arising out of (1) the preparation or approval of drawings, opinions, reports, Change Orders, designs or specifications, or (2) the giving of or the failure to give directions or instructions by the Architect, the Architect's consultants, and agents and employees of any of them provided such giving or failure to give is the primary cause of the injury or damage.

A271-1990 6

4.2.10 The Architect will prepare Change Orders and Change Directives, and may authorize minor changes in the Work as provided in Paragraph 8.4.

4.2.11 The Architect will conduct inspections to determine the date or dates of Substantial Completion and the date of final completion, will receive and forward to the Owner for the Owner's review and records written warranties and related documents required by the Contract and assembled by the Contractor, and will issue a final Certificate for Payment upon compliance with the requirements of the Contract Documents.

4.2.12 If the Owner and Architect agree, the Architect will provide one or more project representatives to assist in carrying out the Architect's responsibilities at the Project premises. The duties, responsibilities and limitations of authority of such project representatives shall be as set forth in an exhibit to be incorporated in the Contract Documents.

4.2.13 The Architect will interpret and decide matters concerning performance under and requirements of the Contract Documents on written request of either the Owner or Contractor. The Architect's response to such requests will be made with reasonable promptness and within any time limits agreed upon. If no agreement is made concerning the time within which interpretations required of the Architect shall be furnished in compliance with this Paragraph 4.2, then delay shall not be recognized on account of failure by the Architect to furnish such interpretations until 15 days after written request is made for them.

4.2.14 Interpretations and decisions of the Architect will be consistent with the intent of and reasonably inferable from the Contract Documents and will be in writing or in the form of drawings. When making such interpretations and decisions, the Architect will endeavor to secure faithful performance by both Owner and Contractor, will not show partiality to either and will not be liable for the results of interpretations or decisons so rendered in good faith.

4.2.15 The Architect's decisions on matters relating to aesthetic effect will be final if consistent with the intent expressed in the Contract Documents.

4.3 CLAIMS AND DISPUTES

4.3.1 Definition. A Claim is a demand or assertion by one of the parties seeking, as a matter of right, adjustment or interpretation of Contract terms, payment of money, extension of time or other relief with respect to the terms of the Contract. The term "Claim" also includes other disputes and matters in question between the Owner and Contractor arising out of or relating to the Contract. Claims must be made by written notice. The responsibility to substantiate Claims shall rest with the party making the Claim.

4.3.2 Decision of Architect. Claims, including those alleging an error or omission by the Architect, shall be referred initially to the Architect for action as provided in Paragraph 4.4. A decision by the Architect, as provided in Subparagraph 4.4.4, shall be required as a condition precedent to arbitration or litigation of a Claim between the Contractor and Owner as to all such matters arising prior to the date final payment is due, regardless of (1) whether such matters relate to execution and progress of the Work or (2) the extent to which the Work has been completed. The decision by the Architect in response to a Claim shall not be a condition precedent to arbitration or litigation in the event (1) the position of Archi-

tect is vacant, (2) the Architect has not received evidence or has failed to render a decision within agreed time limits, (3) the Architect has failed to take action required under Subparagraph 4.4.4 within 30 days after the Claim is made, (4) 45 days have passed after the Claim has been referred to the Architect or (5) the Claim relates to a mechanic's lien.

4.3.3 Time Limits on Claims. Claims by either party must be made within 21 days after occurrence of the event giving rise to such Claim or within 21 days after the claimant first recognizes the condition giving rise to the Claim, whichever is later. Claims must be made by written notice. An additional Claim made after the initial Claim has been implemented by Change Order will not be considered unless submitted in a timely manner.

4.3.4 Continuing Contract Performance. Pending final resolution of a Claim including arbitration, unless otherwise agreed in writing the Contractor shall proceed diligently with performance of the Contract and the Owner shall continue to make payments in accordance with the Contract Documents.

4.3.5 Waiver of Claims: Final Payment. The making of final payment shall constitute a waiver of Claims by the Owner except those arising from:

.1 liens, Claims, security interests or encumbrances arising out of the Contract and unsettled;

.2 failure of the Work to comply with the requirements of the Contract Documents; or

.3 terms of special warranties required by the Contract Documents.

4.3.6 Claims for Concealed or Unknown Conditions. If conditions are encountered at the Project premises which are (1) concealed physical conditions which differ materially from those indicated in the Contract Documents or (2) unknown physical conditions of an unusual nature, which differ materially from those ordinarily found to exist and generally recognized as inherent in activities of the character provided for in the Contract Documents, then notice by the observing party shall be given to the other party promptly before conditions are disturbed and in no event later than 21 days after first observance of the conditions. The Architect will promptly investigate such conditions and, if they differ materially and cause an increase or decrease in the Contractor's cost of, or time required for, performance of any part of the Work, will recommend an equitable adjustment in the Contract Sum or Contract Time, or both. If the Architect determines that the conditions at the premises are not materially different from those indicated in the Contract Documents and that no change in the terms of the Contract is justified, the Architect shall so notify the Owner and Contractor in writing, stating the reasons. Claims by either party in opposition to such determination must be made within 21 days after the Architect has given notice of the decision. If the Owner and Contractor cannot agree on an adjustment in the Contract Sum or Contract Time, the adjustment shall be referred to the Architect for initial determination, subject to further proceedings pursuant to Paragraph 4.4.

4.3.7 Claims for Additional Cost. If the Contractor wishes to make Claim for an increase in the Contract Sum, written notice as provided herein shall be given by the Contractor before proceeding to execute the Work. Prior notice is not required for Claims relating to an emergency endangering life or property arising under Paragraph 11.3. If the Contractor believes additional cost is involved for reasons including but

A271-1990   8

person or entity sought to be joined. No arbitration shall include, by consolidation or joinder or in any other manner, parties other than the Owner, Contractor, a separate contractor as described in Article 6 and other persons substantially involved in a common question of fact or law whose presence is required if complete relief is to be accorded in arbitration. No person or entity other than the Owner, Contractor or a separate contractor as described in Article 6 shall be included as an original third party or additional third party to an arbitration whose interest or responsibility is insubstantial. Consent to arbitration involving an additional person or entity shall not constitute consent to arbitration of a dispute not described therein or with a person or entity not named or described therein. The foregoing agreement to arbitrate and other agreements to arbitrate with an additional person or entity duly consented to by parties to the Agreement shall be specifically enforceable under applicable law in any court having jurisdiction thereof.

4.5.6 Claims and Timely Assertion of Claims. A party who files a notice of demand for arbitration must assert in the demand all Claims then known to that party on which arbitration is permitted to be demanded. When a party fails to include a Claim through oversight, inadvertence or excusable neglect, or when a Claim has matured or been acquired subsequently, the arbitrator or arbitrators may permit amendment.

4.5.7 Judgment on Final Award. The award rendered by the arbitrator or arbitrators shall be final, and judgment may be entered upon it in accordance with applicable law in any court having jurisdiction thereof.

ARTICLE 5
SUBCONTRACTORS

5.1 DEFINITION

5.1.1 A Subcontractor is a person or entity who has a direct contract, purchase order or other authorization with the Contractor to perform a portion of the Work at the Project premises, or to fabricate, transport, supply or install a portion of the Work for the Project. The term "Subcontractor" is referred to throughout the Contract Documents as if singular in number and means a Subcontractor or an authorized representative of the Subcontractor. The term "Subcontractor" does not include a separate contractor or subcontractors of a separate contractor.

5.1.2 A Sub-subcontractor is a person or entity who has a direct or indirect contract, purchase order or other authorization with a Subcontractor to perform a portion of the Work at the Project premises, or to fabricate, transport, supply or install a portion of the Work for the Project. The term "Sub-subcontractor" is referred to throughout the Contract Documents as if singular in number and means a Sub-subcontractor or an authorized representative of the Sub-subcontractor.

5.2 AWARD OF SUBCONTRACTS AND OTHER CONTRACTS FOR PORTIONS OF THE WORK

5.2.1 Unless otherwise stated in the Contract Documents or the bidding requirements, the Contractor, as soon as practicable after award of the Contract, shall furnish in writing to the Owner through the Architect the names of persons or entities (including those who are to furnish furniture, furnishings or equipment fabricated to a special design) proposed for each principal portion of the Work. The Architect will

promptly reply to the Contractor in writing stating whether or not the Owner or the Architect, after due investigation, has reasonable objection to any such proposed person or entity. Failure of the Owner or Architect to reply promptly shall constitute notice of no reasonable objection.

5.2.2 The Contractor shall not contract with a proposed person or entity to whom the Owner or Architect has made reasonable and timely objection. The Contractor shall not be required to contract with anyone to whom the Contractor has made reasonable objection.

5.2.3 If the Owner or Architect has reasonable objection to a person or entity proposed by the Contractor, the Contractor shall propose another to whom the Owner or Architect has no reasonable objection. The Contract Sum shall be increased or decreased by the difference in cost occasioned by such change and an appropriate Change Order shall be issued. However, no increase in the Contract Sum shall be allowed for such change unless the Contractor has acted promptly and responsively in submitting names as required.

5.2.4 The Contractor shall not change a Subcontractor, person or entity previously selected if the Owner or Architect makes reasonable objection to such change.

5.3 SUBCONTRACTUAL RELATIONS

5.3.1 By appropriate agreement, written where legally required for validity, the Contractor shall require each Subcontractor, to the extent of the Work to be performed by the Subcontractor, to be bound to the Contractor by terms of the Contract Documents, and to assume toward the Contractor all the obligations and responsibilities which the Contractor, by these Documents, assumes toward the Owner and Architect. Each subcontract agreement shall preserve and protect the rights of the Owner and Architect under the Contract Documents with respect to the Work to be performed by the Subcontractor so that subcontracting thereof will not prejudice such rights, and shall allow to the Subcontractor, unless specifically provided otherwise in the subcontract agreement, the benefit of all rights, remedies and redress against the Contractor that the Contractor, by the Contract Documents, has against the Owner. Where appropriate, the Contractor shall require each Subcontractor to enter into similar agreements with Sub-subcontractors. The Contractor shall make available to each proposed Subcontractor, prior to the execution of the subcontract agreement, copies of the Contract Documents to which the Subcontractor will be bound, and, upon written request of the Subcontractor, identify to the Subcontractor terms and conditions of the proposed subcontract agreement which may be at variance with the Contract Documents. Subcontractors shall similarly make copies of applicable portions of such documents available to the respective proposed Sub-subcontractors.

5.4 CONTINGENT ASSIGNMENT OF SUBCONTRACTS

5.4.1 Each subcontract agreement for a portion of the Work is assigned by the Contractor to the Owner provided that:

.1 assignment is effective only after termination of the Contract by the Owner for cause pursuant to Paragraph 15.2 and only for those subcontract agreements which the Owner accepts by notifying the Subcontractor in writing; and

.2 assignment is subject to the prior rights of the surety, if any, obligated under bond relating to the Contract.

5.4.2 If the Work has been suspended for more than 30 days, the Subcontractor's compensation shall be equitably adjusted.

AIA DOCUMENT A271 • GENERAL CONDITIONS OF THE CONTRACT FOR FURNITURE, FURNISHINGS AND EQUIPMENT 1990 EDITION • AIA® • ©1990 • THE AMERICAN INSTITUTE OF ARCHITECTS, 1735 NEW YORK AVENUE, N.W., WASHINGTON, D.C. 20006-5209 • ASID® • ©1990 • THE AMERICAN SOCIETY OF INTERIOR DESIGNERS, 608 MASSACHUSETTS AVENUE. N.E., WASHINGTON, D.C. 20002

A271-1990   10

to conform to the Contract Documents, the Owner shall promptly notify the Contractor, and the Contractor shall have an opportunity to remedy the same at the Contractor's own expense within a reasonable time not to exceed the Contract Time.

7.3.2 Notwithstanding any otherwise applicable provision of law or any such inspections or payment on account of furniture, furnishings and equipment delivered, receipt shall not be construed as acceptance of furniture, furnishings or equipment prior to installation and Substantial Completion unless specifically accepted in writing by the Owner.

7.4 OWNER'S RIGHT TO REVOKE ACCEPTANCE

7.4.1 If Work which has been previously accepted, specifically or by the making of payment on Substantial Completion, is found to have defects, damage or deficiencies, or fails to conform to the Contract Documents, for a cause not attributable to the Owner or the Owner's agents or employees, the Owner may revoke acceptance. Such revocation shall be made by giving prompt notice of such conditions to the Contractor, and the Contractor shall promptly remedy the same at the Contractor's expense.

7.4.2 This Paragraph 7.4 shall not be construed as a limitation on remedies otherwise available under the Contract Documents or applicable law.

7.5 CUTTING AND PATCHING OF WORK

7.5.1 The Contractor shall be responsible for cutting, fitting or patching required to complete the Work or to make its parts fit together properly.

7.5.2 The Contractor shall not damage or endanger the premises or a portion of the Work or fully or partially completed construction of the Owner or separate contractors or furniture, furnishings and equipment of the Owner or separate contractors by cutting, patching or otherwise altering such construction or furniture, furnishings and equipment. The Contractor shall not cut or otherwise alter such construction of the Owner or furniture, furnishings and equipment of separate contractors except with written consent of the Owner and of such separate contractor; such consent shall not be unreasonably withheld. The Contractor shall not unreasonably withhold from the Owner or a separate contractor the Contractor's consent to cutting or otherwise altering the Work.

7.6 LABOR JURISDICTION

7.6.1 The Contractor shall become fully informed of the conditions relating to delivery, installation and labor under which the Contractor's Work will be performed. The Contractor shall employ such labor and such means and methods of carrying out the Contractor's Work as are required by such conditions. The Contractor shall, at the time of execution of the Agreement, specify the labor and the means and methods of carrying out the Work which the Contractor intends to employ.

7.6.2 If any trade unions other than those previously indicated by the Contractor under Subparagraph 7.6.1, if any, successfully claim jurisdiction over any of the Work, the Owner shall pay the Contractor the difference in cost necessarily incurred above that of using the labor specified by the Contractor under Subparagraph 7.6.1.

7.7 SECURITY

7.7.1 The Owner shall be responsible for providing security against loss or damage for materials, furniture, furnishings and equipment stored at the Project premises between the dates of delivery and final acceptance by the Owner. Arrangements for such security shall be satisfactory to the Contractor.

7.8 PLACEMENT AND ASSEMBLY

7.8.1 If the Owner requires changes, whether temporary or permanent, in the placement or assembly of furniture, furnishings and equipment from that indicated in the Contract Documents, the Owner shall reimburse the Contractor for additional costs incurred on account of such changes, and an appropriate Change Order shall be issued in accordance with Article 8.

ARTICLE 8

CHANGES IN THE WORK

8.1 CHANGES

8.1.1 Changes in the Work may be accomplished after execution of the Contract, and without invalidating the Contract, by Change Order, Change Directive or order for a minor change in the Work, subject to the limitations stated in this Article 8 and elsewhere in the Contract Documents.

8.1.2 A Change Order shall be based upon agreement among the Owner, Contractor and Architect; a Change Directive requires agreement by the Owner and Architect and may or may not be agreed to by the Contractor; an order for a minor change in the Work may be issued by the Architect alone.

8.1.3 Changes in the Work shall be performed under applicable provisions of the Contract Documents, and the Contractor shall proceed promptly, unless otherwise provided in the Change Order, Change Directive or order for a minor change in the Work.

8.1.4 If unit prices are stated in the Contract Documents or subsequently agreed upon, and if quantities originally contemplated are so changed in a proposed Change Order or Change Directive that application of such unit prices to quantities of Work proposed will cause substantial inequity to the Owner or Contractor, the applicable unit prices shall be equitably adjusted.

8.2 CHANGE ORDERS

8.2.1 A Change Order is a written instrument prepared by the Architect and signed by the Owner, Contractor and Architect, stating their agreement upon all of the following:

.1 a change in the Work;

.2 the amount of the adjustment in the Contract Sum, if any; and

.3 the extent of the adjustment in the Contract Time, if any.

8.2.2 Methods used in determing adjustments to the Contract Sum may include those listed in Subparagraph 8.3.3.

8.3 CHANGE DIRECTIVES

8.3.1 A Change Directive is a written order prepared by the Architect and signed by the Owner and Architect, directing a change in the Work and stating a proposed basis for adjustment, if any, in the Contract Sum or Contract Time, or both. The Owner may by Change Directive, without invalidating the Contract, order changes in the Work within the general scope of the Contract consisting of additions, deletions or other revisions, the Contract Sum and Contract Time being adjusted accordingly.

8.3.2 A Change Directive shall be used in the absence of total agreement on the terms of a Change Order.

A271-1990 12

9.3.3 This Paragraph 9.3 does not preclude recovery of damages for delay by either party under other provisions of the Contract Documents.

ARTICLE 10

PAYMENTS AND COMPLETION

10.1 CONTRACT SUM

10.1.1 The Contract Sum is stated in the Agreement and, including authorized adjustments, is the total amount payable by the Owner to the Contractor for performance of the Work under the Contract Documents.

10.2 SCHEDULE OF VALUES

10.2.1 Before the first Application for Payment, the Contractor shall submit to the Architect a schedule of values allocated to various portions of the Work, prepared in such form and supported by such data to substantiate its accuracy as the Architect may require. If unit prices are stated in the Contract Documents or subsequently agreed upon, they shall be identified in the schedule of values. This schedule, unless objected to by the Architect, shall be used as a basis for reviewing the Contractor's Applications for Payment.

10.3 APPLICATIONS FOR PAYMENT

10.3.1 At least ten days before the date established for each progress payment, the Contractor shall submit to the Architect an itemized Application for Payment for operations completed in accordance with the schedule of values. Such application shall be notarized, if required, and supported by such data substantiating the Contractor's right to payment as the Owner or Architect may require, such as copies of requisitions from Subcontractors and Sub-subcontractors, and reflecting retainage if provided for elsewhere in the Contract Documents.

10.3.1.1 Such applications may include requests for payment on account of changes in the Work which have been properly authorized by Change Directives but not yet included in Change Orders.

10.3.1.2 Such applications may not include requests for payment of amounts the Contractor does not intend to pay to a Subcontractor because of a dispute or other reason.

10.3.2 Unless otherwise provided in the Contract Documents, payments shall be made on account of furniture, furnishings and equipment delivered and suitably stored at the Project premises. If approved in advance by the Owner, payment may similarly be made for furniture, furnishings or equipment suitably stored off the premises at a location agreed upon in writing. Payment for materials, furniture, furnishings or equipment stored on or off the Project premises shall be conditioned upon compliance by the Contractor with procedures satisfactory to the Owner to establish the Owner's title to such materials, furniture, furnishings or equipment or otherwise protect the Owner's interest, and shall include applicable insurance, storage and transportation to the Project premises for such materials, furniture, furnishings and equipment stored off the premises.

10.3.3 The Contractor warrants that title to all Work covered by an Application for Payment will pass to the Owner no later than the time of payment. The Contractor further warrants that upon submittal of an Application for Payment all Work for which Certificates for Payment have been previously issued and payments received from the Owner shall, to the best of the Contractor's knowledge, information and belief, be free and clear of liens, claims, security interests or encumbrances in favor of the Contractor, Subcontractors, Sub-subcontractors, or other persons or entities making a claim by reason of having provided labor, materials, furniture, furnishings and equipment relating to the Work.

10.4 CERTIFICATES FOR PAYMENT

10.4.1 The Architect will, within seven days after receipt of the Contractor's Application for Payment, either issue to the Owner a Certificate for Payment, with a copy to the Contractor, for such amount as the Architect determines is properly due, or notify the Contractor and Owner in writing of the Architect's reasons for withholding certification in whole or in part as provided in Subparagraph 10.5.1.

10.4.2 The issuance of a Certificate for Payment will constitute a representation by the Architect to the Owner, based on the Architect's observations at the Project premises and the data comprising the Application for Payment, that the Work has progressed to the point indicated and that, to the best of the Architect's knowledge, information and belief, quality of the Work is in accordance with the Contract Documents. The foregoing representations are subject to an evaluation of the Work for conformance with the Contract Documents upon Substantial Completion, to results of subsequent tests and inspections, to minor deviations from the Contract Documents correctable prior to completion and to specific qualifications expressed by the Architect. The issuance of a Certificate for Payment will further constitute a representation that the Contractor is entitled to payment in the amount certified. However, the issuance of a Certificate for Payment will not be a representation that the Architect has (1) made exhaustive or continuous inspections to check the quality or quantity of the Work, (2) reviewed the fabrication, shipment, delivery or installation means, methods, techniques, sequences or procedures, (3) reviewed copies of requisitions received from Subcontractors and other data requested by the Owner to substantiate the Contractor's right to payment or (4) made examination to ascertain how or for what purpose the Contractor has used money previously paid on account of the Contract Sum.

10.5 DECISIONS TO WITHHOLD CERTIFICATION

10.5.1 The Architect may decide not to certify payment and may withhold a Certificate for Payment in whole or in part, to the extent reasonably necessary to protect the Owner, if in the Architect's opinion the representations to the Owner required by Subparagraph 10.4.2 cannot be made. If the Architect is unable to certify payment in the amount of the Application, the Architect will notify the Contractor and Owner as provided in Subparagraph 10.4.1. If the Contractor and Architect cannot agree on a revised amount, the Architect will promptly issue a Certificate for Payment for the amount for which the Architect is able to make such representations to the Owner. The Architect may also decide not to certify payment or, because of subsequently discovered evidence or subsequent observations, may nullify the whole or a part of a Certificate for Payment previously issued, to such extent as may be necessary in the Architect's opinion to protect the Owner from loss because of:

  .1 defective Work not remedied;

  .2 third party claims filed or reasonable evidence indicating probable filing of such claims;

  .3 failure of the Contractor to make payments properly to Subcontractors or for labor, materials or equipment;

AIA DOCUMENT A271 • GENERAL CONDITIONS OF THE CONTRACT FOR FURNITURE, FURNISHINGS AND EQUIPMENT
1990 EDITION • AIA® • ©1990 • THE AMERICAN INSTITUTE OF ARCHITECTS, 1735 NEW YORK AVENUE, N.W., WASHINGTON,
D.C. 20006-5209 • ASID® • ©1990 • THE AMERICAN SOCIETY OF INTERIOR DESIGNERS, 608 MASSACHUSETTS AVENUE, N.E.,
WASHINGTON, D.C. 20002

A271-1990   14

286

area to be occupied or portion of the Work to be used in order to determine and record the condition of the Work.

10.9.3 Unless otherwise agreed upon, partial occupancy or use of a portion or portions of the Work shall not constitute acceptance of Work not complying with the requirements of the Contract Documents.

10.10 FINAL COMPLETION AND FINAL PAYMENT

10.10.1 Upon receipt of written notice that the Work is ready for final inspection and acceptance and upon receipt of a final Application for Payment, the Architect will promptly make such inspection and, when the Architect finds the Work acceptable under the Contract Documents and the Contract fully performed, the Architect will promptly issue a final Certificate for Payment stating that to the best of the Architect's knowledge, information and belief, and on the basis of the Architect's observations and inspections, the Work has been completed in accordance with terms and conditions of the Contract Documents and that the entire balance found to be due the Contractor and noted in said final Certificate is due and payable. The Architect's final Certificate for Payment will constitute a further representation that conditions listed in Subparagraph 10.10.2 as precedent to the Contractor's being entitled to final payment have been fulfilled.

10.10.2 Neither final payment nor any remaining retained percentage shall become due until the Contractor submits to the Architect (1) an affidavit that payrolls, bills for materials, furniture, furnishings and equipment, and other indebtedness connected with the Work for which the Owner or the Owner's property might be responsible or encumbered (less amounts withheld by Owner) have been paid or otherwise satisfied, (2) a certificate evidencing that insurance required by the Contract Documents to remain in force after final payment is currently in effect and will not be cancelled or allowed to expire until at least 30 days' prior written notice has been given to the Owner, (3) a written statement that the Contractor knows of no substantial reason that the insurance will not be renewable to cover the period required by the Contract Documents, (4) consent of surety, if any, to final payment and (5), if required by the Owner, other data establishing payment or satisfaction of obligations, such as receipts, releases and waivers of liens, claims, security interests or encumbrances arising out of the Contract, to the extent and in such form as may be designated by the Owner. If a Subcontractor refuses to furnish a release or waiver required by the Owner, the Contractor may furnish a bond satisfactory to the Owner to indemnify the Owner against such lien. If such lien remains unsatisfied after payments are made, the Contractor shall refund to the Owner all money that the Owner may be compelled to pay in discharging such lien, including all costs and reasonable attorneys' fees.

10.10.3 If, after Substantial Completion of the Work, final completion thereof is materially delayed through no fault of the Contractor or by issuance of Change Orders affecting final completion, and the Architect so confirms, the Owner shall, upon application by the Contractor and certification by the Architect, and without terminating the Contract, make payment of the balance due for that portion of the Work fully completed and accepted. If the remaining balance for Work not fully completed or corrected is less than retainage stipulated in the Contract Documents, and if bonds have been furnished, the written consent of surety to payment of the balance due for that portion of the Work fully completed and accepted shall be submitted by the Contractor to the Architect prior to certification of such payment. Such payment shall

be made under terms and conditions governing final payment, except that it shall not constitute a waiver of claims. The making of final payment shall constitute a waiver of claims by the Owner as provided in Subparagraph 4.3.5.

10.10.4 Acceptance of final payment by the Contractor, a Subcontractor or Sub-subcontractor shall constitute a waiver of claims by that payee except those previously made in writing and identified by that payee as unsettled at the time of final Application for Payment. Such waivers shall be in addition to the waiver described in Subparagraph 4.3.5.

ARTICLE 11

PROTECTION OF PERSONS AND PROPERTY

11.1 SAFETY PRECAUTIONS AND PROGRAMS

11.1.1 The Contractor shall be responsible for initiating, maintaining and supervising all safety precautions and programs in connection with the performance of the Contract.

11.1.2 In the event the Contractor encounters on the Project premises material reasonably believed to be asbestos or polychlorinated biphenyl (PCB) which has not been rendered harmless, the Contractor shall immediately stop Work in the area affected and report the condition to the Owner in writing. The Work in the affected area shall not thereafter be resumed except by written agreement of the Owner and Contractor if in fact the material is asbestos or polychlorinated biphenyl (PCB) and has not been rendered harmless. The Work in the affected area shall be resumed in the absence of asbestos or polychlorinated biphenyl (PCB), or when it has been rendered harmless, by written agreement of the Owner and Contractor, or in accordance with final determination by the Architect upon which arbitration has not been demanded, or by arbitration under Article 4.

11.1.3 The Contractor shall not be required pursuant to Article 8 to perform without consent any Work relating to asbestos or polychlorinated biphenyl (PCB).

11.1.4 To the fullest extent permitted by law, the Owner shall indemnify and hold harmless the Contractor, Architect, Architect's consultants and agents and employees of any of them from and against claims, damages, losses and expenses, including but not limited to attorneys' fees, arising out of or resulting from performance of the Work in the affected area if in fact the material is asbestos or polychlorinated biphenyl (PCB) and has not been rendered harmless, provided that such claim, damage, loss or expense is attributable to bodily injury, sickness, disease or death, or to injury to or destruction of tangible property (other than the Work itself) including loss of use resulting therefrom, but only to the extent caused in whole or in part by negligent acts or omissions of the Owner, anyone directly or indirectly employed by the Owner or anyone for whose acts the Owner may be liable, regardless of whether or not such claim, damage, loss or expense is caused in part by a party indemnified hereunder. Such obligation shall not be construed to negate, abridge, or reduce other rights or obligations of indemnity which would otherwise exist as to a party or person described in this Subparagraph 11.1.4.

11.1.5 If reasonable precautions will be inadequate to prevent foreseeable bodily injury or death to persons resulting from a material or substance encountered on the site by the Contractor, the Contractor shall, upon recognizing the condition, immediately stop Work in the affected area and report the condition to the Owner and Architect in writing. The Owner,

A271-1990   16

claims-made basis, shall be maintained without interruption from date of commencement of the Work until date of final payment and termination of any coverage required to be maintained after final payment.

12.1.3 Certificates of Insurance acceptable to the Owner shall be filed with the Owner prior to commencement of the Work. These Certificates and the insurance policies required by this Paragraph 12.1 shall contain a provision that coverages afforded under the policies will not be cancelled or allowed to expire until at least 30 days' prior written notice has been given to the Owner. If any of the foregoing insurance coverages are required to remain in force after final payment and are reasonably available, an additional certificate evidencing continuation of such coverage shall be submitted with the final Application for Payment as required by Subparagraph 10.10.2. Information concerning reduction of coverage shall be furnished by the Contractor with reasonable promptness in accordance with the Contractor's information and belief.

12.2 OWNER'S LIABILITY INSURANCE

12.2.1 The Owner shall be responsible for purchasing and maintaining the Owner's usual liability insurance. Optionally, the Owner may purchase and maintain other insurance for self-protection against claims which may arise from operations under the Contract. The Contractor shall not be responsible for purchasing and maintaining this optional Owner's liability insurance unless specifically required by the Contract Documents.

12.3 PROPERTY INSURANCE

12.3.1 Unless otherwise provided, the Owner shall purchase and maintain, in a company or companies lawfully authorized to do business in the jurisdiction in which the Project is located, property insurance in the amount of the initial Contract Sum as well as subsequent modifications thereto for the entire Work at the Project premises on a replacement cost basis without voluntary deductibles. Such property insurance shall be maintained, unless otherwise provided in the Contract Documents or otherwise agreed in writing by all persons and entities who are beneficiaries of such insurance, until final payment has been made as provided in Paragraph 10.10 or until no person or entity other than the Owner has an insurable interest in the property required by this Paragraph 12.3 to be covered, whichever is earlier. This insurance shall include the interests of the Owner, the Contractor, Subcontractors and Sub-subcontractors in the Work.

12.3.1.1 Property insurance shall be on an all-risk policy form and shall insure against the perils of fire and extended coverage and physical loss or damage including, without duplication of coverage, theft, vandalism, malicious mischief, collapse and debris removal, and shall cover reasonable compensation for Architect's services and expenses required as a result of such insured loss. Coverage for other perils shall not be required unless otherwise provided in the Contract Documents.

12.3.1.2 If the Owner does not intend to purchase such property insurance required by the Contract and with all of the coverages in the amount described above, the Owner shall so inform the Contractor in writing prior to commencement of the Work. The Contractor may then effect insurance which will protect the interests of the Contractor, Subcontractors and Sub-subcontractors in the Work, and by appropriate Change Order the cost thereof shall be charged to the Owner. If the Contractor is damaged by the failure or neglect of the Owner to purchase or maintain insurance as described above, without so notifying the Contractor, then the Owner shall bear all reasonable costs properly attributable thereto.

12.3.1.3 If the property insurance requires minimum deductibles and such deductibles are identified in the Contract Documents, the Contractor shall pay costs not covered because of such deductibles. If the Owner or insurer increases the required minimum deductibles above the amounts so identified or if the Owner elects to purchase this insurance with voluntary deductible amounts, the Owner shall be responsible for payment of the additional costs not covered because of such increased or voluntary deductibles. If deductibles are not identified in the Contract Documents, the Owner shall pay costs not covered because of deductibles.

12.3.1.4 This property insurance will not cover portions of the Work stored off the Project premises or in transit. Unless otherwise provided in the Contract Documents, the Contractor shall maintain insurance to cover these conditions.

12.3.1.5 The insurance required by this Paragraph 12.3 is not intended to cover machinery, tools or equipment owned or rented by the Contractor which are utilized in the performance of the Work but not incorporated into the permanent improvements. The Contractor shall, at the Contractor's own expense, provide insurance coverage for owned or rented machinery, tools or equipment which shall be subject to the provisions of Subparagraph 12.3.6.

12.3.2 Loss of Use Insurance. The Owner, at the Owner's option, may purchase and maintain such insurance as will insure the Owner against loss of use of the Owner's property due to fire or other hazards, however caused. The Owner waives all rights of action against the Contractor for loss of use of the Owner's property, including consequential losses due to fire or other hazards however caused.

12.3.3 If the Contractor requests in writing that insurance for risks other than those described herein or for other special hazards be included in the property insurance policy, the Owner shall, if possible, include such insurance, and the cost thereof shall be charged to the Contractor by appropriate Change Order.

12.3.4 If during the Contract Time the Owner insures properties, real or personal or both, adjoining or adjacent to the Project premises by property insurance under policies separate from those insuring the Project, or if after final payment property insurance is to be provided on the completed Project through a policy or policies other than those insuring the Project during the Contract Time, the Owner shall waive all rights in accordance with the terms of Subparagraph 12.3.6 for damages caused by fire or other perils covered by this separate property insurance. All separate policies shall provide this waiver of subrogation by endorsement or otherwise.

12.3.5 Before an exposure to loss may occur, the Owner shall file with the Contractor a copy of each policy that includes insurance coverages required by this Paragraph 12.3. Each policy shall contain all generally applicable conditions, definitions, exclusions and endorsements related to this Project. Each policy shall contain a provision that the policy will not be cancelled or allowed to expire until at least 30 days' prior written notice has been given to the Contractor.

12.3.6 Waivers of Subrogation. The Owner and Contractor waive all rights against (1) each other and any of their subcontractors, sub-subcontractors, agents and employees, each of the other, and (2) the Architect, Architect's consultants, separate contractors described in Article 6, if any, and any of their subcontractors, sub-subcontractors, agents and employees, for damages caused by fire or other perils to the extent covered by property insurance obtained pursuant to this sonable time fixed by written notice from the Architect, the Owner may remove it and may store the salvable materials, furniture, furnishings or equipment at the Contractor's expense. If the Contractor does not pay costs of such removal and storage within ten days after written notice, the Owner may upon ten additional days' written notice sell such materials, furniture, furnishings and equipment at auction or at private sale and shall account for the proceeds thereof, after deducting costs and damages that should have been borne by the Contractor, including compensation for the Architect's services and expenses made necessary thereby. If such proceeds of sale do not cover costs which the Contractor should have borne, the Contract Sum shall be reduced by the deficiency. If payments then or thereafter due the Contractor are not sufficient to cover such amount, the Contractor shall pay the difference to the Owner.

13.2.5 The Contractor shall bear the cost of correcting destroyed or damaged property, including completed or partially completed construction, of the Owner or separate contractors caused by the Contractor's correction or removal of Work which is not in accordance with the requirements of the Contract Documents.

13.2.6 Nothing contained in this Paragraph 13.2 shall be construed to establish a period of limitation with respect to other obligations which the Contractor might have under the Contract Documents. Establishment of the time period of one year as described in Subparagraph 13.2.2 relates only to the specific obligation of the Contractor to correct the Work, and has no relationship to the time within which the obligation to comply with the Contract Documents may be sought to be enforced, nor to the time within which proceedings may be commenced to establish the Contractor's liability with respect to the Contractor's obligations other than specifically to correct the Work.

13.3 ACCEPTANCE OF NONCONFORMING WORK

13.3.1 If the Owner prefers to accept Work which is not in accordance with the requirements of the Contract Documents, the Owner may do so instead of requiring its removal and correction, in which case the Contract Sum will be reduced as appropriate and equitable. Such adjustment shall be effected whether or not final payment has been made.

ARTICLE 14

MISCELLANEOUS PROVISIONS

14.1 GOVERNING LAW

14.1.1 The Contract shall be governed by the law of the place where the Project is located.

14.2 SUCCESSORS AND ASSIGNS

14.2.1 The Owner and Contractor respectively bind themselves, their partners, successors, assigns and legal representatives to the other party hereto and to partners, successors, assigns and legal representatives of such other party in respect to covenants, agreements and obligations contained in the Contract Documents. Neither party to the Contract shall assign the Contract as a whole without written consent of the other. If either party attempts to make such an assignment without such consent, that party shall nevertheless remain legally responsible for all obligations under the Contract.

14.3 WRITTEN NOTICE

14.3.1 Written notice shall be deemed to have been duly served if delivered in person to the individual or a member

of the firm or entity or to an officer of the corporation for which it was intended, or if delivered at or sent by registered or certified mail to the last business address known to the party giving notice.

14.4 RIGHTS AND REMEDIES

14.4.1 Duties and obligations imposed by the Contract Documents and rights and remedies available thereunder shall be in addition to and not a limitation of duties, obligations, rights and remedies otherwise imposed or available by law.

14.4.2 No action or failure to act by the Owner, Architect or Contractor shall constitute a waiver of a right or duty afforded them under the Contract, nor shall such action or failure to act constitute approval of or acquiescence in a breach thereunder, except as may be specifically agreed in writing.

14.5 TESTS AND INSPECTIONS

14.5.1 Tests, inspections and approvals of portions of the Work required by the Contract Documents or by laws, ordinances, rules, regulations or orders of public authorities having jurisdiction shall be made at an appropriate time. Unless otherwise provided, the Contractor shall make arrangements for such tests, inspections and approvals with an independent testing laboratory or entity acceptable to the Owner, or with the appropriate public authority, and shall bear all related costs of tests, inspections and approvals. The Contractor shall give the Architect timely notice of when and where tests and inspections are to be made so the Architect may observe such procedures. The Owner shall bear costs of tests, inspections or approvals which do not become requirements until after bids are received or negotiations concluded.

14.5.2 If the Architect, Owner or public authorities having jurisdiction determine that portions of the Work require additional inspection, testing or approval not included under Subparagraph 14.5.1, the Architect will, upon written authorization from the Owner, instruct the Contractor to make arrangements for such additional testing, inspection or approval by an entity acceptable to the Owner, and the Contractor shall give timely notice to the Architect of when and where tests and inspections are to be made so the Architect may observe such procedures. The Owner shall bear such costs except as provided in Subparagraph 14.5.3.

14.5.3 If such procedures for testing, inspection or approval under Subparagraphs 14.5.1 and 14.5.2 reveal failure of the portions of the Work to comply with requirements established by the Contract Documents, the Contractor shall bear all costs made necessary by such failure including those of repeated procedures and compensation for the Architect's services and expenses.

14.5.4 Required certificates of testing, inspection or approval shall, unless otherwise required by the Contract Documents, be secured by the Contractor and promptly delivered to the Architect.

14.5.5 If the Architect is to observe tests, inspections or approvals required by the Contract Documents, the Architect will do so promptly and, where practicable, at the normal place of testing.

14.5.6 Tests or inspections conducted pursuant to the Contract Documents shall be made promptly to avoid unreasonable delay in the Work.

14.6 INTEREST

14.6.1 Payments due and unpaid under the Contract Documents shall bear interest from the date payment is due at such rate as the parties may agree upon in writing or, in the absence

AIA DOCUMENT A271 • GENERAL CONDITIONS OF THE CONTRACT FOR FURNITURE, FURNISHINGS AND EQUIPMENT
1990 EDITION • AIA® • ©1990 • THE AMERICAN INSTITUTE OF ARCHITECTS, 1735 NEW YORK AVENUE, N.W., WASHINGTON,
D.C. 20006-5209 • ASID® • ©1990 • THE AMERICAN SOCIETY OF INTERIOR DESIGNERS, 608 MASSACHUSETTS AVENUE, N.E.,
WASHINGTON, D.C. 20002

A271-1990   20

APPENDIX D

California Technical Bulletin 133

**STATE OF CALIFORNIA
DEPARTMENT OF CONSUMER AFFAIRS
BUREAU OF HOME FURNISHINGS AND THERMAL INSULATION
3485 ORANGE GROVE AVENUE
NORTH HIGHLANDS, CALIFORNIA 95660-5595**

TECHNICAL BULLETIN 133

**Flammability Test Procedure for Seating
Furniture for Use in Public Occupancies**

JANUARY 1991

TECHNICAL BULLETIN 133

Flammability Test Procedure for Seating
Furniture for Use in Public Occupancies

I. **Scope**

    A.   This test procedure is designed to test seating furniture for use in occupancies that are identified as or considered to be public occupancies. Such facilities might include, but are not limited to, jails, prisons, nursing care homes, health care facilities, public auditoriums, hotels and motels.

    B.   This test procedure is not intended to be used for the evaluation of residential furniture.

    C.   It is the intent of the Bureau that furniture complying with Technical Bulletin 133 be safer furniture when subjected to the ignition source specified by this test. This type of ignition may be typical of arson or incendiary fires or common accidental fires in public buildings. This Bureau expects manufacturers attempting to comply with this standard will also seek to make safer furniture, and will not attempt to compromise the intent of the standard in any manner.

II. **Test Facility**

    A.   The test burn room shall be 12 x 10 feet or a close approximation with an 8-foot ceiling height. The room shall have no openings other than a doorway opening approximately 38 x 81 inches, located as indicated in Figures 1 and 2, and such other small openings that may be necessary to make test measurements. The test room shall be constructed of wooden or metal studs and lined with fire rated gypsum wallboard. Tests may be conducted in rooms of different physical dimensions than those specified, for example, the proposed ASTM room, when equivalent test results can be demonstrated. In addition, if compliance is claimed using the heat release criteria, tests performed using a furniture calorimeter are acceptable. When using test rooms of different dimensions or a furniture calorimeter the ignition source must be as specified in Section V of this standard.

    B.   The test burn room shall be instrumented to monitor temperature, carbon monoxide concentration, smoke opacity and sample weight loss. Other test room instrumentation may be added as required. In addition, the test facility may be instrumented to measure total heat release and heat release rate when compliance with the alternate heat release criteria is claimed. A typical system used to measure heat release, on the principle of oxygen consumption, is described in Appendix A.

    C.   The test room shall be unfurnished except for the test sample. The test sample shall be positioned as indicated in Figure 1 or 2.

III. Test Sample

The test sample shall consist of typical seating furniture suitable for use in public occupancies, or a full-scale mock-up of the furniture. When a full-scale furniture mock-up is used, the mock-up shall in all respects (including fabrics, filling materials, combustible decorative parts and furniture style) reflect the construction of the actual furniture that it is intended to represent. See Appendix D.

IV. Test Conditioning

The test sample and newsprint shall be conditioned for at least 48 hours prior to testing at 70±5°F and a relative humidity of less than 55%. Test materials shall be tested within 10 minutes of removal from such conditions if test room conditions differ from the above.

V. Test Ignition Source

A.   The test ignition source shall be a square gas burner as described in Appendix C.

B.   An ignition source of five double sheets of loosely wadded newsprint contained in an ignition box, as described in Appendix B, may be used as a screening test.

VI. Test Procedure

A.   Position thermocouple in two test locations (see Figure 1 or 2):

   1.   Over the geometric center of the ignition source, one inch below the ceiling. This shall be designated as the ceiling thermocouple.

   2.   Three feet in front of the ignition source, four feet below the ceiling. This shall be designated as the 4 foot thermocouple.

B.   Position a smoke opacity monitor in one test location (see Figure 1 or 2): Four feet above the floor level. This shall be designated as the 4-foot smoke opacity monitor.

C.   The gas sampling line shall be positioned 6.5 inches below the ceiling and 6.5 inches from the corner (see Figure 1 or 2).

D.   A weighing platform shall support the base of the furniture 5±2 inches above the floor. The furniture and weighing platform shall be positioned in the corner so that the furniture is no more than 10 inches from both walls. If the seating furniture is no more than 40 inches in width, refer to Figure 1. If the seating furniture is more than 40 inches, refer to Figure 2.

E.   If the seating furniture is no more than 40 inches in width, the square gas burner shall be positioned at the center of the crevice area, 2 inches from the furniture back and 1 inch above the seat surface. (See Figures 12D and 13).

293

F.   If the seating furniture is more than 40 inches in width, the square gas burner shall be positioned 5 inches from the left arm crevice or edge of the seating surface. (See Figures 12D and 14).

G.   The gas flow through the square gas burner, described in Appendix C, shall be maintained for 80±2 seconds.

H.   Allow combustion to continue until:

1.   All combustion has ceased; or

2.   1.0 hour of testing has elapsed; or

3.   Flameover or flashover appears to be inevitable.

VII.   Test Criteria

A.   Seating furniture fails to meet the requirements of this test procedure if <u>any</u> of the following criteria are exceeded in a room test using the room instrumentation.

1.   A temperature increase of 200°F or greater at the ceiling thermocouple.

2.   A temperature increase of 50°F or greater at the 4-foot thermocouple.

3.   Greater than 75% opacity at the 4-foot smoke opacity monitor.

4.   Carbon monoxide concentration in the room, as measured in accordance with Section VI, Part C, of 1000 ppm or greater for 5 minutes.

5.   Weight loss due to combustion of 3 pounds or greater in the first 10 minutes of the test.

B.   Seating furniture fails to meet the requirements of this test procedure if any of the following criteria are exceeded in a room test using oxygen consumption calorimetry.

1.   A maximum rate of heat release of 80 kW or greater.

2.   A total heat release of 25 MJ or greater in the first 10 minutes of the test.

3.   Greater than 75% opacity at the 4-foot smoke opacity monitor.

4.   Carbon monoxide concentration in the room, as measured in accordance with Section VI, Part C, of 1000 ppm or greater for 5 minutes.

Note

It is not required that all of the above criteria in VII A and VII B, be measured. Furniture must comply with the criteria described in VII A or VII B. When a furniture calorimeter is used furniture must comply with Criteria B, 1 and 2.

VII.   Caution

Full-scale fire tests may be dangerous. All tests should be supervised by experienced test personnel. Adequate fire suppression equipment and self-contained breathing devices must be available for test personnel. Products of combustion can be irritating and dangerous; therefore, test personnel must avoid exposure to smoke and gases produced during testing as much as possible. Full-scale fire tests should never be left unattended. Test personnel must be certain upon completion of the test that combustion is totally suppressed. The performance of the submitted sample is not necessarily on accurate indication of the performance of the furniture in a real-life fire situation.

APPENDIX A

Calculation of the Rate of Heat release by the Method of Oxygen Consumption

This appendix describes the method of measurement of rate of heat release from burning furniture based on the principle of oxygen depletion. Part I describes the instrumentation required for flow and oxygen depletion measurements. Part II describes the method of, and equations for the calculation of rate of heat release.

PART I   INSTRUMENTATION

The following is a description of the gas sampling technique and instrumentation used by the Bureau of Home Furnishings to determine the rate of heat release - based on oxygen depletion. Alternative techniques and/or equipment that provide accurate determination of oxygen depletion and the rate of heat release are acceptable.

A.   Collection of Combustion Gases and Flow Measurement

A suitable sized collection hood should be installed at the top of the doorway entrance. The hood should be designed and located to ensure a well mixed sample of gases for analysis. The path of the exhaust duct should be at least 20 feet long to ensure accurate flow velocity measurements and may have turning and straightening vanes installed as shown in Figures 9a, 9b and 9c.

B.   Duct Air Velocity Measurement

A bi-directional probe or an equivalent system shall be used to measure gas velocity in the duct. The bi-directional probe shall be mounted at the center line of the duct parallel to the direction of the air flow. A pressure transducer with a range of 0 to 1 torr, or equivalent, shall be used to measure the pressure differential across the bi-directional probe in the duct. A thermocouple shall be installed next to the bi-directional probe to record the temperature of the flowing gases. This temperature along with the pressure differential is required to calculate the velocity of the flow in the exhaust duct.

C.   Gas Sampling Probe in the Duct

In order to determine oxygen depletion due to the combustion of burning articles, a sample of the exhaust gases shall be extracted from the exhaust duct to measure the mole fractions of oxygen, carbon monoxide and carbon dioxide. A stainless steel gas sampling tube shall be used to obtain a continuously flowing sample. The location and configuration of the sampling probe shall ensure collection of a representative sample of well mixed gases. A suitable sampling tube is shown in Figures 10a-d. Alternative designs that allow an integral sampling of gases over the cross-section of the exhaust duct are acceptable.

PART II EQUATIONS

A.   The rate of heat production shall be calculated as follows:

$$\dot{Q} = E'X_{O_2}^\circ V_A \left[\phi - \left(\frac{E'' - E'}{E'} \right) \left(\frac{1 - \phi}{2} \right) \frac{X_{CO}}{X_{O_2}} \right]$$ (1)

where:

E' = net heat of combustion per unit volume of oxygen consumed, 17.2 MJ/m³,

E'' = heat release per unit volume of oxygen consumed in the burning of CO, 23.1 MJ/m³ referred to 25°C.

V_A = the volume flow rate of air into the system corrected to 25°C (including that which enters the room and that which passes directly into the exhaust duct)

X_i = mole fraction of the gas specie i, in the gas analyzer,

X_i° = mole fraction of the gas specie i, entering the system, in the gas analyzer, i.e., the initial mole fractions,

ϕ = oxygen depletion.

B.   The oxygen depletion or the fraction of oxygen consumed is as follows:

$$\phi = \frac{X_{O_2}^\circ - \dfrac{X_{O_2}\left(1 - X_{CO_2}^\circ\right)}{\left(1 - X_{CO_2} - X_{CO}\right)}}{X_{O_2}^\circ \left(1 - \dfrac{X_{O_2}}{\left(1 - X_{CO_2} - X_{CO}\right)}\right)}$$ (2)

C.   The volume flow rate in the exhaust duct is given by,

$$V_s = 1 - \phi V_A + \alpha \phi V_A$$ (3)

Where V_S and V_A are referred to standard conditions (25°C and 1 atm) and α is the expansion factor of the air that is depleted of its oxygen. So

$$V_A = \frac{V_s}{\left(1 + (\alpha - 1)\phi\right)}$$ (4)

The value of α ranges from 1.0 for carbon to 1.175 for cellulose with plastics having values in between. In order to reduce the error incurred when unknown products are burning, α is taken to have an intermediate value of 1.084 which is exact for propane, the calibration burner gas. Setting α=1.084, E'=17.2 MJ/m³ and E"=23.1 MJ/m³, equation (1) becomes:

$$\dot{Q} = 17.2 X_{O_2}^\circ \frac{V_s}{(1+0.084\phi)} \left[\phi - 0.3429 \left(\frac{1-\phi}{2} \right) \frac{X_{CO}}{X_{O_2}} \right] \quad \text{MW} \quad (5)$$

where V_S is measured in the exhaust duct as cubic meters per second.

D. If the gas velocity in the exhaust duct is measured with a pitot-static tube or a bi-directional probe, the standard volume flow rate is given by:

$$V_s = jkA \left[\frac{2\Delta P}{\rho_0} \frac{T_0}{T_s} \right]^{\frac{1}{2}} = 22.4 jkA \left[\frac{\Delta P}{T_s} \right]^{\frac{1}{2}} \quad \text{m}^3/\text{sec} \quad (6)$$

where T_S is the gas temperature in the duct in degrees K and ΔP is the pressure differential across the bi-directional probe (or pitot-static tube) in Pa, A is the cross-sectional area of the duct in m², k is the ratio of the average mass flow rate per unit area to the centerline mass flow rate per unit area, j is a calibration factor equal to unity for a pitot-static tube and 0.926 for a bi-directional probe, and ρ_0 is the density of air, kg/m³, at the reference temperature T_0, °K.

E. When carbon monoxide is not measured in the sampling line or its mole fraction can be neglected compared with the mole fraction of CO_2, the equation for the oxygen depletion can be simplified as:

$$\phi = \frac{X_{O_2}^\circ - \dfrac{X_{O_2} \left(1 - X_{CO_2}^\circ\right)}{\left(1 - X_{CO_2}\right)}}{X_{O_2}^\circ \left(1 - \dfrac{X_{O_2}}{\left(1 - X_{CO_2}\right)}\right)} \quad (7)$$

and the rate of heat release equation will be:

$$\dot{Q} = \frac{17.2 X_{O_2}^\circ V_s \phi}{(1+0.084\phi)} \quad \text{MW} \quad (8)$$

F. The room and ducting shall be calibrated using a porous gas burner with a 12 by 12 inch top surface and a 6 inch depth. A gas burner may be constructed with a 1 inch thick (25 mm) plenum; or alternatively a minimum 4 inch (100 mm) layer of Ottawa sand can be used to provide the horizontal surface through which the gas is supplied. This type of burner is shown in Figure 11. The gas supply to the burner shall be of commercial grade propane and shall have a of propane shall be metered and kept constant throughout the calibration test. A minimum of 2 calibration points shall be obtained. A lower heat release value of 40 kW shall be obtained which is the equivalent of approximately 1.0 standard ft^3/min (28.32 lit/min) of propane. Then a higher heat release value of 169 kW shall be obtained. This is the equivalent of approximately 4.0 standard ft³/min (113.27 lit/min) of propane. Both tests shall be conducted for a period of 10 minutes.

APPENDIX B

Newsprint Ignition Source

A.   This appendix describes the newsprint ignition source which may be used for compliance or screening testing. This ignition source consists of five double sheets of loosely wadded newsprint contained in Ignition Box A, B or C as appropriate. The newsprint shall not be tightly crumpled, but should be loosely wadded to approximately fill the selected ignition box.

B.   One of three ignition boxes shall be used. Ignition Box A shall be used for furniture with a seat/back crevice. Ignition Box B shall be used with furniture that does not have a crevice. Ignition Box C shall be used for furniture that has a gap in the crevice area.

    1.   The following is a description of Ignition Box A:

        a.   The 10 x 10 x 10 inch ignition box shall be constructed of .016 inch thick galvanized steel flashing and one inch hexagonal chicken wire. The steel flashing shall be cut 10 x 20 inches. A 7 inch long x 1.5 inch deep notch shall be cut centrally along a 10 inch side. One-eighth inch diameter holes shall be punched along both 20 inch sides on 1 inch centers, 0.5 inches from the edge of the flashing. The flashing shall be bent to form a right angle producing two 10 x 10 inch sides of the ignition box. Two pieces of chicken wire shall be cut 11 x 11 inches. The chicken wire shall overlap one inch on the outside of the flashing. A 20 gauge wire shall be used to attach the chicken wire to the flashing through the 1/8 inch holes. The two remaining sides of the ignition box shall be left open (see Figure 3). The ignition box shall be used as indicated in Figures 4 and 5.

        b.   Before use, the ignition box should be discolored. This may be accomplished by burning several batches of crumpled newspapers inside the box.

    2.   Ignition Box B shall be similar to Ignition Box A with the following changes:

        a.   Only the side in contact with the seating area shall be left open. An 11 x 12 inch piece of previously described chicken wire shall be used to cover the 10 x 10 inch rear side of the box. Overlap and attachment shall be as previously described.

        b.   The 7 inch long x 1.5 inch deep notch shall be eliminated from the top of the ignition box.

    3.   Ignition Box C shall be similar to Ignition Box B with the following changes:

        a.   A 7 inch long x 1.5 inch deep notch shall be cut centrally from the top of the ignition box. The open side of the box will be in contact with the seating area and the notch will be facing the back of the chair.

C.   Each double sheet of newsprint shall have the approximate dimensions of 23 x 28 inches. Five double sheets of newsprint shall have the combined weight of 90 grams ±5 grams. Newsprint shall be black and white only; sheets with any type of color shall not be used.

APPENDIX C

Square Gas Burner Ignition Source

A.   This appendix describes the square gas burner ignition source which may be used for compliance or screening testing. This ignition source utilizes propane gas as fuel at a volume flow rate of approximately 13 liters per minute for a period of 80 seconds. The propane gas is the same commercial grade as described in Appendix A.

B.   The following is a description of the square gas burner:

The 250 x 250 mm (or approximately 10 x 10 inch) square burner shall be constructed of 1/2 inch OD stainless-steel tubing with 0.035 inch wall thickness (see Figure 12a). The front side shall have 14 holes pointing straight out and spaced 13 mm apart and 9 holes pointing straight down and spaced 13 mm apart. The right and left sides shall have 6 holes pointing straight out and spaced 13 mm apart and 4 holes pointing at 45° angle inward and spaced 50 mm apart. All holes shall be of 1 mm diameter (see Figures 12a-c). The 42 inch straight arm of the burner shall be welded on to the rear of the front side (Figure 12a) in a 30° angle. The burner shall be mounted on an adjustable height pole and be balanced by a counter weight or other appropriate mechanism (Figure 12d).

Note 1:   When the flow of propane to the burner is stopped the burner shall be removed from the chair and away from high temperature gases. If the square gas burner is to be exposed to heat during burning of the test article, arrangements must be made to allow the remaining propane gas inside the tube to be freely released to avoid any possibility of explosion.

Note 2:   Care must be taken to allow free flow of propane through the burner holes. Periodic cleaning of soot deposit and blowing pressurized air through the tube is recommended.

APPENDIX D

Furniture Mock-Up System

Technical Note

In lieu of testing finished products, full-scale mock-up testing may be performed according to the following test procedure.

A. The test sample shall consist of component cushions which duplicate the thickness, construction and design features of a product suitable for use in public occupancies.

B. A metal test frame (Figures 6 and 7) shall be used to support seat and back cushions and, if necessary, arm cushions. The chair frame shall be constructed of slotted "L" angle iron and slotted flat angle iron. The back shall be constructed so that it is adjustable to a maximum angle of 135° from the horizontal plane. The test frame shall be adjustable to accommodate test cushions of various thicknesses and sizes, with or without arm cushions.

C. Component back, seat and arm cushions shall be constructed into mock-up designs of the actual article of furniture. Construction should duplicate all layers found in the actual article of furniture. Cushion construction shall consist of either:

    1. Manufacturer's prefabricated cushions of the appropriate size; or

    2. Custom-made cushions of the appropriate size. Cushions are constructed by covering the face and four edges of the filling material with the appropriate interliners, etc. and cover fabric. On the back of each cushion, a two-inch overlap of the cover fabric is stapled together and a wire is loosely woven through the fabric edges and drawn to produce a close fit (see Figure 8).

D. The constructed seat cushion may be placed horizontally on the seat area of the test frame and pushed against the back of the frame. The constructed back cushion may then be placed vertically against the back support of the test frame. The back cushion shall be held in place by wire to prevent it from falling forward. If arm cushions are used, the constructed arm cushions may be placed between the seat cushion and the arm supports of the test frame. However, the placement of the seat, back and arm cushions should be done to most closely duplicate the design features of the completed article of furniture.

E. The test procedure shall be the same as for completed articles of furniture (see Section VI). The test criteria shall be the same for completed articles of furniture (see Section VII).

F. For upholstered furniture products containing only wood and/or metal frames, the above procedure appears to be an accurate indicator of the open-flame performance of the finished article.   For upholstered furniture products containing plastic frames and plastic decorative parts, this procedure may not be an accurate indicator of the open-flame performance of the finished article unless the plastic parts are included in the mock-up tested.

FIGURE 1

ROOM CONFIGURATION FOR TESTING SEATING ITEMS
NO MORE THAN 40 INCHES ACROSS

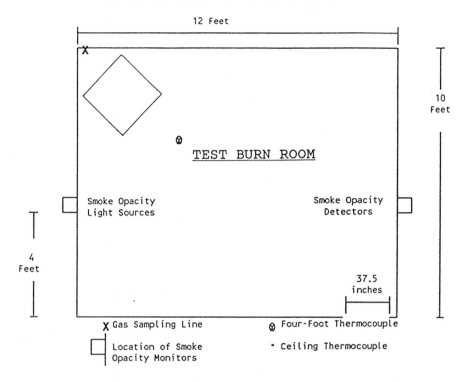

FIGURE 2

ROOM CONFIGURATION FOR TESTING SEATING ITEMS
MORE THAN 40 INCHES ACROSS

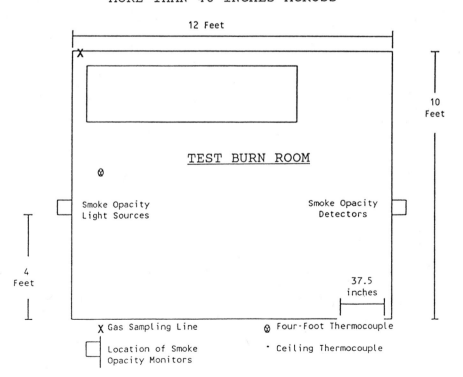

FIGURE 3

IGNITION BOX A

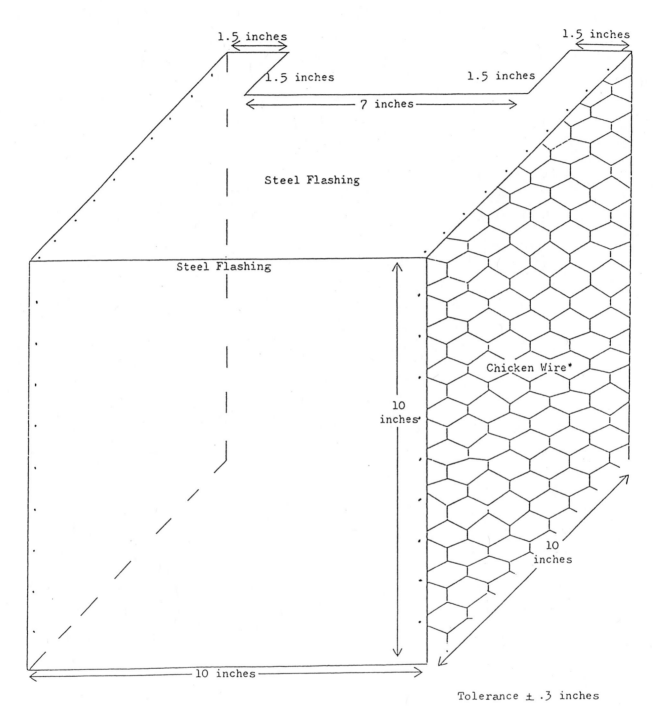

Tolerance ± .3 inches

* Two opposite sides
  are chicken wire

FIGURE 4

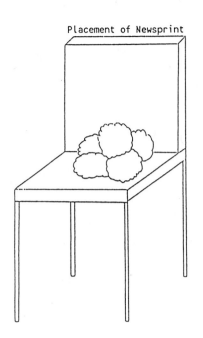

Placement of Newsprint

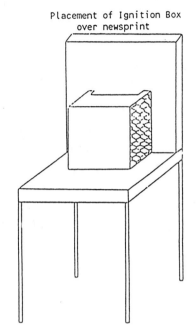

Placement of Ignition Box
over newsprint

FIGURE 5

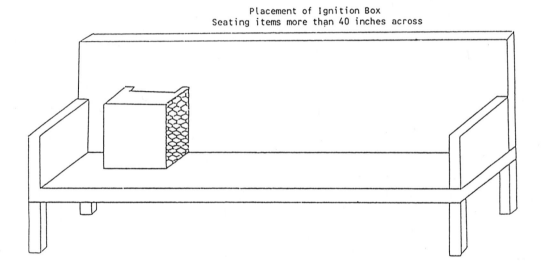

Placement of Ignition Box
Seating items more than 40 inches across

307

FIGURE 6

METAL TEST FRAME

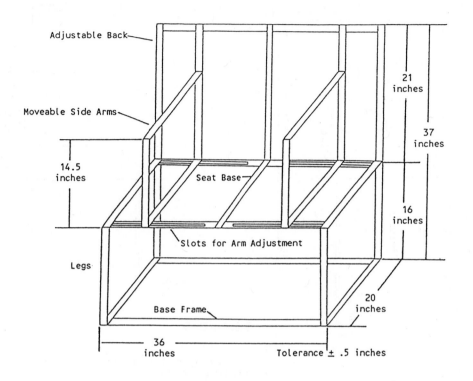

FIGURE 7

METAL TEST FRAME
(END VIEW)

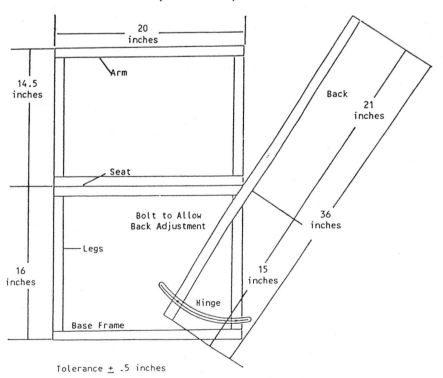

FIGURE 8

BACK VIEW OF CONSTRUCTED CUSHION

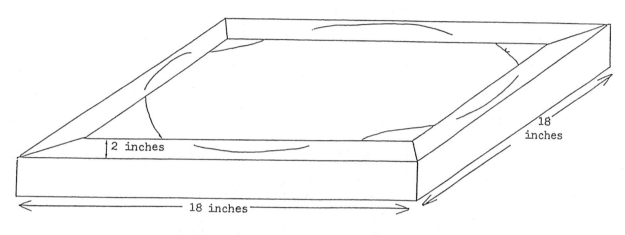

Tolerance ± 1 inch

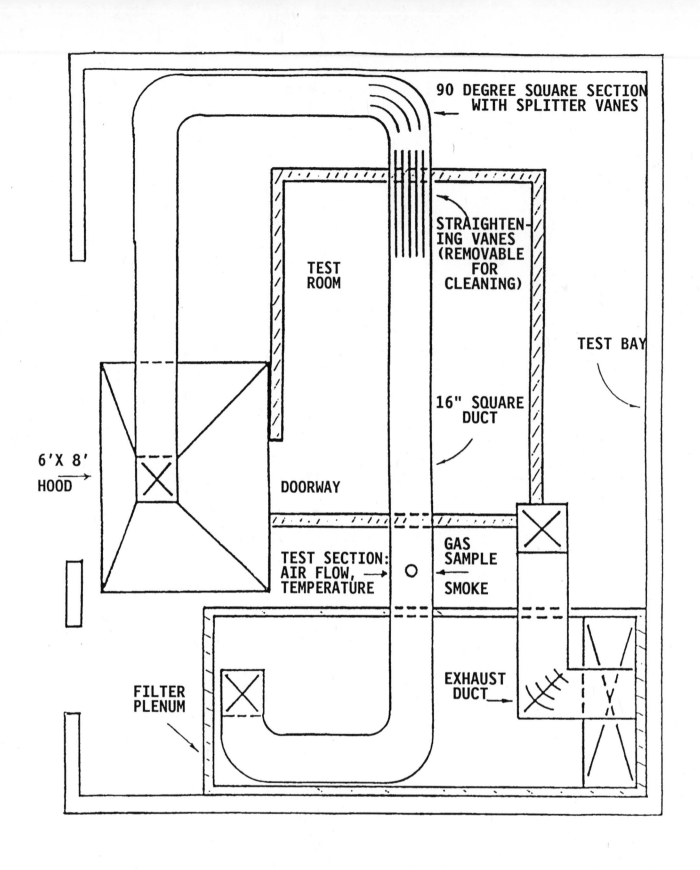

90 DEGREE SQUARE SECTION
WITH SPLITTER VANES

STRAIGHTEN-
ING VANES
(REMOVABLE
FOR
CLEANING)

TEST
ROOM

TEST BAY

16" SQUARE
DUCT

6'X 8'
HOOD

DOORWAY

GAS
SAMPLE

TEST SECTION:
AIR FLOW,
TEMPERATURE

SMOKE

FILTER
PLENUM

EXHAUST
DUCT

PLAN VIEW OF THE TEST ROOM AND EXHAUST DUCT
FIGURE 9a

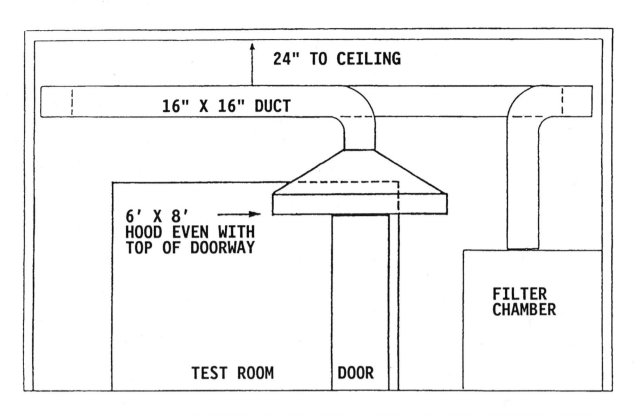

FRONT VIEW OF THE TEST ROOM AND THE EXHAUST DUCT
FIGURE 9b

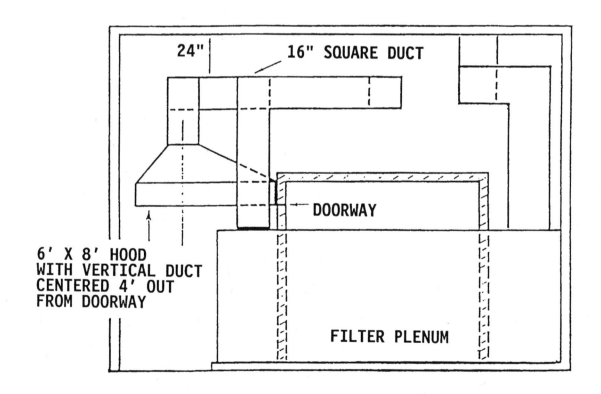

SIDE VIEW OF THE TEST ROOM AND THE EXHAUST DUCT
FIGURE 9c

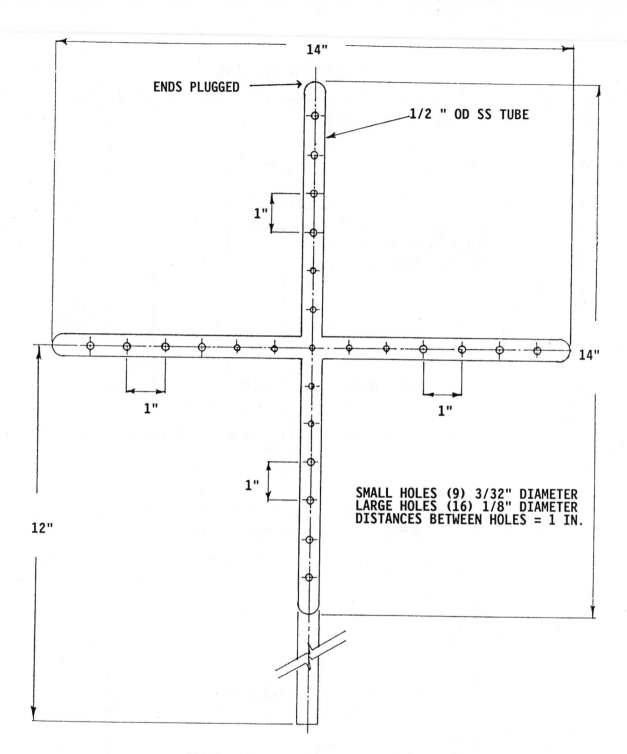

FRONT VIEW OF GAS SAMPLING PROBE
FIGURE 10a

312

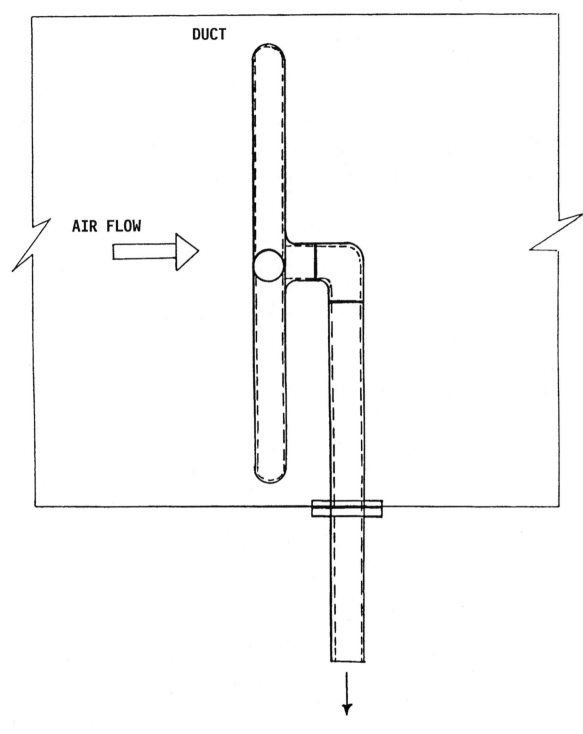

DUCT

AIR FLOW

TO GAS ANALYSIS SYSTEM

SIDE VIEW OF THE GAS SAMPLING PROBE IN THE DUCT
FIGURE 10b

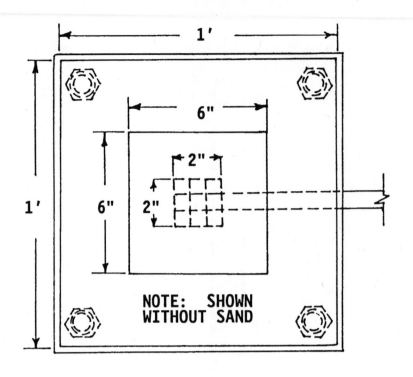

NOTE: SHOWN WITHOUT SAND

PLAN VIEW

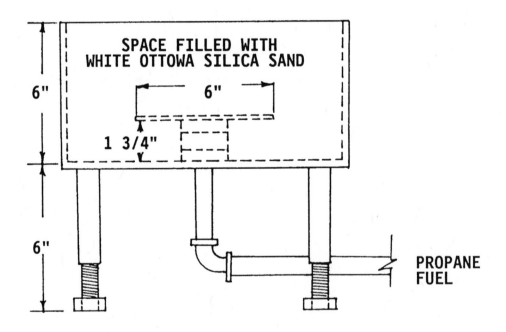

SPACE FILLED WITH
WHITE OTTOWA SILICA SAND

PROPANE
FUEL

ELEVATION

CALIBRATION GAS BURNER
FIGURE 11

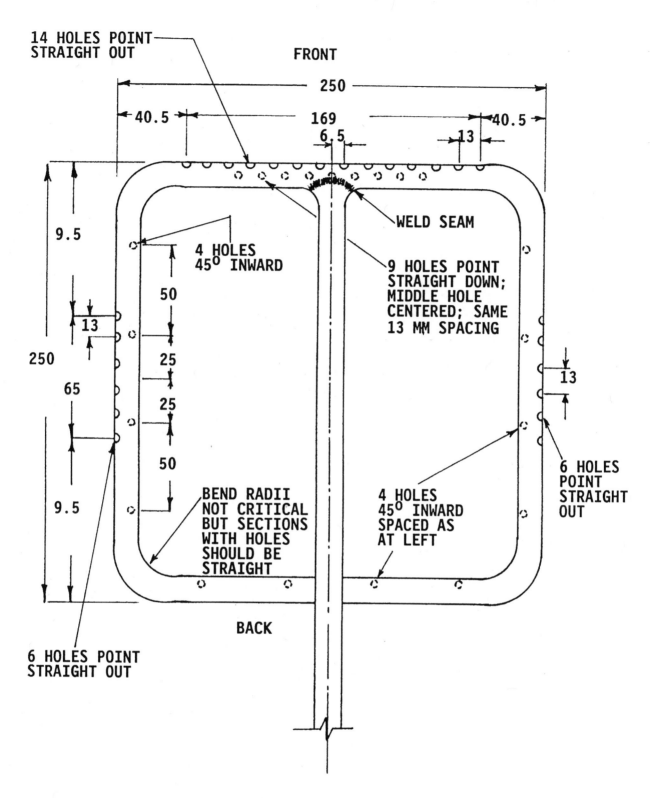

14 HOLES POINT STRAIGHT OUT

FRONT

250

40.5   169   40.5

6.5   13

WELD SEAM

9.5

4 HOLES 45° INWARD

9 HOLES POINT STRAIGHT DOWN; MIDDLE HOLE CENTERED; SAME 13 MM SPACING

13

50

250

25

65

25

13

50

6 HOLES POINT STRAIGHT OUT

BEND RADII NOT CRITICAL BUT SECTIONS WITH HOLES SHOULD BE STRAIGHT

4 HOLES 45° INWARD SPACED AS AT LEFT

9.5

BACK

6 HOLES POINT STRAIGHT OUT

NOTE: 1.   All tubing 1/2" OD, SS, 0.035" wall thickness.
        2.   All holes 1 mm in diameter.
        3.   All units are mm unless otherwise noted.

PLAN VIEW OF SQUARE GAS BURNER
FIGURE 12a

315

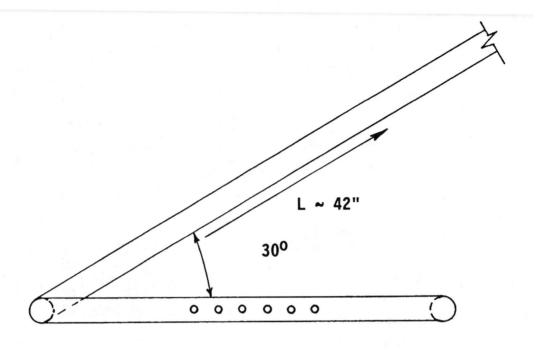

SIDE VIEW OF SQUARE GAS BURNER
FIGURE 12b

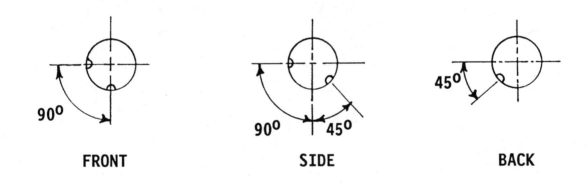

CROSS SECTIONAL VIEW OF EACH SIDE OF SQUARE GAS BURNER
FIGURE 12c

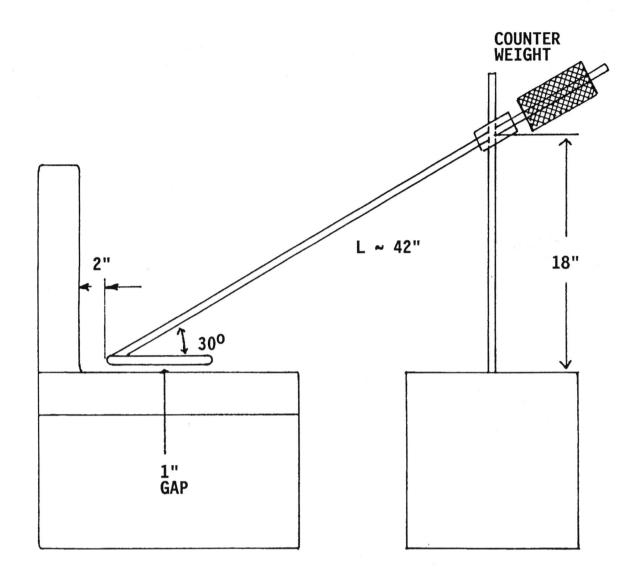

POSITIONING OF SQUARE GAS BURNER ON THE CHAIR
FIGURE 12d

317

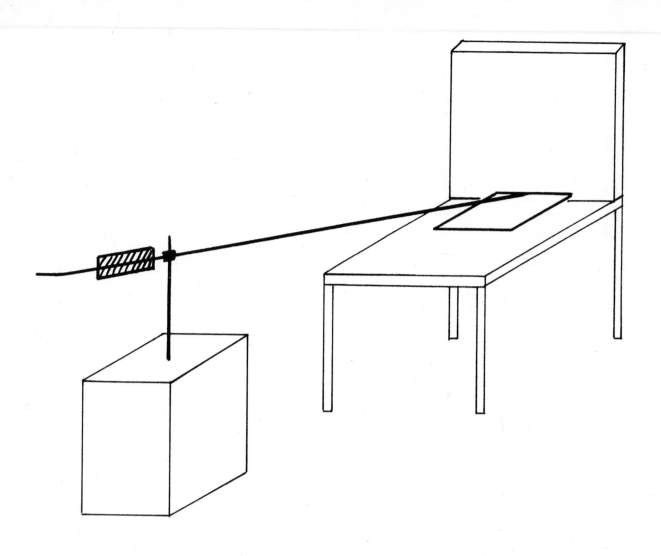

FIGURE 13

Placement of Square Gas Burner
Seating items no more than 40 inches across

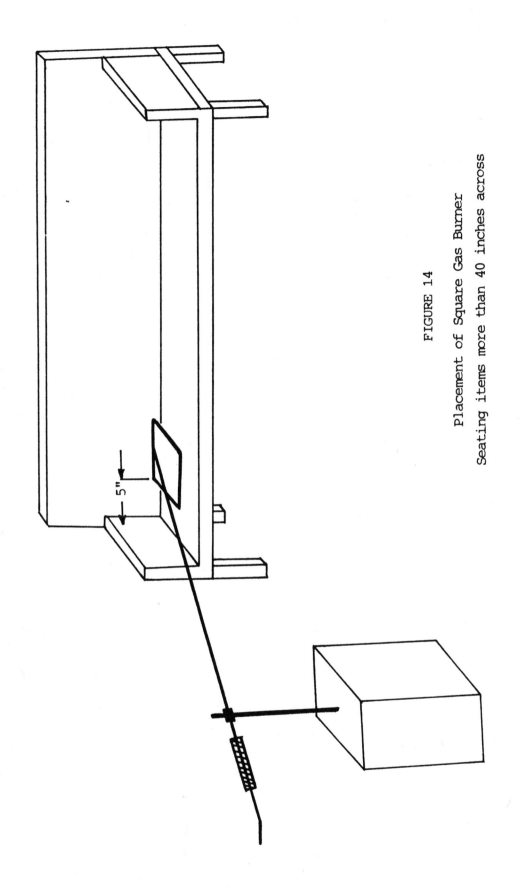

5"

FIGURE 14

Placement of Square Gas Burner
Seating items more than 40 inches across

APPENDIX E

The International System of Units

The International System of Units (Le Système International d'Unités, abbreviated as SI in all languages) is a modernized and expanded version of the metric system. In 1790, just after the French Revolution, one of the first motions of the newly declared democracy, led by the National Assembly, was to request that the French Academy of Sciences develop a system of practical measurements suitable for international adoption. This system was legalized in the United States in 1866, and its implementation is now an officially recognized goal.

TABLE E.1   THE SEVEN BASE UNITS AND TWO SUPPLEMENTARY UNITS OF THE SI SYSTEM. DEFINITIONS ARE TRANSLATIONS OF THE ORIGINAL FRENCH.

Base Units

Quantity	Unit	Symbol	Definition
Length	meter	m	The length of the path traveled by light in a vacuum during a time interval of $\frac{1}{299\ 792\ 458}$ of a second
Mass	kilogram	kg	The mass of the international prototype of the kilogram
Time	second	s	The duration of 9 192 631 770 periods of the radiation corresponding to the transition between the two hyperfine levels of the ground state of the cesium-133 atom
Electric current	ampere	A	That constant current which, if maintained in two straight parallel conductors of infinite length, of negligible circular cross section, and placed one meter apart in a vacuum, would produce between these conductors a force equal to 2×10^{-7} newton per meter of length
Thermodynamic temperature	kelvin	K	$\frac{1}{273.16}$ of the thermodynamic temperature of the triple point of water
Amount of substance	mole	mol	The amount of a substance of a system that contains as many elementary entities as there are atoms in 0.012 kilogram of carbon-12
Luminous intensity	candela	cd	The luminous intensity of a source that emits monochromatic radiation of frequency 540×10^{12} hertz and that has a radiant intensity in that direction of $\frac{1}{683}$ watt per steradian

Supplementary Units

Quantity	Unit	Symbol	Definition
Plane angle	radian	rad	The plane angle between two radii of a circle that cuts off on the circumference an arc equal in length to the radius
Solid angle	steradian	sr	The solid angle which, having its vertex in the center of a sphere, cuts off an area of the surface of the sphere equal to that of a square with sides of length equal to the radius of the sphere

The SI system is a coherent method whereby only one unit is used for each physical quantity so that there are no conversion factors to remember (Table E.1). For example, the meter (and its decimal multiples, the centimeter, millimeter, etc.) is the only measure for length. On the other hand, the customary system has many illogical, unrelated measures for length, including the mil ($^1/_{1000}$ inch), the inch, the foot, the yard, and the mile, to name a few. The SI system (Figure E.1) has seven base units, two supplementary units (Table E.2) and several derived units (Table E.3).

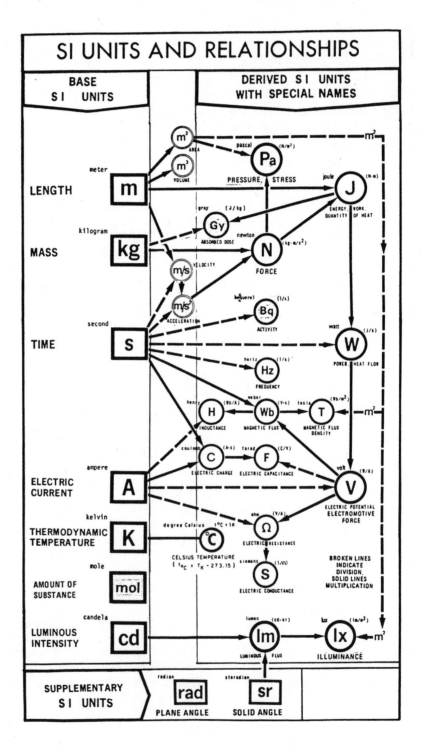

Figure E.1 The SI System has seven base units and two supplementary units. Copyright ASTM. Reprinted with permission.

TABLE E.2   THE DERIVED UNITS OF THE SI SYSTEM. THESE ARE FREQUENTLY
USED IN ENGINEERING CALCULATIONS AND IN THE SCIENCES.

Derived Units		
Quantity	**Name**	**Symbol**
Frequency	hertz	Hz
Force	newton	N
Pressure, stress	pascal	Pa
Energy, work, quantity of heat	joule	J
Power, radiant flux	watt	W
Electric charge, quantity of electricity	coulomb	C
Electric potential	volt	V
Electric capacitance	farad	F
Electric resistance	ohm	Ω
Electric conductance	siemens	S
Magnetic flux	weber	Wb
Magnetic flux density	tesla	T
Inductance	henry	H
Luminous flux	lumen	lm
Illuminance	lux	lx
Celsius temperature	degree	°C
Activity (of a radionuclide)	becquerel	Bq
Absorbed dose	gray	Gy
Dose equivalent	sievert	Sv

TABLE E.3   SI PREFIXES

Multiplication Factor	**SI Prefix**	**Symbol**
1 000 000 000 000 000 000 = 10^{18}	exa	E
1 000 000 000 000 000 = 10^{15}	peta	P
1 000 000 000 000 = 10^{12}	tera	T
1 000 000 000 = 10^{9}	giga	G
1 000 000 = 10^{6}	mega	M
1 000 = 10^{3}	kilo	k
100 = 10^{2}	hecto*	h
10 = 10^{1}	deka*	da
0.1 = 10^{-1}	deci*	d
0.01 = 10^{-2}	centi*	c
0.001 = 10^{-3}	milli	m
0.000 001 = 10^{-6}	micro	μ
0.000 000 001 = 10^{-9}	nano	n
0.000 000 000 001 = 10^{-12}	pico	p
0.000 000 000 000 001 = 10^{-15}	femto	f
0.000 000 000 000 000 001 = 10^{-18}	atto	a

*To be avoided where practical

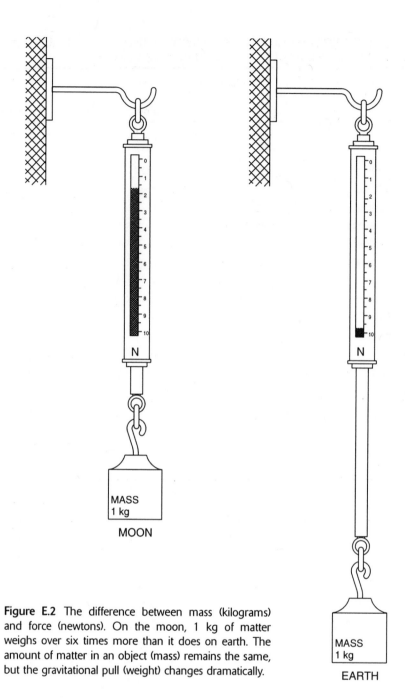

Figure E.2 The difference between mass (kilograms) and force (newtons). On the moon, 1 kg of matter weighs over six times more than it does on earth. The amount of matter in an object (mass) remains the same, but the gravitational pull (weight) changes dramatically.

Although *weight* (pounds and ounces) and *mass* (measured in kilograms) are often erroneously used interchangeably, the distinction between them is particularly important in the fields of science and technology. Mass is different from, but proportional to, weight (Figure E.2). *Mass* is an object's resistance to movement or acceleration. It is the amount of matter in an object. *Weight* is the gravitational force acting on an object. The weight of an object varies with its distance from the center of the earth. Mass is constant and increases only as the velocity of the object approaches that of light.

Table E.4 lists conversion factors for the metric system and the customary system used in the United States.

TABLE E.4 CONVERSION FACTORS

(Underlined values denote exact conversions.)

		Metric to Customary			*Customary to Metric*	
Length		**Multiply by**			**Multiply by**	
	1 km	= 0.621 371	mile (international)	1 mile (international)	= <u>1.609 344</u>	km
	1 m	= 1.093 61	yd	1 yd	= <u>0.914 4</u>	m
	1 m	= 3.280 84	ft	1 ft	= <u>0.304 8</u>	m
				1 ft	= <u>304.8</u>	mm
	1 mm	= 0.039 370 1	in	1 in	= <u>25.4</u>	mm
				1 mil (1/1000 in)	= <u>0.025 4</u>	mm
Area		**Multiply by**			**Multiply by**	
	1 km^2	= 0.386 101	mile^2	1 mile^2	= 2.590 00	km^2
	1 ha	= 2.471 04	acre	1 acre	= 0.404 687	ha
	1 m^2	= 0.000 247	acre	1 acre	= 4 046.856	m^2
	1 m^2	= 1.195 99	yd^2	1 yd^2	= <u>0.836 127 36</u>	m^2
	1 m^2	= 10.7639	ft^2	1 ft^2	= <u>0.092 903 04</u>	m^2
	1 mm^2	= 0.001 550	in^2	1 in^2	= <u>645.16</u>	mm^2
Volume		**Multiply by**			**Multiply by**	
	1 m^3	= 1.307 95	yd^3	1 yd^3	= 0.764 555	m^3
	1 m^3	= 35.3147	ft^3	1 ft^3	= 0.028 316 8	m^3
Fluid Capacity		**Multiply by**			**Multiply by**	
	1 L	= 0.264 172	gal (U.S.)	1 gal (U.S.)	= 3.785 41	L
	1 L	= 1.056 688	qt (U.S.)	1 qt (U.S.)	= 0.946 353	L
	1 L	= 1.056 69	qt (U.S.)	1 qt (U.S.)	= 946.353	mL
	1 mL	= 0.033 814	fl oz (U.S.)	1 fl oz (U.S.)	= 29.5735	mL
Mass (Weight)		**Multiply by**			**Multiply by**	
	1 kg	= 2.204 62	lb	1 lb	= 0.453 592	kg
	1 kg	= 35.2740	oz	1 oz	= 0.028 349 523	kg
	1 g	= 0.035 274	oz	1 oz	= 1.555 17	g
Mass per Unit Length		**Multiply by**			**Multiply by**	
	1 kg/m	= 0.671 969	lb/ft	1 lb/ft	= 1.488 16	kg/m
				1 oz/yd	= 0.031 02	kg/m
				1 oz/in	= 1.116 12	kg/m
Mass per Unit Area		**Multiply by**			**Multiply by**	
	1 kg/m^2	= 0.204 816	lb/ft^2	1 lb/ft^2	= 4.882 43	kg/m^2
				1 lb/in^2	= 703.069 6	kg/m^2
	1 g/m^2	= 0.029 494	oz/yd^2	1 oz/yd^2	= 33.9057	g/m^2
	1 g/m^2	= 3.277 06 × 10^{-3}	oz/ft^2	1 oz/ft^2	= 305.152	g/m^2
				1 oz/ft^2	= 0.305 152	kg/m^2

TABLE E.4 CONTINUED

	Metric to Customary				Customary to Metric		
Density (Mass per Unit Volume)		Multiply by				Multiply by	
	1 kg/m^3	= 0.062 428	lb/ft^3	1 lb/ft^3	= 16.0185		kg/m^3
	1 kg/m^3	= 1.685 56	lb/yd^3	1 lb/yd^3	= 0.593 276		kg/m^3
				1 lb/in^3	= 27.679 90		g/cm^3
				1 oz/yd^3	= 3.711 3 x 10^{-5}		g/cm^3
Temperature Differential		Multiply by				Multiply by	
	1°C	= 1 K= 1.8°F		1°F	= ⅝		°C or K
				1°F	= ⅝ temp. in C= ⅝ K		
Temperature Equivalent		Multiply by				Multiply by	
	1°C	= ⅝ (temp. in F –32)		temp. in F	= ⅝ (temp. in C + 32)		

Bibliography

American Society for Testing and Materials (ASTM). *ASTM E380-89a, Standard Practice for Use of the International System of Units: The Modernized Metric System*. Philadelphia: American Society for Testing and Materials, 1989.

American Society for Testing and Materials (ASTM). *ASTM E621-84, Standard Practice for Use of Metric (SI) Units in Building Design and Construction (Committee E-6 Supplement to E380)*. Philadelphia: American Society for Testing and Materials, 1984.

The Construction Subcommittee of the Metrication Operating Committee of the Interagency Council on Metric Policy. *Metric Guide for Federal Construction*. Washington, D.C.: National Institute of Building Sciences, 1991.

APPENDIX F

Uniform Commercial Code, Article 2 (Abridged)

ARTICLE 2: Sales

Part 1: Short Title

§2–101. Short Title. This Article shall be known and may be cited as Uniform Commercial Code—Sales.

§2–102. Scope; Certain Security and Other Transactions Excluded From This Article.

Unless the context otherwise requires, this Article applies to transactions in goods; it does not apply to any transactions which although in the form of an unconditional contract to sell or present sale is intended to operate only as a security transaction nor does this Article impair or repeal any statute regulating sales to consumers, farmers or other specified classes of buyers.

§2–103. Definitions and Index Definitions.

(**1**) In this Article unless the context otherwise requires

(**a**) "Buyer" means a person who buys or contracts to buy goods.

(**b**) "Good faith" in the case of a merchant means honesty in fact and the observance of reasonable commercial standards of fair dealing on the trade.

(**c**) "Receipt" of goods means taking physical possession of them.

(**d**) "Seller" means a person who sells or contracts to sell goods.

(Text not included for paragraphs (2), (3), and (4) in this abridged version.)

§2–104. Definitions: "Merchant"; "Between Merchants"; "Financing Agency".

(**1**) "Merchant" means a person who deals in goods of the kind or otherwise by his occupation holds himself out as having knowledge or skill peculiar to the practices or goods involved in the transaction or to whom such knowledge or skill may be attributed by his employment of an agent or broker or other intermediary who by his occupation holds himself out as having such knowledge or skill.

(**2**) "Financing agency" means a bank, finance company or other person who in the ordinary course of business makes advances against goods or documents of title or who by arrangement with either the seller or the buyer intervenes in ordinary course to make or collect payment due or claimed under the contract for sale, as by purchasing or paying the seller's draft or making advances against it or by merely taking or for collection whether or not documents of title accompany the draft. "Financing agency" includes also a bank or other person who similarly intervenes between persons who are in the posi-

tion of seller and buyer in respect of the goods (Section 2–707).

(**3**) "Between merchants" means in any transaction with respect to which both parties are chargeable with the knowledge or skill of merchants.

§2–105. Definitions: Transferability; "Goods"; "Future" Goods; "Lot"; "Commercial Unit".

(**1**) "Goods" means all things (including specially manufactured goods) which are movable at the time of identification to the contract for sale other than the money in which the price is to be paid, investment securities (Article 8) and things in action. "Goods" also includes the unborn young of animals and growing crops and other identified things attached to realty as described in the section on goods to be severed from realty (Section 2–107).

(**2**) Goods must be both existing and identified before any interest in them can pass. Goods which are not both existing and identified are "future" goods. A purported present sale if future goods or of any interest therein operates as a contract to sell.

(**3**) There may be a sale of a part interest in existing identified goods.

(**4**) An undivided share in an identified bulk of fungible foods is sufficiently identified to be sold although the quantity of the bulk is not determined. Any agreed proportion if such a bulk or any quantity thereof agreed upon by number, weight or other measure may to the extent of the seller's interest in the bulk be sold to the buyer who then becomes an owner in common.

(**5**) "Lot" means a parcel or a single article which is the subject matter of a separate sale or delivery.

(**6**) "Commercial unit" means such a unit of goods as by commercial usage is a single whole for purposes of sale and division of which materially impairs its character or value on the market or in use. A commercial unit may be a single article (as a machine) or a set of articles (as a suite of furniture or an assortment of sizes) or a quantity (as a bale, gross, or carload) or any other unit treated in use or in the relevant market as a single whole.

§2–106. Definitions: "Contract"; "Agreement"; "Contract for Sale"; "Sale"; "Present Sale"; "Conforming" to Contract; "Termination"; "Cancellation".

(**1**) In this Article unless the context otherwise requires "contract" and "agreement" are limited to those relating to the present or future sale of goods. "Contract for sale" includes both a present sale of goods and a contract to sell goods at a future time. A "sale" consists in the passing of title from the seller to the buyer for a price (Section 2–401). A "present sale" means a sale which is accomplished by the making of the contract.

(**2**) Goods or conduct including any part of a performance are "conforming" or conform to the contract when they are in accordance with the obligations under the contract.

(**3**) "Termination" occurs when either party pursuant to a power created by agreement or law puts an end to the contract otherwise than for its breach.On "termination" all obligations which are still executory on both sides are discharged but any right based on prior breach or performance survives.

(**4**) "Cancellation" occurs when either party puts an end to the contract for breach by the other and its effect is the same as that of "termination" except that the cancelling party also retains any remedy for breach of the whole contract or any unperformed balance.

§2–107. Goods to Be Severed From Realty: Recording. *(Text not included in this abridged version.)*

Part 2: Form, Formation and Readjustment of Contract

§2–201. Formal Requirements; Statute of Frauds.

1) Except as otherwise provided in this section a contract for the sale of goods for the price of $500 or more is not enforceable by way of action or defense unless there is some writing sufficient to indicate that a contract for sale has been made between the parties and signed by the party against whom enforcement is sought or by his authorized gent or broker.A writing is not sufficient because it omits or incorrectly states a term agreed upon but the contract is not enforceable under this paragraph beyond the quantity of goods shown in such writing.

(**2**) Between merchants if within a reasonable time a writing in confirmation of the contract and sufficient against the sender is received and the party receiving it has reason to know its contents, it satisfies the requirements of subsection (1) against such party unless written notice of objection to its contents is given within 10 days after it is received.

(**3**) A contract which does not satisfy the requirements of subsection (1) but which is valid in other respects is enforceable

(**a**) if the goods are to be specially manufactured for the buyer and are not suitable for sale to others in the ordinary course of the seller's business and the seller, before notice of repudiation is received and under circumstances which reasonably indicate that the goods are for the buyer, has made either a substantial beginning of their manufacture of commitments for their procurement; or

(**b**) if the party against whom enforcement is sought admits in his pleading, testimony or otherwise in court that a contract for sale was made, but the contract is not enforceable under this provision beyond the quantity of goods admitted; or

(**c**) with respect to goods for which payment has been made and accepted or which have been received and accepted (Sec. 2–606.)

§2-202. Final Written Expression: Parol or Extrinsic Evidence.
Terms with respect to which the confirmatory memoranda of the parties agree or which are otherwise set forth in a writing intended by the parties as a final expression of their agreement with respect to such terms as are included therein may not be contradicted by evidence of any prior agreement or of a contemporaneous oral agreement but may be explained or supplemented

(**a**) by course of dealing or usage of trade (Section 1-205) or by course of performance (Section 2-208); and

(**b**) by evidence of consistent additional terms unless the court finds the writing to have been intended also as a complete and exclusive statement of the terms of the agreement.

§2-203. Seals Inoperative.
The affixing of a seal to a writing evidencing a contract for sale or an offer to but or sell goods does not constitute the writing a sealed instrument and the law with respect to sealed instruments does not apply to such a contract or offer.

§2-204. Formation in General.

(**1**) A contract for sale of goods may be made in any manner sufficient to show agreement, including conduct by both parties which recognizes the existence of such a contract.

(**2**) An agreement sufficient to constitute a contract for sale may be found even though the moment of its making is undetermined.

(**3**) Even though one or more terms are left open a contract for sale does not fail from indefiniteness if the parties have intended to make a contract and there is a reasonably certain basis for giving an appropriate remedy.

§2-205. Firm Offers.
An offer by a merchant to buy or sell goods in a signed writing which by its terms gives assurance that it will be held open is not revocable, for lack of consideration, during the time stated or if no time is stated for a reasonable time, but in no event may such period of irrevocability exceed three months; but any such term of assurance on a form supplied by the offeree must be separately signed by the offeror.

§2-206. Offer and Acceptance in Formation of Contract.

(**1**) Unless otherwise unambiguously indicated by the language or circumstances

(**a**) an offer to make a contract shall be construed as inviting acceptance in any manner and by any medium reasonable in the circumstances;

(**b**) an order or other offer to buy goods for prompt or current shipment shall be construed as inviting acceptance either by a prompt promise to ship or by the prompt or current shipment of conforming or nonconforming goods, but such a shipment of nonconforming goods does not constitute an acceptance if the seller seasonably notifies the buyer that the shipment is offered only as an accommodation to the buyer.

(**2**) Where the beginning of a requested performance is a reasonable mode of acceptance an offeror who is not notified of acceptance within a reasonable time may treat the offer as having lapsed before acceptance.

§2-207. Additional terms in Acceptance or Confirmation.

(**1**) A definite and seasonable expression of acceptance or a written confirmation which is sent within a reasonable time operates as an acceptance even though it states terms additional to or different from those offered or agreed upon, unless acceptance is expressly made conditional on assent to the additional or different terms.

(**2**) The additional terms are to be construed as proposals for addition to the contract.Between merchants such terms become part of the contract unless:

(**a**) the offer expressly limits acceptance to the terms of the offer;

(**b**) they materially alter it; or

(**c**) notification of objection to them has already been given or is given within a reasonable time after notice of them is received.

(**3**) Conduct by both parties which recognizes the existence of a contract is sufficient to establish a contract for sale although the writings of the parties do not otherwise establish a contract.In such case the terms of the particular contract consist of those terms on which the writings of the parties agree, together with any supplementary terms incorporated under any other provisions of this Act.

§2-208. Course of Performance or Practical Construction.

(**1**) Where the contract for sale involves repeated occasions for performance by either party with knowledge of the nature of the performance and opportunity for objection to it by the other, any course of performance accepted or acquiesced in without objection shall be relevant to determine the meaning of the agreement.

(**2**) The express terms of the agreement and any such course of performance, as well as any course of dealing and usage of trade, shall be construed whenever reasonable as consistent with each other; but when such construction is unreasonable, express terms shall control course of performance and course of performance shall control both course of dealing and usage of trade (Section 1-205).

(**3**) Subject to the provisions of the next section on modification and waiver, such course of performance shall be relevant to show a waiver or modification of any term inconsistent with such course of performance.

§2-209. Modification, Rescission and Waiver.

(**1**) An agreement modifying a contract within this Article needs no consideration to be binding.

(**2**) A signed agreement which excludes modification or rescission except by a signed writing cannot be otherwise modified or rescinded, but except as between merchants such a requirement on a form supplied by the merchant must be separately signed by the other party.

(**3**) The requirements of the statute of frauds section of this Article (Section 2-201) must be satisfied if the contract as modified is within its provisions.

(**4**) Although an attempt at modification or rescission does not satisfy the requirements of subsection (2) or (3) it can operate as a waiver.

(**5**) A party who has made a waiver affecting an executory portion of the contract may retract the waiver by reasonable notification received by the other party that strict performance will be required of any term waived unless the retraction would be unjust in view of a material change of position in reliance on the waiver.

§2-210. Delegation of Performance; Assignment of Rights. *(Text not included in this abridged version.)*

Part 3: General Obligation and Construction of Contract

§2-301. General Obligations of Parties. The obligation of the seller is to transfer and deliver and that of the buyer is to accept and pay in accordance with the contract.

§2-302. Unconscionable Contract or Clause.

(**1**) If the court as a matter of law finds the contract or any clause of the contract to have been unconscionable at the time it was made the court may refuse to enforce the contract, or it may enforce the remainder of the contract without the unconscionable clause, or it may so limit the application of any unconscionable clause as to avoid any unconscionable result.

(**2**) When it is claimed or appears to the court that the contract or any clause thereof may be unconscionable the parties shall be afforded a reasonable opportunity to present evidence as to its commercial setting, purpose and effect to aid the court in making the determination.

§2-303. Allocation or Division of Risks. Where this Article allocates a risk or a burden as between the parties "unless otherwise agreed", the agreement may not only shift the allocation but may also divide the risk or burden.

§2-304. Price Payable in Money, Goods, Realty, or Otherwise. *(Text not included in this abridged version.)*

§2-305. Open Price Term.

(**1**) The parties if they so intend can conclude a contract for sale even though the price is not settled.In such a case the price is a reasonable price at the time for delivery if

(**a**) nothing is said as to price; or

(**b**) the price is left to be agreed by the parties and they fail to agree; or

(**c**) the price is to be fixed on terms of some agreed market or

other standard as set or recorded by a third person or agency and it is not so set or recorded.

(**2**) A price to be fixed by the seller or by the buyer means a price for him to fix in good faith.

(**3**) When a price left to be fixed otherwise than by agreement of the parties fails to be fixed through fault of one party the other may at his option treat the contract as cancelled or himself fix a reasonable price.

(**4**) Where, however, the parties intend not to be bound unless the price be fixed or agreed and it is not fixed or agreed there is no contract.In such a case the buyer must return any goods already received or if unable so to do must pay their reasonable value at the time of delivery and the seller must return any portion of the price paid on account.

§2-306. Output, Requirements and Exclusive Dealings. *(Text not included in this abridged version.)*

§2-307. Delivery in Single Lot or Several Lots. Unless otherwise agreed all goods called for by a contract for sale must be tendered in a single delivery and payment is due only on such tender but where the circumstances give either party the right to make or demand delivery in lots the price if it can be apportioned may be demanded for each lot.

§2-308. Absence of Specified Place for Delivery.Unless otherwise agreed

(**a**) the place for delivery of goods is the seller's place of business or of he has none his residence; but

(**b**) in a contract for sale of identified goods which to the knowledge of the parties at the time of contracting are in some other place, that place is the place for their delivery; and

(**c**) documents of title may be delivered through customary banking channels.

§2-309. Absence of Specific Time Provision; Notice of Termination.

(**1**) The time for shipment or delivery or any other action under a contract if not provided in this Article or agreed upon shall be a reasonable time.

(**2**) Where the contract provides for successive performances but is indefinite in duration it is valid for a reasonable time but unless otherwise agreed may be terminated at any time by either party.

(**3**) Termination of a contract by one party except on the happening of an agreed event requires that reasonable notification be received by the other party and in agreement dispensing with notification is invalid if its operation would be unconscionable.

§2-310. Open Time for Payment or Running of Credit; Authority to Ship Under Reservation. *(Text not included in this abridged version.)*

§2-311. Options and Cooperation Respecting Performance.

(**1**) An agreement for sale which is otherwise sufficiently definite (subsection (3) of Section 2-204) to be a contract is not made invalid by the fact that it leaves particulars of performance to be specified by one of the parties.Any such specification must be made in good faith and within limits set by commercial reasonableness.

(**2**) Unless otherwise agreed specifications relating to assortment of the goods are at the buyer's option and except as otherwise provided in subsection (1)(c) and (3) of Section 2-319 specifications or arrangements relating to shipment are at the seller's options.

(**3**) Where such specifications would materially affect the other party's performance but is not seasonably made or where one party's cooperation is necessary to the agreed performance of the other but is not seasonably forthcoming, the other party in addition to all other remedies

(**a**) is excused for any resulting delay in his own performance; and

(b) may also either proceed to perform in any reasonable manner or after the time for a material part of his own performance treat the failure to specify or to cooperate as a breach by failure to deliver or accept the goods.

§2-312. Warranty of Title and Against Infringement; Buyer's Obligation Against Infringement.

(1) Subject to subsection (2) there is in a contract for sale a warranty by the seller that
(a) the title conveyed shall be good, and its transfer rightful; and
(b) the goods shall be delivered free from any security interest or other lien or encumbrance of which the buyer at the time of contracting has no knowledge.

(2) A warranty under subsection (1) will be excluded or modified only by specific language or by circumstances which give the buyer reason to know that the person selling does not claim title in himself or that he is purporting to sell only such right or title as he or a third person may have.

(3) Unless otherwise agreed a seller who is a merchant regularly dealing in goods of the kind warrants that the goods shall be delivered free of the rightful claim of any third person by way of infringement or the like but a buyer who furnishes specifications to the seller must hold the seller harmless against any such claim which arises out of compliance with the specifications.

§2-313. Express Warranties by Affirmation, Promise, Description, Sample.

(1) Express warranties by the seller are created as follows:
(a) Any affirmation of fact or promise made by the seller to the buyer which relates to the goods and becomes part of the basis of the bargain creates an express warranty that the goods shall conform to the affirmation or promise.
(b) Any description of the goods which is made part of the basis of the bargain creates an express warranty that the goods shall conform to the description.
(c) Any sample or model which is part of the basis of the bargain creates an express warranty that the whole of the goods shall conform to the sample or model.

(2) It is not necessary to the creation of an express warranty that the seller use formal words such as "warrant" or "guarantee" or that he have a specific intention to make a warranty, but an affirmation merely of the value of the goods or a statement purporting to be merely the seller's opinion or commendation of the goods does not create a warranty.

§2-314. Implied Warranty: Merchantability; Usage of Trade.

(1) Unless excluded or modified (Section 2-316), a warranty that the goods shall be merchantable is implied in a contract for their sale if the seller is a merchant with respect to goods of that kind. Under this section the serving for value of food or drink to be consumed either on the premises or elsewhere is a sale.

(2) Goods to be merchantable must be at least such as
(a) pass without objection in the trade under the contract description; and
(b) in the case of fungible goods, are of fair average quality within the description; and
(c) are fit for the ordinary purposes for which such goods are used; and
(d) run, within the variations permitted buy the agreement, of even kind, quality and quantity within each unit and among all units involved; and
(e) are adequately contained, packaged, and labeled as the agreement may require; and
(f) conform to the promises or affirmations of fact made or the container or label if any.

(3) Unless excluded or modified (Section 2-316) other implied warranties may arise from course of dealing or usage of trade.

§2-315. Implied Warranty: Fitness for Particular Purpose.
Where the seller at the time of contracting has reason to know any particular purpose for which the goods are required and that the buyer is relying on the seller's skill or judgment to select or furnish suitable goods, there is unless excluded or modified under the next section an implied warranty that the goods shall be fit for such purposes.

§2-316. Exclusion or Modification of Warranties.

(1) Words or conduct relevant to the creation of an express warranty and words or conduct tending to negate or limit warranty shall be construed wherever reasonable as consistent with each other; but subject to the provisions of this Article on parol or extrinsic evidence (Section 2-202) negation or limitation is inoperative to the extent that such construction is unreasonable.

(2) Subject to subsection (3), to exclude or modify the implied warranty of merchantability or any part of it the language must mention merchantability and in case of a writing must be conspicuous, and to exclude or modify any implied warranty of fitness the exclusion must be by a writing and conspicuous. Language to exclude all implied warranties of fitness is sufficient if it states, for example, that "There are no warranties which extend beyond the description on the face hereof."

(3) Notwithstanding subsection (2)
(a) unless the circumstances indicate otherwise, all implied warranties are excluded by expressions like "as is", "with all faults" or other language which in common understanding calls the buyer's attention to the exclusion of warranties and makes plain that there is no implied warranty; and
(b) when the buyer before entering into the contract has examined the goods or the sample or model as fully as he desired or has refused to examine the goods there is no implied warranty with regard to defects which an examination ought in the circumstances to have revealed to him; and
(c) an implied warranty can also be excluded or modified by course of dealing or course of performance or usage of trade.

(4) Remedies for breach of warranty can be limited in accordance with the provisions of this Article on liquidation or limitation of damages and on contractual modification of remedy (Sections 2-718 and 2-719).

§2-317. Cumulation and Conflict of Warranties Express or Implied.
Warranties whether express or implied shall be construed as consistent with each other and as cumulative but if such construction is unreasonable the intention of the parties shall determine which warranty is dominant. In ascertaining that intention the following rules apply:
(a) Exact or technical specifications displace an inconsistent sample or model or general language of description.
(b) A sample from an existing bulk displaces inconsistent general language of description.
(c) Express warranties displace inconsistent implied warranties other than an implied warranty of fitness for a particular purpose.

§2-318. Third Party Beneficiaries of Warranties Express or Implied.

Note: *If this Act is introduced in the Congress of the United States this section should be omitted. (States to select one alternative.)*

Alternative A—A seller's warranty whether express or implied extends to any natural person who is in the family or household of his buyer or who is a guest in his home if it is reasonable to expect that such person may use, consume or be affected by the foods and who is injured in person by breach of the warranty.

A seller may not exclude or limit the operation of this section.

Alternative B—A seller's warranty whether express or implied extends to any natural person who may reasonably be expected to use, consume or be affected by the goods and who is injured in person by breach of the warranty. A seller may not exclude or limit the operation of this section.

Alternative C—A seller's warranty whether express or implied extends to any person who may reasonably be expected to use, consume or be affected by the goods and who is injured by breach of the warranty. A seller may not exclude or limit the operation of this section with respect to injury to the person of an individual to whom the warranty extends.

§2-319. F.O.B. and F.A.S. Terms.

(**1**) Unless otherwise agreed the term F.O.B. (which means "free on board") at a named place, even though used only in connection with the stated price, is a delivery term under which

(**a**) when the term is F.O.B. the place of shipment, the seller must at that place ship the goods in the manner provided in this Article (Section 2-504) and bear the expense and risk of putting them into the possession of the carrier; or

(**b**) when the term is F.O.B. the place of destination, the seller must at his own expense and risk transport the goods to that place and there tender delivery of them in the manner provided in this Article (Section 2-503);

(**c**) when under either (a) or (b) the term is also F.O.B. vessel, car or other vehicle, the seller must in addition at his own expense and risk load the goods on board. If the term is F.O.B. vessel the buyer must name the vessel and in an appropriate case the seller must comply with the provisions of this Article on the form of bill of lading (Section 2-323).

(**2**) Unless otherwise agreed the term F.A.S. vessel (which means "free alongside") at a named port, even though used only in connection with the stated price, is a delivery term under which the seller must

(**a**) at his own expense and risk deliver the goods alongside the vessel in the manner usual in that port or on a dock designated and provided by the buyer; and

(**b**) obtain and tender a receipt for the goods in exchange for which the carrier is under a duty to issue a bill of lading.

(**3**) Unless otherwise agreed in any case falling within subsection (1)(a) or (c) or subsection (2) the buyer must seasonably give any needed instructions for making delivery, including when the term is F.A.S. or F.O.B. the loading berth of the vessel and in an appropriate case its name and sailing date. The seller may treat the failure of needed instructions as a failure of cooperation under this Article (Section 2-311). He may also at his option move the goods in any reasonable manner preparatory to delivery or shipment.

(**4**) Under the term F.O.B. vessel or F.A.S. unless otherwise agreed the buyer must make payment against tender of the required documents and the seller may not tender nor the buyer demand delivery of the goods in substitution for the documents.

(Text not included for Sections 320-323 in this abridged version.)

§2-320. C.I.F. and C.&F. Terms.

§2-321. C.I.F. or C.&F.: "Net Landed Weights"; "Payment on Arrival"; Warranty of Condition on Arrival.

§2-322. Delivery "Ex-Ship".

§2-323. Form of Bill of Lading Required in Overseas Shipment; "Overseas".

§2-324. "No Arrival, No Sale" Term. Under a term "no arrival, no sale" or terms of like meaning, unless otherwise agreed,

(**a**) the seller must properly ship conforming goods and if they arrive by any means he must tender them on arrival but he assumes no obligation that the goods will arrive unless he has caused the nonarrival; and

(**b**) where without fault of the seller the goods are in part lost or have so deteriorated as no longer to conform to the contract or arrive after the contract time, the buyer may proceed as if there had been casualty to identified goods (Section 2-613).

§2-325. "Letter of Credit" Term; "Confirmed Credit".

(**1**) Failure of the buyer seasonably to furnish an agreed letter of credit is a breach of the contract for sale.

(**2**) The delivery to seller of a proper letter of credit suspends the buyer's obligation to pay. If the letter of credit is dishonored, the seller may on seasonable notification to the buyer require payment directly from him.

(**3**) Unless otherwise agreed the term "letter of credit" or "banker's credit" in a contract for sale means an irrevocable credit issued by a financing agency of good repute and, where the shipment is overseas, of good international repute. The term "confirmed credit" means that the credit must also carry the direct obligation of such agency which does business in the seller's financial market.

§2-326. Sale on Approval and Sale or Return; Consignment Sales and Rights or Creditors.

(**1**) Unless otherwise agreed, if delivered goods may be returned by the buyer even though they conform to the contract, the transaction is

(**a**) a "sale on approval" if the goods are delivered primarily for use, and

(**b**) a "sale or return" if the goods are delivered primarily for resale.

(**2**) Except as provided in subsection (3), goods held on approval are not subject to the claims of the buyer's creditors until acceptance; goods held in sale or return are subject to such claims while in the buyer's possession.

(**3**) Where goods are delivered to a person for sale and such person maintains a place of business at which he deals in goods of the kind involved, under a name other than the name of the person making delivery, then with respect to claims of creditors of the person conducting the business the goods are deemed to be on sale or return. The provisions of this subsection are applicable even though an agreement purports to reserve title to the person making delivery until payment or resale or uses such words as "on consignment" or "on memorandum". However, this subsection is not applicable if the person making delivery

(**a**) complies with an applicable law providing for a consignor's interest or the like to be evidenced by a sign, or

(**b**) establishes that the person conducting the business is generally known by his creditors to be substantially engaged in selling the goods of others, or

(**c**) complies with the filing provisions of the Article on Secured Transaction (Article 9).

(**4**) Any "or return" term of a contract for sale it to be treated as a separate contract for sale within the statute of frauds section of this Article (Section 2-201) and as contradicting the sale aspect of the contract within the provisions of this Article on parol or extrinsic evidence (Section 2-202).

§2-327. Special Incidents of Sale on Approval and Sale or Return.

(**1**) Under a sale on approval unless otherwise agreed

(**a**) although the goods are identified to the contract the risk of loss and the title do not pass to the buyer until acceptance; and

(**b**) use of the goods consistent with the purpose of trial is not acceptance but failure seasonably to notify the seller of election to return the goods is acceptance, and if the goods conform to the contract acceptance of any part is acceptance of the whole; and

(**c**) after due notification of election to return, the return is at the seller's risk and expense but a merchant buyer must follow any reasonable instructions.

(**2**) Under a sale or return unless otherwise agreed (**a**) the option to return extends to the whole or any commercial unit of the goods while in substantially their original condition, but must be exercised seasonably; and

(**b**) the return is at the buyer's risk and expense.

§2-328. Sale by Auction. *(Text not included in this abridged version.)*

Part 4: Title, Creditors and Good Faith Purchasers

§2-401. Passing of Title; Reservation for Security; Limited Application of This Section. Each provision of this Article with regard to the rights, obligations and remedies of the seller, the buyer, purchasers or other third parties applies irrespective of title to the goods except where the provision refers to such title.Insofar as situations are not covered by the other provisions of this Article and matters concerning title become material the following rules apply:

(**1**) Title to goods cannot pass under a contract for sale prior to their identification to the contract (Section 2-501), and unless otherwise explicitly agreed the buyer acquires by their identification a special property as limited by this Act.Any retention or reservation by the seller of the title(property) in goods shipped or delivered to the buyer is limited in effect to a reservation of a security interest.Subject to these provisions and to the provisions of the Article on Secured Transactions (Article 9), title to goods passes from the seller to the buyer in any manner and on any conditions explicitly agreed on by the parties.

(**2**) Unless otherwise explicitly agreed title passes to the buyer at the time and place at which the seller completes his performances with reference or the physical delivery of the goods, despite any reservation of a security interest and even though a document of title is to be delivered at a different time or place; and in particular and despite any reservation of a security interest by the bill of lading

(**a**) if the contract requires or authorizes the seller to send the goods to the buyer but does not require him to deliver them at destination, title passes to the buyer at the time and place of shipment; but

(**b**) if the contract requires delivery at destination, title passes on tender there.

(**3**) Unless otherwise explicitly agreed where delivery is to be made without moving the goods.

(**a**) if the seller is to deliver a document of title, title passes at the time when and the place where he delivers such documents; or

(**b**) if the goods are at the time of contracting already identified and no documents are to be delivered, title passes at the time and place of contracting.

(**4**) A rejection or other refusal by the buyer to receive or retain the goods, whether or not justified, or a justified revocation of acceptance reverts title to the goods in the seller.Such reverting occurs by operation of law and is not a "sale".

§2-402. Rights of Seller's Creditors Against Sold Goods.

(**1**) Except as provided in subsections (2) and (3), rights of unsecured creditors of the seller with respect to goods which have been identified to a contract for sale are subject to the buyer's rights to recover the goods under this Article (Section 2-502 and 2-716).

(**2**) A creditor of the seller may treat a sale or an identification of goods to a contract for sale as void if as against him a retention of possession by the seller is fraudulent under any rule of law if the state where the goods are situated, except that retention of possession in good faith and current course of trade by a merchant-seller for a commercially reasonable time after a

sale or identification is not fraudulent.

(**3**) Nothing in this Article shall be deemed to impair the rights of creditors of the seller

(**a**) under the provisions of the Article on Secured Transactions (Article 9); or

(**b**) where identification to the contract or delivery is made not on current course of trade but in satisfaction of or as security for a pre-existing claim for money, security of the like and is made under circumstances which under any rule of law of the state where the goods are situated would apart from this Article constitute the transaction a fraudulent transfer or voidable preference.

§2-403. Power to Transfer; Good Faith Purchase of Goods; "Entrusting".

(**1**) A purchase of goods acquires all title which his transferor had or had power to transfer except that a purchaser of a limited interest acquires rights only to the extent of the interest purchased.A person with voidable title has power to transfer a good title to a good faith purchaser for value.When goods have been delivered under a transaction of purchase the purchaser had such power even though

(**a**) the transferor was deceived as to the identity of the purchaser, or

(**b**) the delivery was in exchange for a check which is later dishonored, or

(**c**) it was agreed that the transaction was to be a "cash sale", or

(**d**) the delivery was procured through fraud punishable as larcenous under the criminal law.

(**2**) Any entrusting of possession of goods or a merchant who deals in goods of that kind gives him power to transfer all rights of the entrusted to a buyer in ordinary course of business.

(**3**) "Entrusting" includes any delivery and any acquiescence in retention of possession regardless of any condition expressed between the parties to the delivery or acquiescence and regardless of whether the procurement of the entrusting or the possessor's disposition of the goods have been such as to be larcenous under the criminal law.

(**4**) The rights of other purchasers of goods and of lien creditors are governed by the Articles on Secured Transactions (Article 9), Bulk Transfers (Article 6) and Documents of Title (Article 7).

Part 5: Performance

§2-501. Insurable Interest in Goods; Manner of Identification of Goods.

(**1**) The buyer obtains a special property and an insurable interest in goods to which the contract refers even though the goods so identified are non-conforming and he has an option to return or reject them.Such identification can be made at any time and in any manner explicitly agreed to by the parties.In the absence of explicit agreement identification occurs

(**a**) when the contract is made if it is for the sale of goods already existing and identified;

(**b**) if the contract is for sale of future goods other than those described in paragraph (c), when goods are shipped, marked or otherwise designated by the seller as goods to which the contract refers;

(**c**) when the crops are planted or otherwise become growing crops or the young are conceived if the contract is for the sale of unborn young to be born within twelve months after contracting or for the sale of crops to be harvested within twelve months or the next normal harvest season after contracting whichever is longer.

(**2**) The seller retains an insurable interest in goods so long as title to or any security interest in the goods remains in him and where the identification is by the seller alone he may until default or insolvency or notification to the buyer that the identification is final substitute other goods for those identified.

(**3**) Nothing in this section impairs any insurable interest recognized under any other statute or rule of law.

§2-502. Buyer's Right to Goods on Seller's Insolvency.

(**1**) Subject to subsection (2) and even though the goods have not been shipped a buyer who has paid a part or all of the price of goods in which he has a special property under the provisions of the immediately preceding section may on making and keeping goods a tender of any unpaid portion or their price recover them from the seller if the seller becomes insolvent within ten days after receipt of the first installment on their price.

(**2**) If the identification creating his special property has been made by the buyer he acquires the right to recover the goods only if they conform to the contract for sale.

§2-503. Manner of Seller's Tender of Delivery.

(**1**) Tender of delivery requires that the seller put and hold conforming goods at the buyer's disposition and give the buyer any notification reasonably necessary to enable him to take delivery.The manner, time and place from tender are determined by the agreement and this Article, and in particular

(**a**) tender must be at a reasonable hour, and if it is of goods they must be kept available for the period reasonably necessary to enable the buyer to take possession; but

(**b**) unless otherwise agreed the buyer must furnish facilities reasonably suited to the receipt of the goods.

(**2**) Where the case is within the next section respecting shipment tender requires that the seller comply with its provisions.

(**3**) Where the seller is required to deliver at a particular destination tender requires that he comply with subsection (1) and also in any appropriate case tender documents as described in subsections (4) and (5) of this section.

(**4**) Where goods are in the possession of a bailee and are to be delivered without being moved

(**a**) tender requires that the seller either tender a negotiable document for title covering such goods or procure acknowledgment by the bailee of the buyer's right to possession of the goods; but

(**b**) tender to the buyer of a non-negotiable document of title or of a written direction to the bailee to deliver is sufficient tender unless the buyer seasonably objects, and receipt by the bailee of notification of the buyer's rights fixes those rights as against the bailee and all third persons; but risk of loss of the goods and of any failure by the bailee to honor the non-negotiable document of title or to obey the direction remains on the seller until the buyer has had a reasonable time to present the document or direction, and a refusal by the bailee to honor the document or to obey the direction defeats the tender.

(**5**) Where the contract requires the seller to deliver documents

(**a**) he must tender all such documents in correct form, except as provided in this Article with respect to bills of lading in a set (subsection (2) of Section 2-323); and

(**b**) tender through customary banking channels is sufficient and dishonor a draft accompanying the documents constitutes non-acceptance or rejection.

§2-504. Shipment by Seller. Where the seller is required or authorized to send the goods to the buyer and the contract does not require him to deliver them at a particular destination, then unless otherwise agreed he must

(**a**) put the goods in the possession of such a carrier and make such a contract for their transportation as may be reasonable having regard to the nature of the goods and other circumstances of the case; and

(**b**) obtain and promptly deliver or tender in due form any document necessary to enable the buyer to obtain possession of the goods or otherwise required by the agreement or by usage or trade; and

(**c**) promptly notify the buyer of the shipment.

Failure to notify the buyer under paragraph (c) or to make a proper contract under paragraph (a) is a ground for rejection only if material delay or loss ensues.

§2-505. Seller's Shipment under Reservation.

(**1**) Where the seller has identified goods to the contract by or before shipment;

(**a**) his procurement of a negotiable bill of lading to his won order or otherwise reserves in him a security interest in the goods.His procurement of the bill to the order of a financing agency or of the buyer indicates in addition only the seller's expectation of transferring that interest to the person named.

(**b**) a non-negotiable bill of lading to himself or his nominee reserves possession of the goods as security but except in a case of conditional delivery (subsection (2) of Section 2-507) a non-negotiable bill of lading naming the buyer as consignee reserves no security interest even though the seller retains possession of the bill of lading.

(**2**) When shipment by the seller with reservation of a security interest is in violation of the contract for sale it constitutes an improper contract for transportation within the preceding section but impairs neither the rights given to the buyer by shipment and identification of the goods to the contract nor the seller's powers as a holder of a negotiable document.

§2-506. Rights of Financing Agency. *(Text not included in this abridged version.)*

§2-507. Effect of Seller's Tender; Delivery on Condition.

(**1**) Tender of delivery is a condition to the buyer's duty to accept the goods and, unless otherwise agreed, to his duty to pay for them.Tender entitles the seller to acceptance of the goods and to payment according to the contract.

(**2**) Where payment is due and demanded on the delivery to the buyer of goods or documents of title, his right as against the seller to retain or dispose of them is conditional upon his making the payment due.

§2-508. Cure by Seller of Improper Tender or Delivery; Replacement.

(**1**) Where any tender or delivery by the seller is rejected because non-conforming and the time for performance has not yet expired, the seller may seasonably notify the buyer of his intention to cure and may then within the contract time make a conforming delivery.

(**2**) Where the buyer rejects a non-conforming tender which the seller had reasonable grounds to believe would be acceptable with or without money allowance the seller may if he seasonably notifies the buyer have a further reasonable time to substitute a conforming tender.

§2-509. Risk of Loss in the Absence of Breach.

(**1**) Where the contract requires or authorizes the seller to ship the goods by carrier

(**a**) if it does not require to deliver them at a particular destination, the risk of loss passes to the buyer when the goods are duly delivered to the carrier even though the shipment is under reservation (Section 2-505); but

(**b**) if it does require him to deliver them at a particular destination and the goods are there duly tendered while in the possession of the carrier, the risk of loss passes to the buyer when the goods are there duly so tendered as to enable the buyer to take delivery.

(**2**) Where the goods are held by a bailee to be delivered without being moved, the risk of loss passes to the buyer

(**a**) on his receipt of a negotiable document of title covering the goods; or

(b) on acknowledgement by the bailee of the buyer's right to possession of the goods; or

(c) after his receipt of a non-negotiable document of title or other written direction to deliver, as provided in subsection (4)(b) of Section 2-503.

(3) In any case not within subsection (1) or (2), the risk of loss passes to the buyer on his receipt of the goods if the seller is a merchant; otherwise the risk passes to the buyer on tender of delivery.

(4) The provisions of this section are subject to contrary agreement of the parties and to the provisions of this Article on sale on approval (Section 2-327) and on effect of breach on risk of loss (Section 2-510).

§2-510. Effect of Breach on Risk of Loss.

(1) Where a tender or delivery of goods so fails to conform to the contract as to give a right of rejection the risk of their loss remains on the seller until cure or acceptance.

(2) Where the buyer rightfully revokes acceptance he may to the extent of any deficiency in his effective insurance coverage treat the risk of loss as having rested on the seller from the beginning.

(3) Where the buyer as to conforming goods already identified to the contract for sale repudiates or is otherwise in breach before risk of their loss has passed to him, the seller may to the extent of any deficiency in his effective insurance coverage treat the risk of loss as resting on the buyer for a commercially reasonable time.

§2-511. Tender of Payment by Buyer; Payment by Check.

(1) Unless otherwise agreed tender of payment is a condition to the seller's duty to tender and complete any delivery.

(2) Tender of payment is sufficient when made by any means or in any manner current in the ordinary course of business and gives any extension of time reasonably necessary to procure it.

(3) Subject to the provisions of this Act on the effect of an instrument of an obligation (Section 3-310), payment by check is conditional and is defeated as between the parties by dishonor of the check on due presentment.

§2-512. Payment by Buyer Before Inspection.

(1) Where the contract requires payment before inspection non-conformity of the goods does not excuse the buyer from so making payment unless

(a) the non-conformity appears without inspection; or

(b) despite tender of the required documents the circumstances would justify injunction against honor under the provisions of this Act (Section 5-114).

(2) Payment pursuant to subsection (1) does not constitute an acceptance of goods or impair the buyer's right to inspect or any of his remedies.

§2-513. Buyer's Right to Inspection of Goods.

(1) Unless otherwise agreed and subject to subsection (3), where goods are tendered or delivered or identified to the contract for sale, the buyer has a right before payment or acceptance to inspect them at any reasonable place and time and in any reasonable manner. When the seller is required or authorized to send the goods to the buyer, the inspection may be after their arrival.

(2) Expenses of inspection must be borne by the buyer but may be recovered from the seller if the goods but may be recovered from the seller if the goods do not conform and are rejected.

(3) Unless otherwise agreed and subject to the provisions of this Article on C.I.F. contracts (subsection (3) of Section 3-221), the buyer is not entitled to inspect the goods before payment of the price when the contract provides

(a) for delivery "C.O.D." or on other like terms; or

(b) for payment against documents of title, except where such payment is due only after the goods are to become available for inspection.

(4) A place or method of inspection fixed by the parties is presumed to be exclusive but unless otherwise expressly agreed it does not postpone identification or shift the place for delivery or for passing the risk of loss. If compliance becomes impossible, inspection shall be as provided in this section unless the place or method fixed was clearly intended as an indispensable condition failure of which avoids the contract.

§2-514. When Documents Deliverable on Acceptance; When on Payment.
Unless otherwise agreed documents which a draft is drawn are to be delivered to the drawee on acceptance of the draft if it is payable more than three days after presentment; otherwise, only on payment.

§2-515. Preserving Evidence of Goods in Dispute.
In furtherance of the adjustment of any claim or dispute

(a) either party on reasonable notification to the other and for the purpose of ascertaining the facts and preserving evidence has the right to inspect, test and sample the goods including such of them as may be in the possession or control of the other; and

(b) the parties may agree to a third party inspection or survey to determine the conformity or condition of the goods and may agree that the findings shall be binding upon them in any subsequent litigation or adjustment.

Part 6: Breach, Repudiation and Excuse

§2-601. Buyer's Rights on Improper Delivery.
Subject to the provisions of this Article on breach in installment contracts (Section 2-612) and unless otherwise agreed under the section on contractual limitations of remedy (Sections 2-178 and 2-719), if the goods or the tender of delivery fail in any respect to conform to the contract, the buyer may

(a) reject the whole; or

(b) accept the whole; or

(c) accept any commercial unit or units and reject the rest.

§2-602. Manner and Effect of Rightful Rejection.

(1) Rejection of goods must be within a reasonable time after their delivery or tender. It is ineffective unless the buyer seasonably notifies the seller.

(2) Subject to the provisions of the two following sections on rejected goods (Sections 2-603 and 2-604),

(a) after rejection any exercise of ownership by the buyer with respect to any commercial unit is wrongful as against the seller; and

(b) if the buyer has before rejection taken physical possession of goods in which he does not have a security interest under the provisions of this Article (subsection (3) of Section 2-711), he is under a duty after rejection to hold them with reasonable care at the seller's disposition for a time sufficient to permit the seller to remove them; but

(c) the buyer has no further obligations with regard to goods rightfully rejected.

(3) The seller's rights with respect to goods wrongfully rejected are governed by the provisions of this Article on Seller's remedies in general (Section 2-703).

§2-603. Merchant Buyer's Duties as to Rightfully Rejected Goods.

(1) Subject to any security interest in the buyer (subsection (3) of Section 2-711), when the seller has no agent or place of business at the market or rejection a merchant buyer is under a duty after rejection of goods in his possession or control to follow any reasonable instructions received from the seller with respect to the goods and in the absence of such instructions to make reasonable efforts to sell them for the seller's account if they are perishable or

threaten to decline in value speedily. Instructions are not reasonable if on demand indemnity for expenses is not forthcoming.

(2) When the buyer sells goods under subsection (1), he is entitled to reimbursement from the seller or out of the proceeds for reasonable expenses of caring for and selling them, and if the expenses include no selling commission then to such commission as is usual in the trade or if there is none to a reasonable sum not exceeding ten per cent on the gross proceeds.

(3) In complying with this section the buyer is held only to good faith and good faith conduct hereunder is neither acceptance nor conversion nor the basis of an action for damages.

§2-604. Buyer's Options as to Salvage of Rightfully Rejected Goods. Subject to the provisions of the immediately preceding section on perishables if the seller gives no instructions within a reasonable time after notification of rejection the buyer may store the rejected goods for the seller's account or reship them to him or resell them for the seller's account with reimbursement as provided in the preceding section. Such action is not acceptance or conversion.

§2-605. Waiver of Buyer's Objections by Failure to Particularize.

(1) The buyer's failure to state in connection with rejection a particular defect which is ascertainable by reasonable inspection precludes him from relying on the unstated defect to justify rejection or to establish breach

(a) where the seller could have cured it if stated seasonably; or

(b) between merchants when the seller has after rejection made a request in writing for a full and final written statement of all defects on which the buyer proposes to rely.

(2) Payment against documents made without reservation of rights precludes recovery of the payment for defects apparent on the face of the documents.

§2-606. What Constitutes Acceptance of Goods.

(1) Acceptance of goods occurs when the buyer

(a) after a reasonable opportunity to inspect the goods signifies to the seller that the goods are conforming or that he will take or retain them in spite of their non-conformity; or

(b) fails to make an effective rejection (subsection (1) of Section 2-602), but such acceptance does not occur until the buyer has had a reasonable opportunity to inspect them; or

(c) does any act inconsistent with the seller's ownership; but if such act is wrongful against the seller it is an acceptance only if ratified by him.

(2) Acceptance of a part of any commercial unit is acceptance of that entire unit.

§2-607. Effect of Acceptance; Notice of Breach; Burden of Establishing Breach After Acceptance; Notice of Claim or Litigation to Person Answerable Over.

(1) The buyer must pay at the contract rate for any goods accepted.

(2) Acceptance of goods by the buyer precludes rejection of the goods accepted and if made with knowledge of a non-conformity cannot be revoked because of it unless the acceptance was on the reasonable assumption that the non-conformity would be seasonably cured but acceptance does not of itself impair any other remedy provided by this Article for non-conformity.

(3) Where a tender has been accepted

(a) the buyer must within a reasonable time after he discovers or should have discovered any breach notify the seller of breach or be barred from any remedy; and

(b) if the claim is one for infringement or the like (subsection (3) of Section 2-312) and the buyer is sued as a result of such breach he must notify the seller within a reasonable time after he receives notice of the litigation or be barred from any remedy over for liability established by the litigation.

(4) The burden is on the buyer to establish any breach with respect to the goods accepted.

(5) Where the buyer is sued for breach of a warranty or other obligation for which his seller is answerable over

(a) he may give his seller written notice of the litigation. If the notice states that the seller may come in and defend and that if the seller does not do so he will be bound in any action against him by his buyer by any determination of fact common to the two litigations, then unless the seller after seasonable receipt of the notice does come in and defend he is so bound.

(b) if the claim is one for infringement or the like (subsection (3) of Section 2-312) the original seller may demand in writing that his buyer turn over to him control of the litigation in including settlement or else be barred from any remedy over and if he also agrees to bear all expense and to satisfy any adverse judgement, then unless the buyer after seasonable receipt of the demand does turn over control the buyer is so barred.

(6) The provisions of subsections (3), (4) and (5) apply to any obligation of a buyer to hold the seller harmless against infringement or the like (subsection (3) of Section 2-312).

§2-608. Revocation of Acceptance in Whole or in Part.

(1) The buyer may revoke his acceptance of a lot or commercial unit whose nonconformity substantially impairs its value to him if he has accepted it

(a) on the reasonable assumption that its nonconformity would be cured and it has not been seasonably cured; or

(b) without discovery of such nonconformity if his acceptance was reasonably induced either by the difficulty of discovery before acceptance or by the seller's assurances.

(2) Revocation of acceptance must occur within a reasonable time after the buyer discovers or should have discovered the ground for it and before any substantial change in condition of the goods which is not caused by their own defects. It is not effective until the buyer notifies the seller of it.

(3) A buyer who so revokes has the same rights and duties with regard to the goods involved as if he had rejected them.

§2-609. Right to Adequate Assurance of Performance.

(1) A contract for sale imposes an obligation on each party that the other's expectation of receiving due performance will not be impaired. When reasonable grounds for insecurity arise with respect to the performance of either party the other may in writing demand adequate assurance of due performance and until he receives such assurance may if commercially reasonable suspend any performance for which he has not already received the agreed return.

(2) Between merchants the reasonableness of grounds for insecurity and the adequacy of any assurance offered shall be determined according to commercial standards.

(3) Acceptance of any improper delivery or payment does not prejudice the aggrieved party's right to demand adequate assurance of future performance.

(4) After receipt of a justified demand failure to provide within a reasonable time not exceeding thirty days such assurance of due performance as is adequate under the circumstances of the particular case is a repudiation of the contract.

§2-610. Anticipatory Repudiation. When either party repudiates the contract with respect to a performance not yet due the loss of which will substantially impair the value of the contract to the other, the aggrieved party may

(a) for a commercially reasonable time await performance by the repudiating party; or

(b) resort to any remedy for breach (Section 2-703 or Section 2-711), even though he has notified the repudiating party that he would await the latter's performance and has urged retraction;

and

(c) in either case suspend his own performance or proceed in accordance with the provisions of this Article on the seller's right to identify goods to the contract notwithstanding breach or to salvage unfinished goods (Section 2-704).

§2-611. Retraction of Anticipatory Repudiation.

(1) Until the repudiating party's next performance is due he can retract his repudiation cancelled or materially changed his position or otherwise indicated that he considers the repudiation final.

(2) Retraction may be by any method which clearly indicates to the aggrieved party that the repudiating party intends to perform, but must include any assurance justifiably demanded under the provisions of this Article (Section 2-609).

(3) Retraction reinstates the repudiating party's rights under the contract with due excuse and allowance to the aggrieved party for any delay occasioned by the repudiation.

§2-612. "Installment Contract"; Breach.

(1) An "installment contract" is one which requires or authorizes the delivery of goods in separate lots to be separately accepted, even though the contract contains a clause "each delivery is a separate contract" or its equivalent.

(2) The buyer may reject any installment which is nonconforming if the non-conformity substantially impairs the value of that installment and cannot be cured or if the non-conformity is a defect in the required documents, but if the non-conformity does not fall within subsection (3) and the seller gives adequate assurance of its cure the buyer must accept that installment.

(3) Whenever non-conformity or default with respect to one or more installments substantially impairs the value of the whole contract there is a breach of the whole. But the aggrieved party reinstates the contract if he accepts a non-conforming installment without seasonably notifying of cancellation or if he brings an action with respect only to past installments or demands performance as to future installments.

§2-613. Casualty to Identified Goods. Where the contract requires for its performance goods identified when the contract is made, and the goods suffer casualty without fault or either party before the risk of loss passes to the buyer, or in a proper case under a "no arrival, no sale" term (Section 2-234) then

(a) if the loss is total the contract is avoided; and

(b) if the loss is partial or the goods have so deteriorated as no longer to conform to the contract the buyer may nevertheless demand inspection and at his option either treat the contract as avoided or accept the goods with due allowance from the contract price for the deterioration of the deficiency in quantity but without further against the seller.

(Text not included for Sections 614-616 in this abridged version.)

§2-614. Substituted Performance.

§2-615. Excuse by Failure of Presupposed Conditions.

§2-616. Procedure on Notice Claiming Excuse.

Part 7: Remedies

(Text not included for Sections 701-724 in this abridged version.)

§2-701. Remedies for Breach of Collateral Contracts Not Impaired.

§2-702. Seller's on Discovery of Buyer's Insolvency.

§2-703. Seller's Remedies in General.

§2-704. Seller's Right to Identify Goods to the Contract Notwithstanding Breach or to Salvage Unfinished Goods.

§2-705. Seller's Stoppage of Delivery in Transit or Otherwise.

§2-706. Seller's Resale Including Contract for Resale.

§2-707. "Person in the Position of a Seller".

§2-708. Seller's Damages for Non-acceptance or Repudiation.

§2-709. Action for the Price.

§2-710. Seller's Incidental Damages.

§2-711. Buyer's Remedies in General; Buyer's Security Interest in Rejected Goods.

§2-712. "Cover"; Buyer's Procurement of Substitute Goods.

§2-713. Buyer's Damages for Non-Delivery or Repudiation.

§2-714. Buyer's Damages for Breach in Regard to Accepted Goods.

§2-715. Buyer's Incidental and Consequential Damages.

§2-716. Buyer's Right to Specific Performance or Replevin.

§2-717. Deduction of Damages From the Price.

§2-718. Liquidation or Limitation of Damages; Deposits.

§2-719. Contractual Modification or Limitation of Remedy.

§2-720. Effect of "Cancellation" or "Rescission" on Claims for Antecedent Breach.

§2-721. Remedies for Fraud.

§2-722. Who Can Sue Third Parties for Injury to Goods.

§2-723. Proof of Market Price: Time and Place.

§2-724. Admissibility of Market Quotations.

§2-725. Statute of Limitations in Contracts for Sale.

(1) An action for breach of any contract for sale must be commenced within four years after the cause of action has accrued. By the original agreement the parties may reduce the period of limitation to not less than one year but may not extend it.

(2) A cause of action accrues when the breach occurs, regardless of the aggrieved party's lack of knowledge of the breach. A breach of warranty occurs when tender of delivery is made, except that where a warranty explicitly extends to future performance of the goods and discover of the breach must await the time of such performance the cause if action accrues when the breach is or should have been discovered.

(3) Where an action commenced within the time limited by subsection (1) is to terminate as to leave available a remedy by another action for the same breach such other action may be commenced after the expiration of the time limited and within six months after the termination of the first action unless the termination resulted from voluntary discontinuance or from dismissal for failure or neglect to prosecute.

(4) This section does not alter the law on tolling of the statute of limitations nor does it apply to causes of action which have accrued before this Act becomes effective.

Bibliography

Chapter 1

Caplan, Ralph. *The Design of Herman Miller*. New York: Whitney Library of Design, 1976.

Downs, James C., Jr. *Principles of Real Estate Management*. Chicago: Institute of Real Estate Management, 1991.

Pile, John, ed. *Interiors: Second Book of Offices*. New York: Whitney Library of Design, 1969.

Piotrowski, Christine M. *Professional Practice for Interior Designers*. New York: Van Nostrand Reinhold, 1989.

Roberts, Duane F. *Marketing and Leasing of Office Space*. Chicago: Institute of Real Estate Management, 1979.

Steelcase Strafor. *The Responsive Office: People and Change*. Berkshire, England: Polymath Ltd., 1990.

Chapter 2

American Institute of Architects (AIA). *An Architect's Guide to Building Codes & Standards*. 2nd ed. Washington, D.C.: The American Institute of Architects, 1990.

Bare, William K. *Introduction to Fire Science and Fire Protection*. New York: John Wiley & Sons, 1978.

Brown, Gordon W., Edward E. Byers, and Mary Ann Lawlor. *Business Law with UCC Applications*. 7th ed. New York: McGraw-Hill, 1989.

Brummett, William J., and Alec W. Johnson. *Building Code Quick Reference Guide: A Schematic Building Design Timesaver*. Belmont, Calif.: Professional Publications, Inc., 1993.

Bugbee, Percy. *Principles of Fire Protection*. Quincy, Mass.: The National Fire Protection Association, 1978.

The Govmark Organization, Inc. *The Govmark Book on Flammability Standards and Flammability Test Methods of Textiles, Plastics and Other Materials Used in Home and Contract Furnishings*. 3rd ed. Bellmore, N.Y.: The Govmark Organization, Inc., 1992.

Miller, Roger, and Gaylord Jentz. *Fundamentals of Business Law*. St. Paul, Minn.: West Publishing Company, 1990.

Chapter 3

Architectural Woodwork Institute (AWI). *Decorative Laminates for Architectural Surfacing*. Arlington, Va.: Architectural Woodwork Institute, 1987.

Architectural Woodwork Institute (AWI). *Fine Factory Finishing*. Arlington, Va.: Architectural Woodwork Institute, 1987.

Athalye, A.S. *Plastics Materials Handbook*. Bombay: Multi-tech Publishing Co., 1980.

Casper, Douglas P. "Stainless Steel Finishes." *The Construction Specifier* (April, 1994): 113-119.

Coppes, Wayne F., ed. *Metal Finishes Manual for Architectural Metals and Metal Products*. Oak Park, Ill.: National Association of Architectural Metal Manufacturers, 1988.

Dan River Inc. *A Dictionary of Textile Terms.* 13th ed. Danville, Va.: Dan River Inc., 1980.

Jackman, Dianne R. *The Guide to Textiles for Interior Designers.* Winnipeg, Canada: Peguis Publishers Limited, 1983.

Lyle, Dorothy. *Modern Textiles.* New York: John Wiley & Sons, 1976.

Modern Plastics Encyclopedia. New York: McGraw-Hill, 1992.

Olin, Harold B., J. Schmidt, and W. Lewis. *Construction: Principles, Materials, and Methods.* New York: Van Nostrand Reinhold, 1990.

Pile, John. *Furniture Modern and Postmodern.* 2nd ed. New York: John Wiley & Sons, 1990.

Rosato, Dominick V. *Rosato's Plastics Encyclopedia and Dictionary.* New York: Hanser Publishers, 1993.

The Spinneybeck Leather Handbook. Amherst, N.Y.: Spinneybeck, 1993.

Teddy and Arthur Edelman, Ltd. *A Leather Handbook.* Hawleyville, Conn.: Teddy and Arthur Edelman, Ltd., 1994.

Chapter 4

American Institute of Architects (AIA). *Masterspec.* Washington, D.C.: The American Institute of Architects, 1995.

Banov, Abel. *Paints & Coatings Handbook for Contractors, Architects and Builders.* Farmington, Mich.: Structures Publishing Co., 1973.

Busch, Jennifer Theile. "Painting the Future." *Contract Design* (February, 1995): 70-72.

Egan, David. *Architectual Acoustics.* New York: McGraw-Hill, 1988.

Harriman, Lew. "Drying Concrete." *The Construction Specifier* (March, 1995): 54-64.

Harris, David A., ed. *Noise Control Manual: Guidelines for Problem-Solving in the Industrial/Commercial Acoustical Environment.* New York: Van Nostrand Reinhold, 1991.

Painting and Decorating Contractors of America. *Architectural Specification Manual: Painting, Repainting, Wallcovering, and Gypsum Wallboard Finishing.* Kent, Wash.: Specification Services, Washington State Council, Painting and Decorating Contractors of America, 1986.

Pulgram, William L., *Designing the Automated Office: A Guide for Architects, Interior Designers, Space Planners, and Facility Managers.* New York: Whitney Library of Design, 1984.

Thompson, Sheri. "Paint Failures." *The Construction Specifier* (November, 1994): 27-28.

Weismantel, Guy E., ed. *Paint Handbook.* New York: McGraw-Hill Book Co., 1981.

Chapter 5

American Institute of Architects (AIA). *Masterspec.* Washington, D.C.: The American Institute of Architects, 1995.

Architectural Woodwork Institute (AWI). *Architectural Woodwork Quality Standards.* 6th ed. Arlington, Va.: Architectural Woodwork Institute, 1987.

Architectural Woodwork Institute (AWI). *Decorative Laminates for Architectural Surfacing.* Arlington, Va.: Architectural Woodwork Institute, 1987.

J & J Industries. *The Carpet Specifier's Handbook.* Dalton, Ga.: J & J Industries, 1990.

Reznikoff, Sivon. *Specifications for Commercial Interiors.* New York: Whitney Library of Design, 1989.

Glossary

above base building standard Materials and constructions that are not included in the base building standard.

absorption The process of soaking up energy.

acid-curing finish A solvent-based wood floor finish.

acknowledgment A confirmation of the purchaseorder, in regards to the purchase orders.

acrylic (1) A clear, transparent plastic material widely used for skylights and security glazing. (2) A manufactured fiber composed primarily of acrylonitrile.

addenda Contract modifications made to the bidding documents.

additive Substance added to another in relatively small amounts to impart or improve desirable characteristics.

administrative law That body of law, including decrees and legal decisions, generated by administrative agencies, boards, and commissions. Involves the administration of law by nonjudicial agencies created by the executive or legislative branches of the government.

agency A legal agreement between two persons, whereby one is designated the agent of the other.

agent A person authorized to act on behalf of another and subject to the other's control in dealing with third parties.

agreement The contract document that briefly states the work of the contract, the project time, and the contract sum. It includes other contract documents by reference.

alkaline A material having a pH greater than 7.0 in water.

alkyd A resin formed by the combination of alcohol and acid.

alloy A metal made from mixing various metals to combine their desirable properties.

annealed glass Glass cooled under conditions to minimize internal stresses.

anodize A finish applied principally to aluminum which involves passing an electrical current across a solution, most commonly sulfuric acid, in which the aluminum is immersed.

application rate The amount of paint that must be applied to a surface to achieve the desired perfomance, given as the area of substrate in square feet that should be covered by a gallon of paint, or *sq ft/gal*. For example, an intumescent paint may have to be applied at a rate of 190 sq ft/gal to achieve the required coating thickness, whereas a regular paint may have an application rate of 300 sq ft/gal.

aramid A manufactured fiber with low flammability and high strength used in firefighter's apparel, barrier fabrics between upholstery cushions and fabric, and in bullet-resistant vests.

austenitic A process by which steel is heated above a certain temperature causing certain components to transform to austentite making the steel nonmagnetic; named after Sir William Roberts-Austen who invented the process.

Axminster A woven carpet in which successive weft-wise rows of pile are inserted during the weaving process according to a predetermined arrangement of colors.

base building The commercial office building shell and core, including essential services such as the elevator, HVAC system, and toilet rooms.

base building standard A package of typical tenant improvements provided by, and sometimes required by, the landlord. Sometimes called the building standard.

beck dyeing A textile dye method consisting of advancing a continuous loop of textile through a dye bath.

bill of lading A document evidencing the receipt of goods for shipment and issued by a person engaged in the business of transporting or forwarding goods.

bill of sale   A written statement evidencing the transfer of personal property from one person to another.

blackout lining   A fabric backing used with a drapery to darken a room completely.

book match   The back of the top wood veneer leaf is matched to the face of the lower leaf, creating a mirror image and continuity in grain, much like the open leaves of a book.

brass   A copper-zinc alloy.

bronze   Origionally a copper-tin alloy, the term today is used to identify other alloys with a bronze color.

building code   A set of laws that set forth the minimum requirements for design and construction to protect public health and safety.

building gross area   The floor area within the exterior face of the building including the thickness of the exterior wall.

bulked continuous filament (BCF)   Continuous strands of synthetic fiber which are formed into yarn bundles without the need for spinning.

butt master carrier   A drapery carrier that holds the drapery end traversing the rod and joins it to the other drapery end with no overlap. Butt master carriers are often used in roll pleat and stack pleat draperies.

calendering   A process used to manufacture vinyl wallcovering that squeezes vinyl to the consistency of dough over a series of hot metal rollers, flattening the compound into a sheet.

calfskin   The hide of a young animal.

carbon steel   Steel containing up to 1.20% carbon with, generally, no other alloying elements added.

carrier   A business that undertakes to transport persons or goods, or both.

cascade   A lined window treatment with folds of fabric hanging from the top of a drapery heading.

casement   A sheer or semisheer fabric window treatment, often used with operable over-drapes or fixed side panels.

casework   Cabinets, cases, fixtures, or other storage units that are built in or attached to the building.

cast   Produced by pouring molten material into a mold.

catalyzed laquer   A laquer containing nitrocellulose which dries harder and faster than noncatalyzed laquer, but cannot be easily touched up.

cattle hide   The skin of a fully grown cow.

Ceiling Sound Transmission Class (CSTC)   A value that correlates with the reduction of sound, expressed in increments of 5. The higher the CSTC, the better the sound reduction capability of the ceiling system.

cementitious backerboard   Smooth, lightweight boards made of portland cement or treated gypsum and lightweight aggregate and are reinforced with galss fiber that are sometimes used as an underlayment for thin-set installations. They are designed to provide a water-resistant base for ceramic tile installations regularly exposed to water (for example, in a shower surround).

ceramic mosaic tile   Tile with a face area of less than 150 sq. mm (6 sq. in.)

change directive   A written contract modification when the consequent alteration of the contract sum or schedule has not yet been agreed upon.

change order   A written contract modification altering the contract sum. Only the owner can authorize a change order.

chemical finish   For metals, a finish produced by the reaction of a metal surface to various chemical solutions.

C.I.F.   (cost, insurance, and freight) Terms instructing a carrier to collect the cost of goods shipped, insurance, and freight charges.

code   A compilation of statutes. A set of laws.

C.O.L.   Customer's own leather. Leather that is not supplied by the product manufacturer.

colorfastness   The ability of a material to retain its origional hue.

colorthrough   A term used to describe high pressure decorative laminates that are a uniform color throughout the thickness of the sheet.

colorway   A set of colors for a given pattern or texture. Fabric or wall covering manufacturers offer a pattern in a variety of colorways to suit different color schemes.

C.O.M.   Customer's own material. Material, typically fabric, that is not supplied by the product manufacturer.

common areas   Corridors, lavatories, elevator vestibules, and other areas that the tenants share in common.

common carrier   A company that transports goods or persons for compensation and offers its facilities to the general public without discrimination. Compare *contract carrier*.

common law   The body of recorded court decisions that courts refer to and rely upon when making legal decisions. Past judicial decisions and reasoning; involves the application of precedent in applying the law.

compression modulus   An indication of a foam's support, calculated by indenting the foam to 65% of its original height and dividing it by the IFD.

concealed grid ceiling system   A suspended ceiling system where the grid supporting the ceiling tiles is not visible in the finished ceiling. Also referred to as concealed spline systems.

conditions of the contract The document that establishes the duties and responsibilities of the construction or FF&E contractor, the owner, and the designer. The conditions of the contract consist of the general conditions and the supplementary conditions.

conduction The transfer of heat energy through a substance.

consideration In contract law, the mutual promise to exchange benefits and sacrifices between the parties.

constitution The basic law of a nation or state.

constitutional law That body of law which involves a constitution and its interpretation.

continuous piece dyeing A textile dye method in which the greige goods travel through a long production line. First, an applicator spreads dye on the greige goods, then the dye is fixed in a steamer, and the piece is washed and dried.

contract An agreement between two or more component parties, based on mutual promises to do or to refrain from doing some particular thing that is neither illegal nor impossible. The agreement results in an obligation or a duty that can be enforced in a court of law.

contract carrier A carrier that provides transportation for compensation only to those people with whom it desires to do business. Compare with *common carrier*.

contract documents The documents that describe the work included in the contract. Contract documents consist of the contract forms (including the agreement, bonds, and certificates) the conditions of the contract, the specifications, the drawings, and the addenda.

contract for construction An agreement between the owner and the construction contractor to provide expertise and service.

contract for FF&E An agreement between the owner and the FF&E contractor to provide services such as warehousing, delivery, and installation. It is primarily a sale-of-goods contract.

contract modifications Changes to the construction or FF&E documents, including addenda, change orders, change directives, and supplemental instructions.

convection The transfer of heat energy through air.

cork The outer layer of the cork oak tree that is harvested for use as, among other things, resilient flooring.

crocking Rubbing off.

curtain A hanging textile window treatment. Usually refers to an unlined treatment with a gathered or shirred heading.

dealer The local or regional presence of a manufacturer who processes sales and provides various support and follow-up services to the consumer.

dedicated circuit An electrical circuit with three conductors, consisting of hot, neutral, and ground, between th final overcurrent device protecting the circuit and the outlets that are reserved only for use with specific equipment.

delamination The separation of two materials that had been bonded together.

delivery The transfer of possession from one person to another.

demised premises That portion of a property covered by a lease agreement, usually defined by the walls and other structures that separate one tenant's space from that of another.

demising walls The partitions that separate one tenant's space from another.

denier A unit of yarn measurement equal to the weight in grams of 9000 meters of the yarn.

density The mass per unit volume.

descriptive specification Specifications that detail the requirements for products, materials, and workmanship.

design-award-build The traditional approach to a construction contract where the designer prepares the contract documents, the contract is awarded to a construction contractor, and the project is built.

design/build A construction contract process where one party is responsible for both the design and the construction.

destination contract A contract under which the seller is required to deliver goods to a place of destination. Title passes to the buyer when the seller delivers the goods.

dimension stone Quarried stone with usually one or more mechanically dressed surfaces.

dimension stone tile Dimension stone that is less than 19 mm (¾ in) thick.

direct glue-down The most common method of commercial carpet installation where the carpet is glued directly to the floor without a cushion. This is the most dimensionally stable carpet installation method and is often required for stair or ramp applications.

direct sales force A selling team that represents the product's manufacturer, not the manufacturer's dealer.

double glue-down A carpet installation method where the carpet cushion is adhered to the floor and the carpet is then glued to the cushion.

drapery A hanging, textile window treatment. Usually refers to lined treatments with a stiffened, constructed heading requiring a traversing rod and carriers.

drawings Graphic representations describing the shape and form of the space and the quantities, sizes, and locations of materials and goods. Part of the contract documents.

drop shipment A shipment whereby goods are shipped to a destination different from that of the party who ordered and paid for them.

dry film thickness (DFT) The thickness of the cured paint or coating finish measured in mils (1/1000 in.).

electrolyte A liquid that conducts electricity.

emissivity No or low reflectivity. If a surface has high reflectivity, it has low emissivity.

end A yarn loop in the surface of a carpet.

end match Wood veneers are book matched, and then the ends of the sheets are matched, creating a long and wide matching veneer piece.

exposed grid ceiling systyem A ceiling suspension system of square or rectilinear frames that are visible in the finished ceiling and hold attached or loose laid panels.

express warranty An oral or written statement, promise, or other representation about the quality of a product.

extruded Produced by forcing semi-molten material through a die.

face weight The weight of the carpet pile yarn in ounces per square yard; also referred to as pile weight or yarn weight.

fast-track A construction contract process where construction begins before the project design is complete. Separate construction contracts are defined, and contract documents are prepared for each phase. Fast tracking often increases construction cost due to decreased labor efficiency.

ferrous Consisting mostly of iron; from the Latin *ferrum,* meaning iron.

fiber A fine hairlike strand that forms the basis of a yarn.

fiber cushion A carpet cushion made by needlepunching natural fiber, synthetic fiber, or a combination of the two, into a feltlike pad.

fiberglass Glass in fibrous form used in making various products.

filament fiber A long, continuous fiber measured in meters or yards.

filament yarn Continuous strands of synthetic fiber from a spinerette or of silk, twisted together.

fire resistant A substance that resists the spread of fire by not contributing to the flame.

flame-retardant A substance that slows the rate at which a fire spreads.

flammability, n. The ability to support combustion.

flammability standard A specified level of flammability performance.

flammability test method A group of procedures carried out by a testing laboratory to measure whether or not a product conforms to the stated acceptance criteria or classification cited by the flammability standard.

flash cove An integral, monolithic wall base for finish flooring.

flitch (1) The section of the wood log ready to be sliced into leaves; (2) The bundle of leaves stacked in sequence after slicing.

float glass Glass sheet manufactured by cooling a layer of liquid glass on a bath of molten tin.

F.O.B. Defined by the UCC as "free on board." It is the place where title to the goods and risk of loss pass from the seller to the buyer.

F.O.B. factory-freight prepaid Terms indicating that the buyer has title to the goods during transit, but the supplier pays the transportation charges to the destination.

F.O.B. the place of destination Terms indicating that goods will be delivered free to the place of destination.

F.O.B. the place of shipment Terms indicating that goods will be delivered free to the place from which the goods are to be shipped.

French pleat A traditional, folded and stitched drapery heading, sometimes referred to as a pinch pleat.

full-grain leather Leather with the original, genuine grain of the hide; the most expensive type of hides.

fullness In reference to draperies and curtains, fullness is the ratio of the total fabric used, less allowances for side hems and seams, to the finished drapery width. For example, a drapery with 100% fullness is 100% wider than the width of the drapery in a closed position, or twice the finished drapery width.

full warranty Under the Magnuson-Moss Warranty Act, a defective product will be fixed or replaced free within a reasonable time after a complaint has been made about the product.

furnish To supply and deliver to the project site, ready for unloading, unpacking, assembly, installation, and similar operations.

furniture dealer The local or regional presence of the furniture manufacturer who processes furniture sales and provides various support and follow-up services.

fusion bonded carpet A thermoplastic carpet tile manufacturing process where yarns are attached to a backing material by means of adhesion rather than tufting or weaving.

galvanic corrosion Metal corrosion caused by an electrolyte.

galvanize The application of zinc to the surface of cast iron, steel, or steel alloys to prevent corrosion.

gauge The measure of the spacing of the tufting needles, center to center, in a tufted carpet.

gel coat A pigmented polyester coating that is applied to the inside surface of a mold and becomes an integral part of a finished piece, for example, a cultured marble countertop.

general conditions of the contract Standardized documents establishing the duties and responsibilities of the construction or FF&E contractor, the owner, and the designer. The general conditions are modified through the supplementary conditions of the contract. See *conditions of the contract.*

glass reinforced gypsum (GRG) A high strength, high density gypsum reinforced with extruded glass fibers, that is molded to the required shape.

glazed tile A ceramic tile with an impervious finish composed of ceramic materials fused to the face of the tile. The body of a glazed tile may be nonvitreous, semivitreous, vitreous, or impervious.

gloss The relative luminous reflectance. Defined by ASTM D 523 *Standard Test Method for Specular Gloss.*

goods All things (including specially manufactured goods) which are movable at the time they are sold, other than money in which the price is to be paid, investment securities, and intangible items.

greige goods An unfinished fabric just off the loom or knitting machine.

gypsum Hydrous calcium sulfate.

gypsum board An interior facing panel made from a gypsum core sandwiched between paper faces; also called *drywall, sheet rock,* or *plasterboard.*

hand A fabric's tactile qualities, e.g., softness, firmness, drapability, and resiliency.

hardboard A very dense panel product manufactured in a manner similar to medium density fiberboard (MDF) but under higher pressure, often without adhesive.

hardwood Wood from a deciduous tree.

heat-strengthened glass Glass that has been strengthened by heat treatment, but not to the extent of fully-tempered glass.

heat-treated glass Glass that has been strengthened by heat treatment; either fully-tempered glass or heat-strengthened glass.

honed A satin smooth stone finish with a dull sheen.

high pressure decorative laminate (HPDL) Plastic laminate; commonly used for countertops.

hygrometer A device that measures relative humidity.

Impact Noise Rating (INR) A measurement of the sound insulation of a floor and ceiling assembly.

implied warranty A warranty imposed by law rather than by statements, descriptions, or samples given by the seller.

Indentation Force Deflection (IFD) A measure of foam firmness.

install To set up for use or service including unloading, unpacking, assembly, erection, placing, anchoring, applying, working to dimension, finishing, curing, protecting, cleaning, and similar operations.

Interzone Attenuation and Articulation Class (AC) A single figure rating measuring the sound reflective characteristics of ceiling systems in spaces with partial-height walls.

intumescent Swelling and charring when exposed to flame. An intumescent substance expands to form an insulating char when exposed to fire.

jacquard loom A loom used for figured fabrics such as tapestries, brocades, and damask weaves. Jacquard weaving uses a series of punched cards. Each card perforation controls the action of one warp yarn.

lacquer A coating that dries extremely quickly through the evaporation of a volatile solvent.

lamb's wool Wool sheared from sheep under 8 months of age.

laminated glass A glazing material consisting of outer layers of glass laminated to an inner layer of plastic.

landlord A person who owns real property and who rents or leases it to someone else; a lessor.

law A set of rules created by the governing body of a society to ensure the orderly maintenance of that society.

lease A contract granting the use of certain real property to another for a specified period of time in return for payment of rent.

leaves Individual wood veneer slices cut from a log section.

limited warranty Under the Magnuson-Moss Warranty Act, a warranty that is not a full warranty.

lining A fabric backing used to enhance certain qualities of a fabric, e.g., drapability, energy performance, and protection from ultraviolet (UV) radiation.

linoleum A resilient flooring material composed of oxidized linseed oil or other resins, mixed with cork or wood flour, mineral fillers, and pigments; derived from the botanical terms for "flax," *linum,* and "oil," *oleum.*

MasterFormat A list of 6-digit numbers and titles that classify the materials and requirements of construction and FF&E projects, promulgated by the Construction Specification Institute (CSI).

mastic   A paste-like adhesive.

mechanical finish   For metals, a finish accomplished by buffing, grinding, polishing, or otherwise texturing the metal surface.

medium density fiberboard (MDF)   A panel product manufactured by breaking down wood particles into fibers by steam pressure, mixing them with adhesive resins, and pressing them into panels.

mercerization   A treatment of cotton yarn or fabric to increase its luster and affinity for dyes. The material is immersed under tension in a cold sodium hydroxide solution and is later neutralized in acid. The process causes a permanent swelling of the fiber and thus increases its luster.

merchant   A person who deals in goods of the kind sold in the ordinary course of business or who otherwise claims to have knowledge or skills peculiar to those goods.

mineral tanning   A leather tanning process using a tanning solution based on chromium salts. Mineral tanned hides accept dyes well, including rich, vibrant colors. About 90% of leather today is tanned by this method.

natural fiber   Textile fiber from animal, plant, or mineral sources.

needlepunched carpet   A method of manufacturing carpet by layering tick fiber batts (typically polypropylene) over a support fabric and punching barbed needles through the support fabric.

Noise Reduction Coefficient (NRC)   A rating of the sound absorbing efficiency of a material.

noncatalyzed laquer   An easy to apply, touch up, and recoat, solvent-based laquer, forming a monolithic finish. Sometimes referred to as standard laquer.

nonferrous   Containing little or no iron.

nonvitreous   An absorption of 7.0% or more when used to describe ceramic tile.

nonvolatile   Does not readily evaporate.

oil-modified polyurethane   An easy to apply, affordable wood floor finish which tends to amber (turn slightly orange) as it ages.

olefin   A manufactured fiber of light weight, high strength, and good abrasion resistance. It is used primarily in the manufacture of indoor-outdoor carpet.

on center   Spacing measured from the center of one component to the center of the next.

one-way draw   A drapery or curtain operation that opens entirely to one side, designated as either *full left* or *full right*, indicating the direction in which the drapery stacks as you face it. For example, if you are looking at an open drapery stacked on the right, it is a right draw.

ordinance   A statute or regulation enacted by a municipal (city or town) government.

oriented strand board (OSB)   A panel product manufactured from thin, narrow strands of both hardwood and softwood which are blended with adhesive and formed into a multilayer panel.

overlap master carrier   A drapery carrier that holds the drapery end traversing the rod and joins it to the other drapery end with an overlap. Overlap master carriers are often used in conventional pleated draperies.

PageFormat   A page organization for specifications promulgated by the Construction Specification Institute (CSI).

panel   When referring to window treatments, a panel is a single drapery unit of one or more fabric widths.

parquet   Wood flooring consisting of small lengths of wood strips, either individual slats or preconfigured into tiles, that are arranged to form patterns.

particleboard   A panel product manufactured from wood particles and fibers which are bonded under heat and pressure with an adhesive resin.

patina   A thin layer of corrosion resulting from oxidation.

paver tiles   Ceramic tiles with a face size of 1150 sq. mm (6 sq. in) or more.

performance specification   Specifications that describe the required results.

pH   A numeric scale used to indicate how acidic or basic (alkaline) a solution is.

piece dyeing   The dyeing of fabrics after weaving or knitting, as opposed to dyeing in the form of yarn.

pigment   An insoluble substance used as coloring.

pile   In carpets, the face yarn, as opposed to the backing yarn.

pile density   The weight of the pile yarn in a given volume of carpet face.

pile height   The length of a carpet tuft from the backing to the tip of the tuft.

pile weight   See *face weight*.

pinch pleat   A traditional, folded and stitched drapery heading, sometimes referred to as a French pleat.

pitch   The number of ends (yarn loops) in a 27 inch (685 mm) width of carpet.

plain sawn   Cuts made tangentially to the annual growth ring of a tree. This sawing method produces the least waste and requires the least labor.

plain weave One of the three fundamental weaves: plain, satin, and twill. Each weft yarn passes successively over and under each warp yarn, alternating each row.

plastisol A method of manufacturing vinyl wallcovering which spreads liquid vinyl onto a backing material as it is rolled by. The materials are then fused together under high temperatures.

pleat to The width of the drapery after it has been pleated. For example, if a 121.92 cm (48 in) width of fabric is 48.26 cm (19 in) after it has been pleated, it is specified as "pleat to 48.26 cm (19 in)."

plenum The space between a finished ceiling and the structure above.

plywood A sandwich of wood or wood products between two layers of wood veneer, top and bottom.

polyester A manufactured fiber of high strength that is resistant to shrinking and stretching; a quick drying fiber with good crease retention and wrinkle resistance.

polymer A giant molecule composed of many identical simple molecules.

polymerization The process by which polymers are formed; the basic formation of plastics.

polyurethane A large group of resins and plastic compounds used in varnishes, insulation foam, and sealants.

precedent A model case that a court can follow when facing a similar situation.

prescriptive specifications Specifications that delineate product or material attributes.

primer A substance that prepares a surface for the application of a finish by increasing the surface adhesion.

private carrier A company that transports goods or persons under individual contract with those seeking its service. A private carrier is not required to serve all requests, unlike a common carrier.

project site The space available to the construction or FF&E contractor for performance of construction or installation activities. The extent of the project site should be shown on the drawings.

proprietary specifications Specifications requiring a specific product from a specific manufacturer.

pro rata Proportionately.

provide To furnish and install, complete and ready for the intended use.

purchase order The form used to order goods. It contains a description of the goods, the supplier's catalog identification code, the number of items required, and the price.

purchase order acknowledgment A confimation of the purchase order.

quarry tile A tile that is extruded from either natural clay or shale.

quarter sawn Cuts made with the growth rings at 60° to 90° angles to the face of the board. This sawing method is not available for all species of wood.

R-value The insulating effect of a material; a material's resistance to the flow of heat.

radiation The transmission of energy by invisible light waves independent of a substance or air.

railroading Fabric applied in a horizontal manner, the way in which it is unrolled from the bolt, with the selvage edge parallel to the seat cushion edge.

rayon A manufactured fiber composed of regenerated cellulose; originally known as artificial silk.

real property The ground and anything permanently attached to it including land, buildings, and growing trees and shrubs; the air space above it and the land is also included.

receipt Taking physical possession of goods.

reducing strip An extruded piece that creates a smooth transition and connection between floorings of different types, and possibly heights.

reference standard specifications Specifications based on the requirements set by an accepted authority.

reflection Energy bending back from and not penetrating a surface.

regulation A governmental order with the force of law.

rentable area The floor area that a tenant pays rent on; usually defined as the interior floor area excluding vertical penetrations through the floor, e.g., air shafts, elevators, and stairways.

repeat Distance between two identical patterns in a length of material, typically fabric or wallcovering.

resilient flooring A manufactured sheet or tile of polyvinyl chloride, linoleum, cork, or other material with resilience.

resin A nonvolatile (does not readily evaporate) component of paints, coatings, and plastics.

return In reference to window treatments, the return is the distance from the traversing rod to the wall or the depth of the projection.

rift sawn Cuts made with growth rings at 30° to 60° angles to the face of the board.

roll pleat A soft, rounded, uncreased drapery heading.

rotary cutting A wood veneer slicing method that produces wide sheets of veneer. The log is mounted on a lathe and the veneer is sliced off as the log spins around.

rows The number of ends (yarn loops) per inch in a lengthwise section of Axminster carpet.

safety glass Glazing material that complies with ANSI Z97.1 *Safety Glazing Materials Used in Buildings.*

sale The passing of title to goods from the seller to the buyer for a price.

samples Examples of materials or workmanship.

satin weave One of the three fundamental weaves: plain, satin, and twill. The face of the fabric consists almost completely of floating warp yarns. Satin-weave fabrics have a characteristic smooth, lustrous surface.

SectionFormat A 3-part format for the organization of specification sections, promulgated by the Construction Specification Institute (CSI).

selvage (also *selvedge*) The narrow edge of woven fabric that runs parallel to the warp. It is made with stronger yarns in a tighter construction than the body of the fabric to prevent raveling.

semivitreous An absorption of more than 3.0%, but not more than 7.0% when used to describe ceramic tile.

sericulture The growth of silk moths for their silk production.

setting material A substance used to fix tile including the traditional mortars and the relatively new adhesives.

shading coefficient (SC) A measure of a window systems ability to reduce heat gain.

sheen The reflectance of a surface.

shop drawings Detailed drawings prepared by a fabricator to guide the production of the item, e.g., casework.

silicone A polymer used for high-range sealants and water repellents.

skein dyeing The dyeing of yarn in the form of skeins.

slip match Adjacent wood veneer leaves are laid side by side in sequence, in a repeating pattern with no continuity in grain.

softwood Wood from a coniferous tree.

solid surfacing material A thick, dense synthetic sheet, uniform through the depth of the material; known by the trade name Corian, manufactured by Du Pont.

specifications Written contract documents that describe the quality of materials and their construction or installation.

split leather Leather made by slicing the hide into two or three layers. The inside layer is often finished as suede.

sponge rubber cushion A carpet cushion made of either flat sponge, ripple (waffle) sponge, or reinforced foam rubber. Sponge rubber cushions are generally open cell forms.

spun yarn Staple fibers twisted together to form a continuous strand.

stack back The width of a window treatment in a fully open position beside the window.

stack pleat A creased drapery heading with the pleeat crease sewn front and back for the length of the drapery.

stain A transparent or opaque coating which penetrates and colors a wood surface without masking its inherent grain.

standard A material specification, practice, or test method based on technical research and testing by industry experts.

staple fiber A short fiber, typically measured in centimeters or inches. All natural fibers except silk are staple fibers.

static generation The tendency of a substance to generate static electricity.

statute A law passed by legislature.

statutory law The body of law which includes statutes and ordinances.

stitches The number of ends sewn by the needles down the length of a tufted carpet.

stretch-in installation The traditional method of carpet installation whereby the carpet is stretched over a cushion and attached at the perimeter with a tack strip.

strike off A small printed sample of a custom order for the designer's review and approval.

stock dyeing The dyeing of fibers in staple form.

subfloor The load bearing surface beneath the finish surface.

supplemental instructions An interpretation or clarification of the contract documents by the designer does not alter the contract sum or schedule.

supplementary conditions of the contract Customized document modifying the duties and responsibilities of the construction or FF&E contractor, the owner, and the designer as described in the general conditions. See *conditions of the contract.*

swag A textile window treatment heading with draped soft folds at the tops of drapery.

synthetic fiber Textile fibers that are man-made.

tempered glass Glass that has been heat-treated to increase its toughness and its resistance to breakage.

tenant A person who has temporary possession of an interest in the real property of another.

tenant improvement Materials and construction that form the infill responding to the tenant's needs.

tenant improvement allowance A sum of money allowed for tenant improvements typically including standard items that will be installed at no cost to the tenant. The quantity of tenant improvements in the allowance is usually described per square foot of rentable space.

tender An offer or performance by one party to a contract which, if unjustifiably refused, places the other party in default and permits the party making the tender to exercise remedies for breach of contract.

terrazzo A floor finish material consisting of concrete with an aggregate of marble chips selected for color and size, which is ground and polished smooth after curing.

testing laboratory An independent entity engaged to perform specific inspections or tests, either at the project site or elsewhere, and to report on and, if required, to interpret the results.

textile Fabric made of fibers, whether woven, knitted, felted, or manufactured by some other means.

thermal finish A stone finish achieved by the application of intense flaming heat to the surface of the stone. Thermal finishes are usually applied to granite.

thermoplastics Plastics that become soft when heated and can be remolded repeatedly without affecting the properties of the plastic.

thermosets Plastics which are permanently hardened after undergoing an irreversible chemical change during processing.

thick set A ceramic tile setting method using a thick bed of portland cement mortar.

thinner That portion of a paint or coating that is volatile (readily evaporates); the thinner does not become part of the cured film.

thin set A ceramic tile setting method using a thin layer of dry-set mortar or latex-portland cement mortar.

title The right of ownership to goods. A subdivision of a code containing all the statutes that deal with a particular area of law.

top-grain leather Leather in which the original surface pattern, including scars from barbed wire or brands, is removed by abrasion. This skinless surface is embossed with a pattern, typically resembling the grain of the skin that was removed.

transmission The penetration of energy through a substance.

tuft A cluster of yarns drawn through a fabric or backing and projecting from the surface in the form of cut yarns or loops.

tuft bind The force required to pull a tuft out of a finished carpet. The industry standard for measuring tuft bind is *ASTM D 1335 Standard Test Method for Tuft Bind of Pile Floor Covering.*

tufted carpet Carpet produced by a tufting machine instead of a loom; much as in sewing, the needles are forced through a backing material forming loops, or tufts.

twill weave One of the three fundamental weaves: plain, satin, and twill. A weave characterized by diagonal lines produced by a series of staggered floating warp threads.

two-way draw A drapery or curtain operation that parts drapery panels that meet in the center, opening to either side.

underlayment A panel laid smooth over a subfloor to create a smooth, stiff surface for the application of the finish flooring.

Uniform Commercial Code (UCC) A set of statutory laws relating to certain commercial transactions, including the sale of goods, commercial paper, bank deposits and collections, letters of credit, bulk transfers, warehouse receipts, bills of lading, and secured transactions. Sales law is contained in the UCC.

upholstered wall system A site-constructed wallcovering that stretches fabric taut over a frame and infill material.

up-the-bolt Fabric applied in a vertical manner, with the selvage edge perpendicular to the seat cushion edge.

useable area The floor area that is inhabitable by the tenant.

variance An exemption or an exception permitting a use that differs from those permitted under the existing zoning law.

varnish A slow drying transparent coating.

vegetable tanning A leather tanning method using a tanning solution based on tree bark, typically oak. The hides are submerged in the solution, and the tannins (tanning materials) from the bark swell the hides.

vehicle That portion of a paint or coating that conveys the ingredients which remain on the substrate after the paint or coating has cured.

velvet (1) A woven carpet in which the pile ends are lifted over wires that are inserted in the same manner as the weft and that cut the pile as they are drawn. (2) A fabric with a short, dense cut pile that produces a rich appearance and soft texture.

vinyl composition tile (VCT) Resilient flooring tiles composed mostly of fillers with a comparatively small amounts of binder and pigments.

virgin wool Wool made into yarn for the first time.

vitreous Glasslike; ceramic tile with an absorption of 0.5% or less.

volatile   Readily evaporates.

volatile organic compounds (VOC)   Those components of paints and coatings that evaporate readily. VOCs adversely affect human health and the environment.

wall base   A strip of material that conceals the joint where a wall meets the floor.

wall liner   A nonwoven sheet used under wallcovering where wall surfaces cannot be prepared by conventional means. Wall liners can be used to prevent cracks, holes, and gaps from telegraphing through the wallcovering.

warehouse   A building in which any goods, particularly wares or merchandise, are stored.

warp   Yarns that run lengthwise and parallel to the selvage in woven fabrics.

warranty   A statement, promise, or other representation that an item has certain qualities; also, an obligation imposed by law, that an item will have certain qualities. Warranties made by means of a statement or other affirmation of fact are called express warranties; those imposed by law are implied warranties.

warranty of fitness for a particular purpose   An implied warranty that goods will be fit for a particular purpose. This warranty is given by the seller to the buyer of goods whenever the seller has reason to know of any particular purpose for which the goods are needed and the buyer relies on the seller's skill and judgment to select the goods.

warranty of merchantability   An implied warranty that the goods are fit for the ordinary purpose for which such goods are used. Unless excluded, this warranty is always given by a merchant who sells goods in the ordinary course of business.

water-based polyurethane   A low VOC, nonyellowing, expensive wood floor finish.

weft   Yarns that run from selvage to selvage at right angles to the warp in woven fabrics.

Wilton   A woven carpet in which the pile yarns are an integral part of the carpet, being held in place by the weft, usually made on a Jacquard loom.

wire   The number of ends (yarn loops) per inch in a lengthwise section of Wilton or velvet carpet.

wired glass   Glass in which a wire mesh is embedded during the manufacturing process.

wire height   The pile height of woven carpet.

work letter   A document that describes the improvements to the leased space. It is attached to, and a part of, the lease.

wrought   Produced by rolling semi-molten material into sheets and punching or cutting out the required shape.

yarn   A continuous strand formed by twisting fibers together.

yarn count   A relative gage of a spun yarn's weight; heavier yarns are designated by lower yarn count numbers.

yarn weight   See *face weight*.

zoning law   A local regulation or ordinance that restricts certain areas to specific uses; for example, areas zoned for residential, commercial, agricultural, industrial or other uses.

Index